WEIGHT IN AMERICA

OBESITY, EATING DISORDERS, AND OTHER HEALTH RISKS

ISSN 1551-2118

WEIGHT IN AMERICA

OBESITY, EATING DISORDERS, AND OTHER HEALTH RISKS

Barbara Wexler

INFORMATION PLUS® REFERENCE SERIES
Formerly Published by Information Plus, Wylie, Texas

GALE
CENGAGE Learning™

Detroit • New York • San Francisco • New Haven, Conn • Waterville, Maine • London

Weight in America: Obesity, Eating Disorders, and Other Health Risks

Barbara Wexler

Kepos Media, Inc.: Paula Kepos and Janice Jorgensen, Series Editors

Project Editors: Elizabeth Manar, Kathleen J. Edgar

Rights Acquisition and Management: Barb McNeil, Edna Shy

Composition: Evi Abou-El-Seoud, Mary Beth Trimper

Manufacturing: Cynde Lentz

For product information and technology assistance, contact us at **Gale Customer Support, 1-800-877-4253.**
For permission to use material from this text or product, submit all requests online at **www.cengage.com/permissions.**
Further permissions questions can be e-mailed to **permissionrequest@cengage.com**

Cover photograph: Image copyright Ljupco Smokovski, 2010. Used under license from Shutterstock.com.

Gale
27500 Drake Rd.
Farmington Hills, MI 48331-3535

ISBN-13: 978-0-7876-5103-9 (set)   ISBN-10: 0-7876-5103-6 (set)
ISBN-13: 978-1-4144-4123-8   ISBN-10: 1-4144-4123-1

ISSN 1551-2118

This title is also available as an e-book.
ISBN-13: 978-1-4144-7003-0 (set)
ISBN-10: 1-4144-7003-7 (set)
Contact your Gale sales representative for ordering information.

Printed in the United States of America
1 2 3 4 5 6 7 14 13 12 11 10

TABLE OF CONTENTS

PREFACE

Weight in America: Obesity, Eating Disorders, and Other Health Risks is part of the *Information Plus Reference Series*. The purpose of each volume of the series is to present the latest facts on a topic of pressing concern in modern American life. These topics include the most controversial and studied social issues in the 21st century: abortion, capital punishment, care for the elderly, crime, health care, the environment, immigration, minorities, social welfare, women, youth, and many more. Even though this series is written especially for high school and undergraduate students, it is an excellent resource for anyone in need of factual information on current affairs.

By presenting the facts, it is the intention of Gale, Cengage Learning to provide its readers with everything they need to reach an informed opinion on current issues. To that end, there is a particular emphasis in this series on the presentation of scientific studies, surveys, and statistics. These data are generally presented in the form of tables, charts, and other graphics placed within the text of each book. Every graphic is directly referred to and carefully explained in the text. The source of each graphic is presented within the graphic itself. The data used in these graphics are drawn from the most reputable and reliable sources such as from the various branches of the U.S. government and from major organizations and associations. Every effort has been made to secure the most recent information available. Readers should bear in mind that many major studies take years to conduct and that additional years often pass before the data from these studies are made available to the public. Therefore, in many cases the most recent information available in 2010 is from 2007 or 2008. Older statistics are sometimes presented as well, if they are landmark studies or of particular interest and no more-recent information exists.

Even though statistics are a major focus of the *Information Plus Reference Series*, they are by no means its only content. Each book also presents the widely held positions and important ideas that shape how the book's subject is discussed in the United States. These positions are explained in detail and, where possible, in the words of their proponents. Some of the other material to be found in these books includes historical background, descriptions of major events related to the subject, relevant laws and court cases, and examples of how these issues play out in American life. Some books also feature primary documents or have pro and con debate sections that provide the words and opinions of prominent Americans on both sides of a controversial topic. All material is presented in an even-handed and unbiased manner; readers will never be encouraged to accept one view of an issue over another.

HOW TO USE THIS BOOK

The United States has a serious weight problem. The majority of Americans weigh more than they should, and roughly one-third of them are considered obese. Overweight and obesity have serious health consequences, and their epidemic levels in the United States have had a major impact on society. Yet, overweight and obesity are not the only problems that Americans face when it comes to food. Some suffer from eating disorders, such as anorexia nervosa and bulimia, that can have a devastating effect on their health. This book brings together information from academic and governmental sources on every aspect of overweight, obesity, and eating disorders, including their prevalence in the United States, their consequences, public opinion about them, and methods of combating them.

Weight in America: Obesity, Eating Disorders, and Other Health Risks consists of 11 chapters and 3 appendixes. Each chapter is devoted to a particular aspect of weight in the United States. For a summary of the information covered in each chapter, please see the synopses provided in the Table of Contents. Chapters generally begin with an overview of the basic facts and background information on the chapter's topic, then proceed to examine subtopics of particular interest. For example, Chapter 3: The Influences of Mental Health and Culture on Weight and Eating Disorders begins by considering the relationship between psychological and emotional well-being and eating, diet, and weight. This is followed by a detailed discussion of the origins and prevalence of eating disorders. The next section describes the treatment of and recovery from eating disorders and the strategies and programs that are used to prevent eating disorders. The chapter concludes with a section that examines changing social and cultural norms about weight, thinness, and satisfaction with body image. Readers can find their way through a chapter by looking for the section and subsection headings, which are clearly set off from the text. They can also refer to the book's extensive index if they already know what they are looking for.

Statistical Information

The tables and figures featured throughout *Weight in America: Obesity, Eating Disorders, and Other Health Risks* will be of particular use to readers in learning about this issue. These tables and figures represent an extensive collection of the most recent and important statistics on weight and related issues. For example, graphics cover the percentage of obese adults by state, race, and ethnicity; the prevalence of obesity among adults; the names for added sugars found on ingredients labels; dubious diet claims; and the percentage of Americans who say they are trying to lose weight, by weight status. Gale, Cengage Learning believes that making this information available to readers is the most important way to fulfill the goal of this book: to help readers understand the issues and controversies surrounding overweight and obesity in the United States and reach their own conclusions about them.

Each table or figure has a unique identifier appearing above it, for ease of identification and reference. Titles for the tables and figures explain their purpose. At the end of each table or figure, the original source of the data is provided.

To help readers understand these often complicated statistics, all tables and figures are explained in the text. References in the text direct readers to the relevant statistics. Furthermore, the contents of all tables and figures are fully indexed. Please see the opening section of the index at the back of this volume for a description of how to find tables and figures within it.

Appendixes

Besides the main body text and images, *Weight in America: Obesity, Eating Disorders, and Other Health Risks* has three appendixes. The first is the Important Names and Addresses directory. Here, readers will find contact information for a number of government and private organizations that can provide further information on aspects of weight and eating disorders and their impact on health. The second appendix is the Resources section, which can also assist readers in conducting their own research. In this section, the author and editors of *Weight in America: Obesity, Eating Disorders, and Other Health Risks* describe some of the sources that were most useful during the compilation of this book. The final appendix is the detailed index, which facilitates reader access to specific topics in this book.

ADVISORY BOARD CONTRIBUTIONS

The staff of Information Plus would like to extend its heartfelt appreciation to the Information Plus Advisory Board. This dedicated group of media professionals provides feedback on the series on an ongoing basis. Their comments allow the editorial staff who work on the project to continually make the series better and more user-friendly. The staff's top priority is to produce the highest-quality and most useful books possible, and the Information Plus Advisory Board's contributions to this process are invaluable.

The members of the Information Plus Advisory Board are:

- Kathleen R. Bonn, Librarian, Newbury Park High School, Newbury Park, California

- Madelyn Garner, Librarian, San Jacinto College, North Campus, Houston, Texas

- Anne Oxenrider, Media Specialist, Dundee High School, Dundee, Michigan

- Charles R. Rodgers, Director of Libraries, Pasco-Hernando Community College, Dade City, Florida

- James N. Zitzelsberger, Library Media Department Chairman, Oshkosh West High School, Oshkosh, Wisconsin

COMMENTS AND SUGGESTIONS

The editors of the *Information Plus Reference Series* welcome your feedback on *Weight in America: Obesity, Eating Disorders, and Other Health Risks*. Please direct all correspondence to:

Editors
Information Plus Reference Series
27500 Drake Rd.
Farmington Hills, MI 48331-3535

CHAPTER 1
AMERICANS WEIGH IN OVER TIME

More die in the United States of too much food than of too little.

—John Kenneth Galbraith, *The Affluent Society* (1998)

In 2009 more Americans were fatter than ever before—in fact, they were the heaviest since the U.S. government started tracking patterns of body weight of the U.S. adult population in the first half of the 20th century. The Centers for Disease Control and Prevention (CDC) reports in "Obesity—Halting the Epidemic by Making Health Easier: At a Glance 2009" (December 17, 2009, http://www.cdc.gov/NCCDPHP/publications/AAG/obesity.htm) that more than one-third of adults in the United States—an estimated 72 million—are considered obese. In *Health, United States, 2008* (2008, http://www.cdc.gov/nchs/data/hus/hus08.pdf), the National Center for Health Statistics (NCHS) notes that from 2003 to 2006, the most recent period for which data were available as of early 2010, 66.9% of American adults were overweight, including 34.1% who were classified as obese. Despite billions of dollars spent on diet programs, overweight and obesity are widespread and increasingly prevalent throughout the United States.

Even though Americans' body weight had been increasing incrementally during the last century, overweight and obesity skyrocketed between 1985 and 2008. The CDC indicates in *U.S. Obesity Trends 1985–2008* (November 20, 2009, http://www.cdc.gov/obesity/data/trends.html) that during this period obesity among adults more than doubled and obesity among adolescents tripled. Normal-weight adults are now a minority in the United States; nearly one-third of the adult population is obese, and childhood obesity is at an all-time high. In 1990, 10 states had obesity prevalence rates of less than 10% and no states had rates at or above 15%. By 2008 just only one state, Colorado, had an obesity prevalence rate of less than 20%, 31 states had rates of 25% or higher, and six of these states (Alabama, Mississippi, Oklahoma, South Carolina, Tennessee, and West Vir-

ginia) reported rates of 30% or greater. (The prevalence rate is the number of cases of a disease or condition present during a specified interval of time, usually a year, divided by the population.) Figure 1.1 maps the geographic distribution of obesity throughout the United States in 1990, 1999, and 2008.

The prevalence of obesity varies by state. According to the CDC, in 2008 Colorado reported the lowest percentage of obesity (18.5%), followed by Massachusetts (20.9%), Connecticut (21%), and Rhode Island (21.5%). Mississippi reported the highest rate of obesity (32.8%), followed by Alabama (31.4%), West Virginia (31.2%), and Tennessee (30.6%).

An analysis of data from the CDC 2006–08 Behavioral Risk Factor Surveillance System reveals that the obesity epidemic affects men and women of all ages, races, ethnic origins, smoking status, and educational attainment. Even though the prevalence of obesity among U.S. adults disproportionately affects older age groups, African-Americans, and Hispanics, and declines with increasing educational attainment, no group remains untouched by this epidemic.

In "Differences in Prevalence of Obesity among Black, White, and Hispanic Adults—United States, 2006–2008" (*Morbidity and Mortality Weekly Report*, vol. 58, no. 27, July 17, 2009), Liping Pan et al. of the CDC report that compared with the prevalence of obesity among whites, African-Americans' obesity prevalence rates were 51% higher and Hispanics were 21% higher. These differences were consistent across most states and were greater among women than men. Non-Hispanic African-American women had the greatest prevalence (39.2%), followed by non-Hispanic African-American men (31.6%), Hispanic women (29.4%), Hispanic men (27.8%), non-Hispanic white men (25.4%), and non-Hispanic white women (21.8%). Figure 1.2 shows the percentage of obese adults in each state by race and

FIGURE 1.1

Obesity trends* among U.S. adults, 1990, 1999, and 2008

(*BMI ≥30, or about 30 lbs. overweight for 5'4" person)

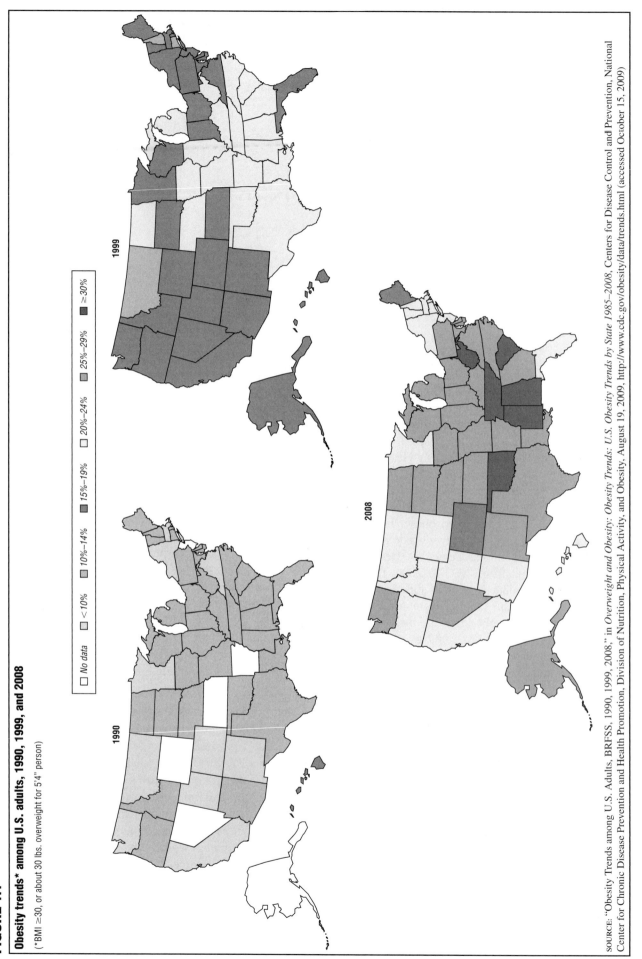

SOURCE: "Obesity Trends among U.S. Adults, BRFSS, 1990, 1999, 2008," in *Overweight and Obesity: Obesity Trends: U.S. Obesity Trends by State 1985–2008,* Centers for Disease Control and Prevention, National Center for Chronic Disease Prevention and Health Promotion, Division of Nutrition, Physical Activity, and Obesity, August 19, 2009, http://www.cdc.gov/obesity/data/trends.html (accessed October 15, 2009)

FIGURE 1.2

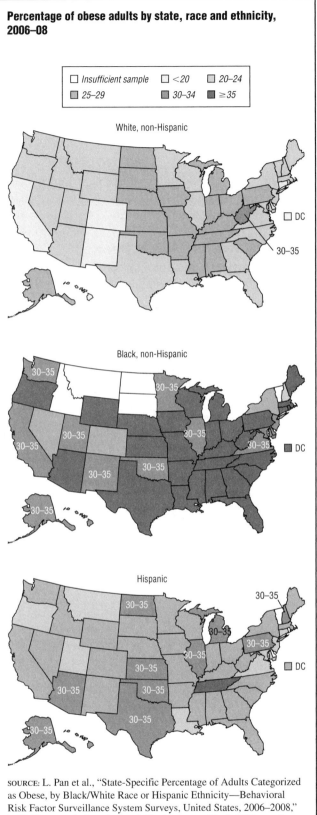

Percentage of obese adults by state, race and ethnicity, 2006–08

Legend:
- □ Insufficient sample
- □ <20
- ▨ 20–24
- ▨ 25–29
- ▨ 30–34
- ■ ≥35

White, non-Hispanic

Black, non-Hispanic

Hispanic

SOURCE: L. Pan et al., "State-Specific Percentage of Adults Categorized as Obese, by Black/White Race or Hispanic Ethnicity—Behavioral Risk Factor Surveillance System Surveys, United States, 2006–2008," in "Differences in Prevalence of Obesity among Black, White, and Hispanic Adults—United States, 2006–2008," *Morbidity and Mortality Weekly Report*, vol. 58, no. 27, July 17, 2009, http://www.cdc.gov/mmwr/preview/mmwrhtml/mm5827a2.htm (accessed October 16, 2009)

ethnicity from 2006 to 2008. In most states non-Hispanic African-Americans had the greatest prevalence of obesity, followed by Hispanics and non-Hispanic whites. In the states where there were enough non-Hispanic African-American respondents to analyze, the state-specific prevalence of obesity for this group ranged from a low of 23% in New Hampshire to 45.1% in Maine. In 40 of the 45 states reporting, the prevalence was greater than 30%, and in five states—Alabama, Maine, Mississippi, Ohio, and Oregon—it exceeded 40%.

In the United States many researchers believe that obesity is the second-leading cause of preventable death after smoking. There is conclusive scientific evidence that mortality (death) risk increases with increasing weight and that even slightly overweight adults—people of average height who are 10 to 20 pounds (4.5 to 9.1 kg) above their ideal weight—are at increased risk of premature death. The rising prevalence of overweight and obesity not only foretells increasing adverse effects on health and longevity but also guarantees increased costs for medical care. Overweight and obesity increase the risk of developing a range of ailments including: heart disease; stroke; selected cancers; sleep apnea (interrupted breathing while sleeping); respiratory problems; osteoarthritis (loss of joint bone and cartilage); gallbladder disease; fatty liver disease (the deposition of fats, such as triglycerides in the liver, which may lead to an enlarged liver and elevated liver enzymes); and Type 2 diabetes. (Insulin is necessary for the body to be able to use sugar, the basic fuel for the cells in the body. People with diabetes do not produce enough insulin or their cells are resistant to the effects of the insulin.) Jeffrey Levi et al. of the Trust for America's Health observe in *F as in Fat: How Obesity Policies Are Failing in America, 2009* (July 2009, http://healthyamericans.org/reports/obesity 2009/Obesity2009Report.pdf) that more than a quarter of U.S. health care costs are related to obesity and that between 20% and 30% of the increase in health care spending since 1979 is attributable to the dramatic rise in obesity.

Overweight and obesity also exact a personal toll, with affected individuals at increased risk for emotional, psychological, and social problems. Overweight children, teens, and adults suffer from depression, low self-esteem, and other mental health and emotional problems more than their normal-weight counterparts. Along with a physical inability to participate in many activities, people who are overweight or obese may encounter weight-based stigmatization, bias, and discrimination in school and at the workplace and may be excluded from social opportunities.

TRENDS IN U.S. BIRTH WEIGHTS

Americans are not born overweight. In fact, Joyce A. Martin et al. of the CDC indicate in "Births: Final

Data for 2006" (*National Vital Statistics Reports*, vol. 57, no. 7, January 7, 2009) that the mean (average) birth weight of infants born as singletons (births of one infant as opposed to twins or other multiple births) has steadily declined since 1990. In 2006 the mean birth weight of all singletons was approximately 7 pounds, 4 ounces (3,298 g), and the average non-Hispanic white singleton (7 pounds, 6 ounces, or 3,357 g) weighed 9 ounces (257 g) more than the average non-Hispanic African-American singleton (6 pounds, 13 ounces, or 3,100 g).

Even though ideal birth weight varies based on the expectant mother's ethnicity, for women in the United States the average ideal birth weight is approximately 7 pounds, 8 ounces (3,402 g), close to the average weight of singletons born in 2006. In the United States the percent of babies born with low birth weight (LBW)— less than 5 pounds, 8 ounces (2,500 g)—has risen steadily since the 1980s. (See Table 1.1.) According to Martin et al., the LBW rate rose from 7.6% in 2000 to 8.3% in 2006, the highest level reported in more than three decades. The percent of infants with very low birth weight (VLBW)—less than 3 pounds, 4 ounces (1,500 g)— remained nearly steady between 2000 (1.43%) and 2006 (1.49%).

LBW and VLBW are major predictors of infant morbidity (illness or disease) and mortality. For LBW infants, the risk of dying during the first year of life is more than five times that of infants born at normal weight; the risk for VLBW infants is nearly 100 times higher. The risk of delivering an LBW infant is greatest among the youngest and oldest mothers; however, many of the LBW births among older mothers are attributable to their higher rates of multiple births.

Birth Weight Influences Risk of Disease

Even though the relationship between birth weight and development of disease in adulthood is an emerging field of research, and scientists cannot yet fully explain

TABLE 1.1

Percentage of live births, very low and low birthweight, by race and Hispanic origin of mother, 1981–2006

Year	Very low birthweight[d]				Low birthweight[e]			
		Non-Hispanic				Non-Hispanic		
	All races[a]	White[b]	Black[b]	Hispanic[c]	All races[a]	White[b]	Black[b]	Hispanic[c]
2006	1.49	1.20	3.15	1.19	8.3	7.3	14.0	7.0
2005	1.49	1.21	3.27	1.20	8.2	7.3	14.0	6.9
2004	1.48	1.20	3.15	1.20	8.1	7.2	13.7	6.8
2003	1.45	1.18	3.12	1.16	7.9	7.0	13.6	6.7
2002	1.46	1.17	3.15	1.17	7.8	6.9	13.4	6.5
2001	1.44	1.17	3.08	1.14	7.7	6.8	13.1	6.5
2000	1.43	1.14	3.10	1.14	7.6	6.6	13.1	6.4
1999	1.45	1.15	3.18	1.14	7.6	6.6	13.2	6.4
1998	1.45	1.15	3.11	1.15	7.6	6.6	13.2	6.4
1997	1.42	1.12	3.05	1.13	7.5	6.5	13.1	6.4
1996	1.37	1.08	3.02	1.12	7.4	6.4	13.1	6.3
1995	1.35	1.04	2.98	1.11	7.3	6.2	13.2	6.3
1994	1.33	1.01	2.99	1.08	7.3	6.1	13.3	6.2
1993	1.33	1.00	2.99	1.06	7.2	5.9	13.4	6.2
1992[f]	1.29	0.94	2.97	1.04	7.1	5.7	13.4	6.1
1991[f]	1.29	0.94	2.97	1.02	7.1	5.7	13.6	6.1
1990[g]	1.27	0.93	2.93	1.03	7.0	5.6	13.3	6.1
1989[h]	1.28	0.93	2.97	1.05	7.0	5.6	13.6	6.2
1988	1.24	—	—	—	6.9	—	—	—
1987	1.24	—	—	—	6.9	—	—	—
1986	1.21	—	—	—	6.8	—	—	—
1985	1.21	—	—	—	6.8	—	—	—
1984	1.19	—	—	—	6.7	—	—	—
1983	1.19	—	—	—	6.8	—	—	—
1982	1.18	—	—	—	6.8	—	—	—
1981	1.16	—	—	—	6.8	—	—	—

—Data not available.
[a]Includes races other than white and black and origin not stated.
[b]Race and Hispanic origin are reported separately on birth certificates. Persons of Hispanic origin may be of any race. Race categories are consistent with the 1977 Office of Management and Budget (OMB) standards. In 2006, 23 states reported multiple-race data. Multiple-race data for these states were bridged to the single-race categories of the1977 OMB standards for comparability with other states. Multiple race reporting areas vary for 2003–2006.
[c]Includes all persons of Hispanic origin of any race.
[d]Less than 1,500 grams (3 lb. 4 oz.).
[e]Less than 2,500 grams (5 lb. 8 oz.).
[f]Data by Hispanic origin exclude New Hampshire, which did not report Hispanic origin.
[g]Data by Hispanic origin exclude New Hampshire and Oklahoma, which did not report Hispanic origin.
[h]Data by Hispanic origin exclude New Hampshire, Oklahoma, and Louisiana, which did not report Hispanic origin.

SOURCE: Adapted from Joyce A. Martin et al., "Table 33. Percentage of Live Births Very Preterm and Preterm and Percentage of Life Births of Very Low Birthweight and Low Birthweight, by Race and Hispanic Origin of Mother: United States, 1981–2006," in "Births: Final Data for 2006," *National Vital Statistics Reports*, vol. 57, no. 7, January 7, 2009, http://www.cdc.gov/nchs/data/nvsr/nvsr57/nvsr57_07.pdf (accessed October 16, 2009)

how and why birth weight is a predictor of health and illness in later life, mounting evidence indicates that both LBW and higher-than-average birth weight are linked to future health problems. Research reveals that LBW infants are more likely than normal-weight infants to develop disease in later life. Male infants with LBW who gain weight rapidly before their first birthday appear to be at the highest risk. Researchers hypothesize that LBW infants have fewer muscle cells at birth and that rapid weight gain during the first year of life may lead to disproportionate amounts of fat to muscle and above average body mass. Infants with LBW who later develop above average body mass are at an increased risk for developing diseases such as Type 2 diabetes, hypertension (high blood pressure), and cardiovascular disease (heart disease and stroke).

Thiemo Pfab et al. find in "Low Birth Weight, a Risk Factor for Cardiovascular Diseases in Later Life, Is Already Associated with Elevated Fetal Glycosylated Hemoglobin at Birth" (*Circulation*, vol. 114, no. 16, October 2006) an inverse relationship between birth weight and cardiovascular disease. In general, rates of cardiovascular disease decreased with increasing birth weight. The association was strong, did not depend on adjustment for size in later childhood, and was independent of social class and other maternal and pregnancy characteristics.

LBW has also been linked to the development of asthma. In "Is the Association between Low Birth Weight and Asthma Independent of Genetic and Shared Environmental Factors?" (*American Journal of Epidemiology*, vol. 169, no. 11, February 2009), a study of 21,588 twins, Eduardo Villamor, Anastasia Iliadou, and Sven Cnattingius find that LBW is associated with asthma during childhood and adult life. Claudia Brufani et al. indicate in "Obese Children with Low Birth Weight Demonstrate Impaired-Cell Function during Oral Glucose Tolerance Test" (*Journal of Clinical Endocrinology and Metabolism*, vol. 94, no. 11, November 2009) that both LBW and abnormally high birth weight are associated with a risk of developing diabetes later in life.

Evidence also indicates that birth weight is related to a risk of developing breast cancer. Xiaohui Xu et al. consider 18 epidemiological (population) studies that detail 16,424 cases of breast cancer to determine whether birth weight influenced the risk of developing breast cancer in adulthood. The results of the study were published in "Birth Weight as a Risk Factor for Breast Cancer: A Meta-analysis of 18 Epidemiological Studies" (*Journal of Women's Health*, vol. 18, no. 8, August 2009). The researchers find that women who, when they were born, weighed more than 8 pounds, 13 ounces (4,000 g) were at greater risk for breast cancer than those with birth weights of less than 5 pounds, 8 ounces to

6 pounds, 10 ounces (2,500 to 3,000 g) and that risk followed a classic dose-response pattern—each incremental increase in birth weight increased the risk of developing the disease.

Athanasios Michos, Fei Xue, and Karin B. Michels indicate in "Birth Weight and the Risk of Testicular Cancer: A Meta-Analysis" (*International Journal of Cancer*, vol. 121, no. 5, September 1, 2007) that both low and high birth weight increase the risk of testicular cancer in men. Men with LBW were 18% more likely to develop testicular cancer, and men with high birth weight were 12% more likely to develop the cancer than men of average birth weight.

In "Aerobic Capacity, Strength, Flexibility, and Activity Level in Unimpaired Extremely Low Birth Weight (≤800 g) Survivors at Seventeen Years of Age Compared with Term-Born Control Subjects" (*Pediatrics*, vol. 116, no. 1, July 2005), Marilyn Rogers et al. note that infants born either prematurely or with an extremely low birth weight (ELBW)—1 pound, 12 ounces (800 g)—were significantly more likely to suffer a lower level of fitness later in life, including less strength, endurance, and flexibility, and a greater risk of health problems as adults. When compared with teens born at normal weight, the ELBW teens had lower aerobic capacity, grip strength, leg power, and vertical jump. They were unable to perform as many push-ups, had less abdominal strength as measured by curl-ups, showed less flexibility in their lower backs, and had tighter hamstrings. The ELBW teens reported less previous and current sports participation, lower physical activity levels, and poorer coordination compared with term-born control subjects. ELBW teens also had more trouble maintaining rhythm and tempo than their peers who were born at normal weight.

The only action that can alter the birth weight of an infant is if the mother modifies her weight gain during the pregnancy. In 2009 most health professionals concurred that for normal-weight women the optimal weight gain during pregnancy ranges from 15 to 25 pounds (6.8 to 11.3 kg) of fat and lean mass. Furthermore, Nancy F. Butte et al. of the Children's Nutrition Research Center in Houston, Texas, reveal in "Composition of Gestational Weight Gain Impacts Maternal Fat Retention and Infant Birth Weight" (*American Journal of Obstetrics and Gynecology*, vol. 189, no. 5, November 2003) that a newborn's birth weight and the mother's postpregnancy weight are influenced not only by how much weight is gained during the pregnancy but also by the source of the excess weight. The researchers conducted body scans of 63 women before, during, and after their pregnancies and recorded changes in the women's weight from water, protein, fat, and potassium—a marker for changes in muscle tissue, which is one component of lean mass.

They find that increases in lean mass, and not fat mass, appeared to influence infant size. Independent of how much fat the women gained during pregnancy, only lean body mass increased the birth weight of the infant, with women who gained more lean body mass giving birth to larger infants.

FIRST WEEK OF LIFE MAY DETERMINE ADULT OBESITY. Research demonstrates that low birth weight and low weight gain during infancy are associated with coronary heart disease. Similarly, research indicates that rapid weight gain in infancy is shown to predict obesity in childhood. In 2004 a landmark study funded by the National Institutes of Health and conducted at the Children's Hospital of Philadelphia, University of Pennsylvania School of Medicine, and the Fomon Infant Nutrition Unit, University of Iowa, sought to determine which periods of weight gain in infancy might be associated with adult obesity.

In "Weight Gain in the First Week of Life and Overweight in Adulthood: A Cohort Study of European American Subjects Fed Infant Formula" (*Circulation*, vol. 111, no. 15, April 2005), Nicolas Stettler et al. reviewed data for 653 subjects who had been weighed on seven occasions during infancy and were contacted when they were young adults, aged 20 to 32 years, when they again reported their height and weight. The researchers pinpointed the period between birth and age eight days as potentially critical because weight gain during the first week of life was associated with adulthood overweight status. The formula-fed babies who gained weight rapidly during their first week of life were significantly more likely to be overweight decades later. Stettler et al. conclude that "in formula-fed infants, weight gain during the first week of life may be a critical determinant for the development of obesity several decades later." The researchers also observe that their findings reinforce the recommendation by the American Academy of Pediatrics that infants should be exclusively breast-fed for the first six months of life. Among the many health benefits associated with breast-feeding is the fact that breast-fed babies are much less likely than formula-fed babies to become obese adults.

Janis Baird et al. report in "Being Big or Growing Fast: Systematic Review of Size and Growth in Infancy and Later Obesity" (*British Medical Journal*, vol. 331, no. 929, October 14, 2005) that big babies who grow quickly in the first two years of life risk being obese in childhood and adulthood. The researchers looked at 24 studies that found an association between infant size or growth during the first two years of life and obesity later in life. Baird et al. note that the heaviest infants and those who gained weight rapidly during the first and second year of life faced a ninefold risk of obesity in childhood, adolescence, and adulthood. Their findings suggest that factors in infant growth are probably influencing the risk of later obesity. Baird et al. do not know why big and

fast-growing babies have a higher risk of obesity, but they believe that some factors related to how infants grow are important in influencing their later risk of obesity and suggest that the timing of weaning and social circumstances are factors that merit further investigation.

In "Rapid Postnatal Weight Gain and Visceral Adiposity in Adulthood: The Fels Longitudinal Study" (*Obesity*, April 2009), Ellen W. Demerath et al. report that rapid infant weight gain is not only associated with increased risk for obesity but also with excess deposits of fat in the abdomen and in the abdomen surrounding internal organs. Abdominal obesity is associated with an increased risk for heart disease, diabetes, fatty liver, and other health problems.

DEFINING AND ASSESSING IDEAL WEIGHT, OVERWEIGHT, AND OBESITY

Historically, the determination of desirable, healthy, or ideal weights have been derived from demographic and actuarial statistics (data compiled to assess insurance risk and formulate insurance premiums). The NCHS compiles and analyzes demographic data—the heights and weights of a representative sample of the U.S. population to develop standards for desirable weight. In 1943 the Metropolitan Life Insurance Company (MetLife) introduced standard weight-for-height tables for men and women based on an analysis of actuarial data. The MetLife weight-for-height tables assisted adults in determining if their weight was within an appropriate range for height and frame size. Revised in 1959 and 1983, the tables were based on actuarial data, in which desirable or ideal weight was defined as the weight for height associated with the lowest mortality rate, or longest life span, among the client population of adults (policyholders) insured by MetLife.

Even though the MetLife and other weight-for-height tables remained in use in 2009, many health professionals and medical researchers believe these tables have limited utility. Nearly every weight-for-height table shows different acceptable weight ranges for men and women, and considerable debate continues among health professionals over which table to use. The tables lack information about body composition, such as the ratio of fat to lean muscle mass; their data are derived primarily from white populations and do not represent the entire U.S. population; they generally do not take age into consideration; and it is often unclear how the frame size is determined. Furthermore, it is now known that ideal, healthy, or low-risk weight varies for different populations and varies for the same population at different times and in relation to different causes of morbidity and mortality.

The limitations of weight-for-height tables have prompted health care practitioners and researchers to adopt other measures that allow comparison of weight independent of height and frame across populations to define desirable or healthy weight as well as overweight and obesity. For example, the *Dietary Guidelines for Americans, 2005* (January 2005, http://www.health.gov/ dietaryguidelines/dga2005/document/pdf/DGA2005.pdf), which is published jointly by the U.S. Department of Health and Human Services and the U.S. Department of Agriculture (USDA), includes updated weight-for-height tables for adults that incorporate height, weight, and body mass index (BMI). (See Table 1.2.)

Overweight is generally defined as excess body weight in relation to height, when compared with a pre-determined standard of acceptable, desirable, or ideal weight. One definition characterizes individuals as over-weight if they are between 10 and 30 pounds (4.5 and 13.6 kg) heavier than the desirable weight for height. Overweight does not necessarily result from excessive body fat; people may become overweight as the result of an increase in lean muscle. For example, even though muscular bodybuilders with minimal body fat frequently weigh more than nonathletes of the same height, they are overweight because of their increased muscle mass rather than increased fat.

Rather than viewing overweight and obesity as distinct conditions, many researchers prefer to consider weight as a curve or continuum with obesity at the far end of the curve. People who are obese constitute a subset of the overweight population. In this definition, only some over-weight people are obese, but all obese people are over-weight.

Similarly, there is still no uniform definition of obe-sity. Some health professionals describe anyone who is more than 30 pounds (13.6 kg) above his or her desirable weight for height as obese. Others assert that body weight 20% or more above desirable or ideal body weight con-stitutes obesity. Extreme or clinically severe obesity is often defined as weight twice the desirable weight or 100 pounds (45.3 kg) more than the desirable weight. Obesity is also defined as an excessively high amount of adipose tissue (body fat) in relation to lean body mass such as muscle and bone. The amount of body fat (also known as adiposity), the distribution of fat throughout the body, and the size of the adipose tissue deposits are also used to assess obesity because the location and distribution of body fat are important predictors of the health risks associated with obesity. The location and distribution of body fat may be measured by the ratio of waist-to-hip circumference. High ratios are associated with higher risks of morbidity and mortality.

Overweight and obese body types may be character-ized as apple- or pear-shaped, depending on the anatom-ical site where fat is more prominent. In the apple or android type of obesity, fat is mainly located in the trunk (upper body, nape of the neck, shoulder, and abdomen).

Gynoid obesity, or the pear-shape, features rounded hips and more fat located in the buttocks, thighs, and lower abdomen. Fat cells around the waist, flank, and abdomen are more active metabolically than those in the thighs, hips, and buttocks. This increased metabolic activity is thought to produce the increased health risks associated with android obesity. In general, women are more likely to have gynoid obesity. However, those women with the android type of obesity are subject to similar health risks as males with android overweight.

There are many ways to measure body fat. Weighing an individual underwater in a laboratory with specialized equipment provides a highly accurate assessment of body fat. By performing hydrostatic or underwater weighing, an examiner obtains an estimate of whole-body density and uses this to calculate the percentage of the body that is fat. First, the subject is weighed on a land scale. The subject then puts on a diver's belt with weights to prevent floating during the weighing procedure, sits on a chair that is suspended from a precision scale, and is com-pletely submerged. When maximum expiration of breath is achieved, the subject remains in this submerged posi-tion for about 10 seconds while the investigator reads the scale. This procedure is repeated as many as 10 times to obtain reliable, consistent values. The weight of the diver's belt and chair are subtracted from this weight to obtain the true value of the subject's mass in water.

Simpler, but potentially less accurate assessments of body fat include skinfold thickness measurements, which involve measuring subcutaneous (immediately below the skin) fat deposits using an instrument called a caliper in locations such as the upper arm. Skinfold thickness meas-urements rely on the fact that a certain fraction of total body fat is subcutaneous and by using a representative sample of that fat, the overall body fatness (density) may be predicted. Several skinfold measurements are obtained, and the values are used in equations to calculate body density. Using a caliper, the examiner grasps a fold of skin and subcutaneous fat firmly, pulling it away from the underlying muscle tissue that follows the natural contour of the skin. The caliper jaws exert a relatively constant tension at the point of contact and measure skinfold thickness in millimeters. Most obesity research-ers believe there is an acceptable correlation between skinfold thickness and body fat—that it is possible to estimate body fatness from the use of skinfold calipers. Skinfold thickness measurements are considered more subjective than underwater weights because the accuracy of measurements of skinfold thickness depends on the skill and technique of the examiner, and there may be variations in readings from one examiner to another.

Another technique used to evaluate body fat is bio-electric impedance analysis (BIA). BIA offers an indirect estimate of body fat and lean body mass. It entails passing

TABLE 1.2

Adult BMI (body mass index) chart

BMI Height	19	20	21	22	23	24	25	26	27	28	29	30	31	32	33	34	35
	Healthy weight						Overweight					Obese					
							Weight in pounds										
4'10"	91	96	100	105	110	115	119	124	129	134	138	143	148	153	158	162	167
4'11"	94	99	104	109	114	119	124	128	133	138	143	148	153	158	163	168	173
5'	97	102	107	112	118	123	128	133	138	143	148	153	158	163	168	174	179
5'1"	100	106	111	116	122	127	132	137	143	148	153	158	164	169	174	180	185
5'2"	104	109	115	120	126	131	136	142	147	153	158	164	169	175	180	186	191
5'3"	107	113	118	124	130	135	141	146	152	158	163	169	175	180	186	191	197
5'4"	110	116	122	128	134	140	145	151	157	163	169	174	180	186	192	197	204
5'5"	114	120	126	132	138	144	150	156	162	168	174	180	186	192	198	204	210
5'6"	118	124	130	136	142	148	155	161	167	173	179	186	192	198	204	210	216
5'7"	121	127	134	140	146	153	159	166	172	178	185	191	198	204	211	217	223
5'8"	125	131	138	144	151	158	164	171	177	184	190	197	203	210	216	223	230
5'9"	128	135	142	149	155	162	169	176	182	189	196	203	209	216	223	230	236
5'10"	132	139	146	153	160	167	174	181	188	195	202	209	216	222	229	236	243
5'11"	136	143	150	157	165	172	179	186	193	200	208	215	222	229	236	243	250
6'	140	147	154	162	169	177	184	191	199	206	213	221	228	235	242	250	258
6'1"	144	151	159	166	174	182	189	197	204	212	219	227	235	242	250	257	265
6'2"	148	155	163	171	179	186	194	202	210	218	225	233	241	249	256	264	272
6'3"	152	160	168	176	184	192	200	208	216	224	232	240	248	256	264	272	279

Notes: Locate the height of interest in the left-most column and read across the row for that height to the weight of interest. Follow the column of the weight up to the top row that lists the BMI. BMI of 18.5–24.9 is the healthy range, BMI of 25–29.9 is the overweight range, and BMI of 30 and above is the obese range.

SOURCE: "Figure 2. Adult BMI Chart," in *Dietary Guidelines for Americans, 2005*, 6th ed., U.S. Department of Health and Human Services and U.S. Department of Agriculture, January 2005, http://www.health.gov/dietaryguidelines/dga2005/document/pdf/DGA2005.pdf (accessed October 16, 2009)

an electrical current through the body and assessing the body's ability to conduct the current. It is based on the principle that resistance is inversely proportional to total body water when an electrical current (with a frequency of 70 megahertz) is applied through several electrodes placed on body extremities. Because greater conductivity occurs when there is a higher percent of body water and because a higher percent of body water indicates larger amounts of muscle and other lean tissue (fat cells contain less water than muscle cells), people with less fat are better able to conduct electrical current. BIA has been shown to correlate well with total body fat assessed by other methods.

Other means of estimating the location and distribution of body fat include waist-to-hip circumference ratios and imaging techniques such as ultrasound, computed tomography, or magnetic resonance imaging.

Waist Circumference and Waist-to-Hip Ratio

Along with height and weight, waist circumference is a common measure used to assess abdominal fat content. An excess of body fat in the abdomen or upper body is considered to increase the risk of developing heart disease, high blood pressure, diabetes, stroke, and certain cancers. Like body fat, health risks increase as the waist circumference increases. For men, a waist circumference greater than 40 inches (101.6 cm) is considered to confer increased health risks. Women are considered at increased risk when a waist measurement is 35 inches (88.9 cm) or greater. Waist circumference measures lose their incremental predictive value in people with a BMI greater than or equal to 35 because these individuals generally exceed the cutoff points for increased risk. Table 1.3 shows the relationship between BMI, waist circumference, and disease risk for people who are underweight, normal weight, overweight, obese, and extremely obese.

In fact, research demonstrates that clothing size, which serves as a surrogate for waist circumference, can help predict disease risk. Laura A. E. Hughes et al. find that skirt and trouser sizes correlated well with waist circumference measurements and that bigger skirt and trouser sizes were associated with a greater risk of developing selected cancers. In "Self-Reported Clothing Size as a Proxy Measure for Body Size" (*Epidemiology*, vol. 20, no. 5, September 2009), the researchers indicate that the skirt size predicts the risk for endometrial cancer (cancer of the lining of the uterus) and the trouser size predicts the risk for renal cell carcinoma (kidney cancer).

The waist-to-hip ratio is the ratio of waist circumference to hip circumference, which is calculated by dividing waist circumference by hip circumference. For men and women, a waist-to-hip ratio of 1 or more is considered to place them at greater risk. Most people store body fat at the waist and abdomen (android body fat distribution) or at the hips (gynoid body fat distribution). Interestingly, even though overweight and obesity both increase health risks, body fat that is concentrated in the lower body is thought to be less harmful in terms of morbidity and mortality than abdominal fat.

Body Mass Index

BMI is a single number that evaluates an individual's weight status in relation to height. It does not directly measure the percent of body fat; however, it offers a more accurate assessment of overweight and obesity than weight alone. It is a direct calculation based on height and weight, and it is not gender specific. BMI is the preferred measurement of health care professionals and obesity researchers to assess body fat and is the most common method of tracking overweight and obesity among adults. BMI, which is calculated by dividing weight in kilograms by the square of height in meters,

TABLE 1.3

Classification of overweight and obesity by body mass index (BMI), waist circumference, and associated disease risk

	BMI (kg/m²)	Obesity class	Disease risk[a] relative to normal weight and waist circumference	
			Men ≤ 102 cm (≤ 40 in) Women ≤ 88 cm (≤ 35 in)	> 102 cm (> 40 in) > 88 cm (> 35 in)
Underweight	<18.5		—	—
Normal[b]	18.5–24.9		—	—
Overweight	25.0–29.9		Increased	High
Obesity	30.0–34.9	I	High	Very high
	35.0–39.9	II	Very high	Very high
Extreme obesity	≥40	III	Extremely high	Extremely high

[a]Disease risk for type 2 diabetes, hypertension, and cardiovascular disease.
[b]Increased waist circumference can also be a marker for increased risk even in persons of normal weight.

SOURCE: "Table ES-4. Classification of Overweight and Obesity by BMI, Waist Circumference, and Associated Disease Risk," in *Clinical Guidelines on the Identification, Evaluation, and Treatment of Overweight and Obesity in Adults: The Evidence Report*, National Institutes of Health, National Heart, Lung, and Blood Institute in cooperation with The National Institute of Diabetes and Digestive and Kidney Diseases, September 1998, http://www.ncbi.nlm.nih.gov/bookshelf/br.fcgi?book=obesity&part=A54 (accessed October 16, 2009)

TABLE 1.4

How to calculate body mass index (BMI)

You can calculate BMI as follows

$$BMI = \frac{Weight\ (kg)}{Height\ squared\ (m^2)}$$

If pounds and inches are used

$$BMI = \frac{Weight\ (pounds) \times 703}{Height\ squared\ (inches^2)}$$

Calculation directions and sample

Here is a shortcut method for calculating BMI. (Example: for a person who is 5 feet 5 inches tall weighing 180 lbs.)

1. Multiply weight (in pounds) by 703

180 × 703 = 126,540

2. Multiply height (in inches) by height (in inches)

65 × 65 = 4,225

3. Divide the answer in step 1 by the answer in step 2 to get the BMI.

126,540/4,225 = 29.9

BMI = 29.9

SOURCE: "You Can Calculate BMI as Follows," in *The Practical Guide: Identification, Evaluation, and Treatment of Overweight and Obesity in Adults*, National Institutes of Health, National Heart, Lung, and Blood Institute, North American Association for the Study of Obesity, October 2000, http://www.nhlbi.nih.gov/guidelines/obesity/prctgd_b.pdf (accessed October 16, 2009)

classifies people as underweight, normal weight, overweight, or obese. Table 1.4 shows the formula used to calculate BMI when height is measured in either inches or centimeters and weight is measured in either pounds or kilograms.

The World Health Organization and the National Institutes of Health consider individuals overweight when their BMI is between 25 and 29.9, and they are classified as obese when their BMI exceeds 30. Table 1.2 shows the relationship between height, weight, and BMI. Table 1.3 shows the classification of overweight and obesity by BMI and distinguishes between three levels of obesity.

Even though BMI is a simple, inexpensive tool for assessing weight, it has several limitations. BMI may deem muscular athletes overweight when they are extremely fit and excess weight is the result of a larger amount of lean muscle. It may similarly misrepresent the health of older adults who as the result of muscle wasting (loss of muscle mass) may be considered to have a normal or healthy weight when they may actually be nutritionally depleted or overweight in terms of body fat composition. Even though it is an imperfect method for assessing individuals, BMI is extremely useful for tracking weight trends in the population.

Definitions and Estimates of Prevalence Vary

Historically, varying definitions of, and criteria for, overweight and obesity have affected prevalence statistics

and made it difficult to compare data. Some overweight- and obesity-related prevalence rates are crude or unadjusted estimates; others are age-adjusted estimates that offer different values. Early efforts to track overweight and obesity in the U.S. population relied on the 1943, 1959, and 1983 MetLife tables of desirable weight-for-height as the reference standard for overweight. During the last three decades, most government agencies and public health organizations have estimated overweight using data from a series of surveys conducted by the NCHS. These surveys include the National Health Examination Surveys, the National Health and Nutrition Examination Surveys (NHANES), and the Behavioral Risk Factor Surveillance System.

Despite changing definitions of overweight and obesity and various methods to track changes in the U.S. population, there is irrefutable evidence that the prevalence of overweight and obesity has steadily increased among people of both genders, all ages, all racial and ethnic groups, all educational levels, and all smoking levels. The prevalence of obesity in the United States was first reported in the 1960 National Health Examination Survey, and subsequent reports were derived from three NHANES: NHANES I, 1971; NHANES II, 1976–80; and NHANES III, 1988–94. Most obesity data referenced in the medical literature in 2009 were drawn from the NHANES study conducted between 2003 and 2004 and the 1997 to 2009 National Health Interview Studies, along with several other national studies. Data from the National Health Examination Survey, NHANES I, and NHANES II indicated that the prevalence of obesity was relatively constant from 1960 to 1980; however, the results of the NHANES III indicated a sharp increase in the prevalence of obesity.

Overweight and obesity have steadily progressed at an alarming rate over the course of the past three decades. The National Health and Nutrition Examination findings reported in *Health, United States, 2008* reveal that even though the proportion of American adults who are overweight but not obese held steady at about one-third from 1971–1974 through 2003–2006, the prevalence of obesity (BMI of 30 or more) more than doubled from 15% from 1971–1974 to 34% in 2003–2006 for adults aged 20 to 74 years. Among adults aged 20 and older, the prevalence of obesity rose 8% in less than a little over a decade—from 19% in 1997 to 28% in 2008. (See Figure 1.3.)

The prevalence of overweight and obesity generally increases with advancing age, then starts to decline among people over the age of 60 years. In 2009, for men and women combined, the prevalence of obesity was highest among adults aged 40 to 59 (31%) and lowest among adults aged 20 to 39 (24%). (See Figure 1.4.) There was no significant difference in the prevalence of obesity between men and women in all three age groups.

FIGURE 1.3

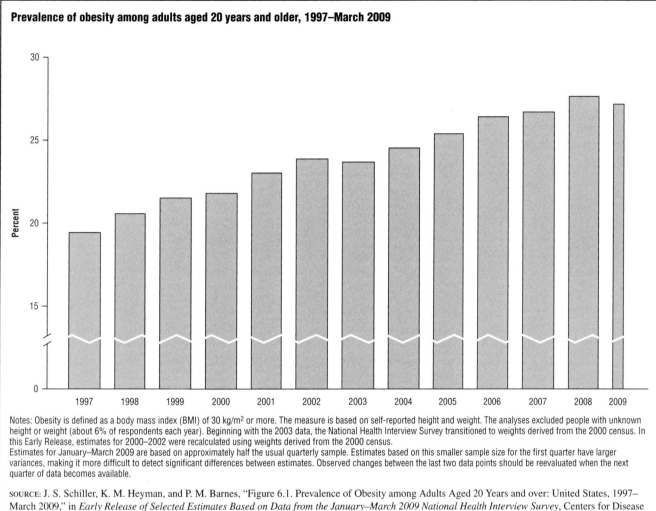

Prevalence of obesity among adults aged 20 years and older, 1997–March 2009

Notes: Obesity is defined as a body mass index (BMI) of 30 kg/m² or more. The measure is based on self-reported height and weight. The analyses excluded people with unknown height or weight (about 6% of respondents each year). Beginning with the 2003 data, the National Health Interview Survey transitioned to weights derived from the 2000 census. In this Early Release, estimates for 2000–2002 were recalculated using weights derived from the 2000 census.
Estimates for January–March 2009 are based on approximately half the usual quarterly sample. Estimates based on this smaller sample size for the first quarter have larger variances, making it more difficult to detect significant differences between estimates. Observed changes between the last two data points should be reevaluated when the next quarter of data becomes available.

SOURCE: J. S. Schiller, K. M. Heyman, and P. M. Barnes, "Figure 6.1. Prevalence of Obesity among Adults Aged 20 Years and over: United States, 1997–March 2009," in *Early Release of Selected Estimates Based on Data from the January–March 2009 National Health Interview Survey*, Centers for Disease Control and Prevention, National Center for Health Statistics, September 2009, http://www.cdc.gov/nchs/data/nhis/earlyrelease/200909_06.pdf (accessed October 16, 2009)

The age-adjusted prevalence of obesity in racial and ethnic minorities, especially minority women, is generally higher than in whites in the United States. According to J. S. Schiller, K. M. Heyman, and P. M. Barnes of the NCHS, in *Early Release of Selected Estimates Based on Data from the January–March 2009 National Health Interview Survey* (September 2009, http://www.cdc.gov/nchs/data/nhis/earlyrelease/200909_06.pdf), in 2009 for both genders, non-Hispanic African-Americans were more likely than Hispanics and non-Hispanic whites to be obese. The age-adjusted prevalence of obesity was highest among non-Hispanic African-American women (46.5%) and lowest among non-Hispanic white women (23.1%). (See Figure 1.5.) Earlier studies, including the NHANES, reported a higher prevalence of overweight and obesity among Hispanics and Native Americans and a lower prevalence of overweight and obesity in Asian-Americans than in the U.S. population as a whole.

WHY ARE SO MANY AMERICANS OVERWEIGHT?

Historically, overweight and obesity were largely attributed to gluttony—solely the result of inappropriate eating. The scientific study of obesity has identified genetic, biochemical, viral, and metabolic alterations in humans and experimental animals, as well as the complex interactions of psychosocial and cultural factors that create susceptibility to overweight and obesity. Even though obesity is thought to result from multiple causes, for the overwhelming majority of Americans, overweight and obesity result from excessive consumption of calories and inadequate physical activity—eating too much and exercising too little.

Some observers maintain that Americans were destined to become overweight when their diets remained unchanged even as the inventions of the Industrial Revolution such as cars, automation, and a variety of laborsaving devices sharply reduced levels of physical activity. The

FIGURE 1.4

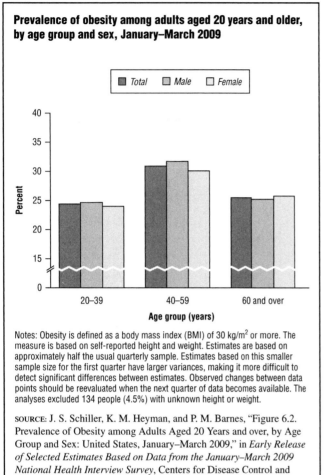

Prevalence of obesity among adults aged 20 years and older, by age group and sex, January–March 2009

Notes: Obesity is defined as a body mass index (BMI) of 30 kg/m² or more. The measure is based on self-reported height and weight. Estimates are based on approximately half the usual quarterly sample. Estimates based on this smaller sample size for the first quarter have larger variances, making it more difficult to detect significant differences between estimates. Observed changes between data points should be reevaluated when the next quarter of data becomes available. The analyses excluded 134 people (4.5%) with unknown height or weight.

SOURCE: J. S. Schiller, K. M. Heyman, and P. M. Barnes, "Figure 6.2. Prevalence of Obesity among Adults Aged 20 Years and over, by Age Group and Sex: United States, January–March 2009," in *Early Release of Selected Estimates Based on Data from the January–March 2009 National Health Interview Survey*, Centers for Disease Control and Prevention, National Center for Health Statistics, September 2009, http://www.cdc.gov/nchs/data/nhis/earlyrelease/200909_06.pdf (accessed October 16, 2009)

FIGURE 1.5

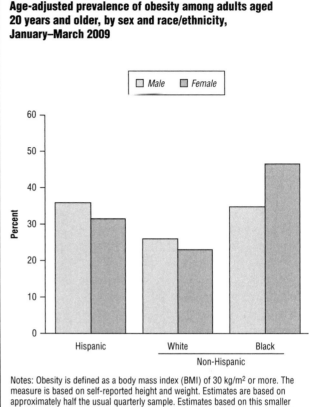

Age-adjusted prevalence of obesity among adults aged 20 years and older, by sex and race/ethnicity, January–March 2009

Notes: Obesity is defined as a body mass index (BMI) of 30 kg/m² or more. The measure is based on self-reported height and weight. Estimates are based on approximately half the usual quarterly sample. Estimates based on this smaller sample size for the first quarter have larger variances, making it more difficult to detect significant differences between estimates. Observed changes between data points should be reevaluated when the next quarter of data becomes available. The analyses excluded 134 people (4.5%) with unknown height or weight. Estimates are age adjusted using the projected 2000 U.S. population as the standard population and using five age groups: 20–24 years, 25–34 years, 35–44 years, 45–64 years, and 65 years and over.

SOURCE: J. S. Schiller, K. M. Heyman, and P. M. Barnes, "Figure 6.3. Age-Adjusted Prevalence of Obesity among Adults Aged 20 Years and over, by Sex and Race/Ethnicity: United States, January–March 2009," in *Early Release of Selected Estimates Based on Data from the January–March 2009 National Health Interview Survey*, Centers for Disease Control and Prevention, National Center for Health Statistics, September 2009, http://www.cdc.gov/nchs/data/nhis/earlyrelease/200909_06.pdf (accessed October 16, 2009)

widespread availability of high-caloric foods and less physically demanding jobs conspired to make Americans fatter. Others contend that the rise in overweight and obesity began during the 1970s, when Americans came to rely on processed, convenient, and calorie-dense, saturated-fat-laden fast foods. In "The Epidemic of Childhood Obesity: A Case for Primary Prevention and Action" (*Bariatric Nursing and Surgical Patient Care*, vol. 4, no. 3, September 22, 2009), Renee Ellen Fox and Deborah E. Trautman cite the interaction of myriad biological and social factors including "dramatic decreases in the amount of calories expended daily, increases in calorie intake and portion sizes, societal changes such as women entering the workforce in large numbers, more meals eaten in restaurants, and changes in television and video game viewing patterns."

Recent research even implicates a viral cause of obesity. Vincent van Ginnekan, Laura Sitnyakowsky, and Jonathan E. Jeffery note in "Infectobesity: Viral Infections (Especially with Human Adenovirus-36: Ad-36) May Be a Cause of Obesity" (*Medical Hypotheses*, vol. 72, no. 4,

April 2009) that the human adenovirus-36 (Ad-36) is capable of inducing adiposity in experimentally infected animals and is known to increase the replication, differentiation, lipid accumulation, and insulin sensitivity in fat cells. (Adenoviruses typically produce respiratory infections.) Recent research finds that in the United States antibodies to Ad-36 are more prevalent in obese subjects (30%) than in nonobese subjects (11%).

The American Diet Has Changed

The American diet has changed dramatically since the middle of the 20th century. According to the USDA, in *Agriculture Fact Book, 2001–2002* (March 2003, http://www.usda.gov/factbook/2002factbook.pdf), during the 1950s food production in the United States provided about 800 fewer calories per person per day than in 2000.

Of the 3,800 calories produced per person per day in 2000, the USDA estimates that about 1,100 calories were wasted, either through spoilage, plate waste, or cooking, leaving an average of about 2,700 calories per person per day. The USDA data reveal that between 1970 and 2000 the average number of calories consumed daily rose by 530 calories, an increase of 24.5%. This 24.5% increase consisted of 9.5 percentage points of grains (primarily refined grain products), 9 percentage points of added fats and oils, 4.7 percentage points of added sugars, 1.5 percentage points of fruits and vegetables, and 1 percentage point of meats and nuts. There was a 1.5 percentage point decline in dairy product and egg consumption.

The USDA states that Americans consumed an average of 4 pounds (1.8 kg) more fish and shellfish, 7 pounds (3.2 kg) more red meat, and 46 pounds (20.9 kg) more poultry per person per year in 2000 than they did during the 1950s. Americans consumed more meat—57 pounds (25.9 kg) more per year in 2000 than they did during the 1950s. Despite record-high per capita (per person) consumption of meat in 2000, the proportion of fat in the U.S. food supply from meat, poultry, and fish declined from one-third (33%) in the 1950s to one-quarter (24%) in 2000. This decline resulted from the marketing of lower-fat ground and processed meat products, a shift away from red meat to poultry, and closer trimming of outside fat on meat, which commenced in 1986.

According to the USDA, the consumption of milk dropped from an annual average of 36.4 gallons (137.8 L) per person in the 1950s to 22.6 gallons (85.6 L) in 2000, a decrease of 38%. The USDA posits a link between the trend toward dining out and the reduction in beverage milk consumption. According to the USDA, soft drinks, fruit drinks, and flavored teas appear to be displacing milk as the beverages of choice for Americans. By contrast, Americans ate more cheese, from 7.7 pounds (3.5 kg) in the 1950s to 29.8 pounds (13.5 kg) in 2000.

The average use of added fats and oils increased 67%, from 44.6 pounds (20.2 kg) in the 1950s to 74.5 pounds (33.8 kg) in 2000. Added fats include butter, shortenings, and oils used in commercially prepared foods. All fats that naturally occur in foods, such as those in milk and meat, were excluded from the USDA analysis. Americans consumed an average of 23% more salad and cooking oil in 2000 than they did during the 1950s, and more than twice as much shortening. During the same period, the consumption of butter and margarine declined by about the same proportion—25%. During the 1950s added fats and oils accounted for the largest proportion of fat in the food supply (41%), followed by animal proteins—meat, poultry, and fish group (32%). By 2000 added fats and oils accounted for 53% of total fat consumption, most likely because Americans' appetites for fried foods in fast-food outlets and high-fat snack foods grew, as did the use of

salad dressings. USDA food consumption surveys, which assess the prevalence of discretionary fats in Americans' diets, continue to find that margarine, salad dressing, and mayonnaise, along with cakes and other sweet baked goods, are among the top 10 food sources of fat in the American diet.

The USDA indicates that the consumption of fruit and vegetables increased 20%, from 587.5 pounds (266.5 kg) in the 1970s to 707.7 pounds (321 kg) in 2000. The USDA attributes some of the increase to the introduction of convenient, ready-to-eat, pre-cut, and packaged fruit and vegetables and to increasing consumer health awareness. Despite these gains, the CDC explains in *State Indicator Report on Fruits and Vegetables, 2009* (September 29, 2009, http://www.fruitsandveggiesmatter.gov/downloads/StateIndicatorReport2009.pdf), a state-by-state study of fruit and vegetable consumption, that no state met the national objectives for fruit and vegetable consumption outlined in Healthy People 2010 (http://www.healthypeople.gov/), the nation's framework for health priorities. The CDC finds that just 32.8% of adults met the recommended two or more servings of fruit and only 27.4% consumed the recommended three or more servings of vegetables in 2009. (See Figure 1.6.) Fruit and vegetable consumption by adolescents was even worse—32.2% said they ate at least two servings of fruit daily and 13.2% said they ate at least three servings of vegetables each day.

According to the USDA, the per capita use of flour and cereal products reached 199.9 pounds (90.7 kg) in 2000, from an annual average of 155.4 pounds (70.5 kg)

FIGURE 1.6

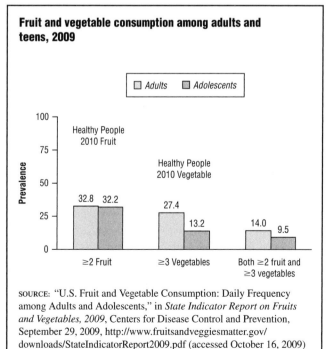

Fruit and vegetable consumption among adults and teens, 2009

SOURCE: "U.S. Fruit and Vegetable Consumption: Daily Frequency among Adults and Adolescents," in *State Indicator Report on Fruits and Vegetables, 2009*, Centers for Disease Control and Prevention, September 29, 2009, http://www.fruitsandveggiesmatter.gov/downloads/StateIndicatorReport2009.pdf (accessed October 16, 2009)

in the 1950s and 138.2 pounds (62.7 kg) in the 1970s, when grain consumption was at a record low. This increase reflects plentiful grain stocks, robust consumer demand for store-bought bakery items and grain-based snack foods, and increased consumption of fast-food products such as buns, pizza dough, and tortillas. Despite the overall increase in grain consumption, the average American's diet contained mostly refined grain products and fell short of the recommended minimum three daily servings of whole grain products.

The USDA cites a variety of factors that have contributed to the changes in the American diet over the past 50 years, including fluctuations in food prices and availability, increases in real (adjusted for inflation) disposable income, and more food assistance for the poor. New products, particularly the expanding array of convenience foods, also alter patterns of consumption, as do more imports, growth in the away-from-home food market, intensified advertising campaigns, and increases in nutrient-enrichment standards and food fortification. The social and demographic trends driving changes in food choices include smaller households, more two-wage earner households, more single-parent households, an aging population, and increased ethnic diversity.

Americans Enjoy Eating Out

A variety of societal trends are thought to contribute to Americans' propensity to overeat, including eating outside the home, as well as ready access to and preference for sugar- and fat-laden foods. Table 1.5 shows how expenditures for eating away from home have steadily increased, and more than doubled from $280 billion in 1993 to $565.3 billion in 2008. This finding is surprising in light of the economic downturn that began in late 2007, which presumably may have prompted some Americans to limit their eating out. Lydia Saad of the Gallup Organization observes in *Restaurant Dining Mostly Holding up Despite Recession* (December 30, 2008, http://www.gallup.com/poll/113617/Restaurant-Dining-Mostly-Holding-Despite-Recession.aspx) that Americans' inclination to dine out in 2008 was relatively unchanged from 2003 and 2005 and that the number of frequent restaurant patrons (people eating out three or more times per week) increased slightly, from 15% in 2005 to 18% in 2008. (See Figure 1.7 and Figure 1.8.)

Many nutritionists and obesity researchers assert that controlling portion size, which is key to controlling calorie consumption, is more difficult in restaurants, where portions are frequently quite large. Increasingly, restaurants have translated consumer demand for value into more food for less money. Because humans are genetically programmed to eat when food is abundant, larger portions trigger the natural impulse to eat more.

Barbara Rolls, Erin L. Morris, and Liane S. Roe of Pennsylvania State University confirm in "Portion Size

of Food Affects Energy Intake in Normal-Weight and Overweight Men and Women" (*American Journal of Clinical Nutrition*, vol. 76, no. 6, December 2002) the notion that when presented with larger portions, people will generally consume more. When they offered research subjects a five-cup portion of macaroni and cheese, the subjects all responded by eating 30% more than they had when they were given portions half that size. Rolls, Morris, and Roe observe that both "restrained and unrestrained eaters" ate more when offered larger portions and assert that Americans have become accustomed to eating too much at one sitting. The problem of portion size is compounded by the observation that Americans are eating larger portions of foods that are high in calories and fat.

In "External Cues in the Control of Food Intake in Humans: The Sensory-Normative Distinction" (*Physiology & Behavior*, vol. 94, no. 5, August 2008), C. Peter Herman and Janet Polivy verify that external cues such as portion size exert a strong influence on food intake—when presented with larger portions, people will generally consume more. Furthermore, Herman and Polivy assert that most people are affected by external cues such as portion size, but that sensory cues, such as the extent to which the food is perceived as tasty, have a more powerful affect on people who are obese than they do on people who have a healthy weight.

BIGGER PORTIONS IN RESTAURANTS. Samara Joy Nielsen and Barry M. Popkin of the University of North Carolina, Chapel Hill, looked at portion size consumed in the United States to determine whether average portion sizes had increased over time. They reported their findings in "Patterns and Trends in Food Portion Sizes, 1977–1998" (*Journal of the American Medical Association*, vol. 289, no. 4, January 22, 2003). In this landmark study, Nielsen and Popkin analyzed data collected by national nutrition surveys—the Nationwide Food Consumption Survey and the Continuing Survey of Food Intake by Individuals—conducted in the United States in 1977, 1989, 1994, and 1996, detailing the consumption habits of more than 63,000 people. For each survey year, the researchers analyzed the average portion sizes consumed of specific food items (salty snacks, desserts, soft drinks, fruit drinks, French fries, hamburgers, cheeseburgers, pizza, and Mexican food) by eating location (home, restaurant, and fast-food outlet). Nielsen and Popkin report that over the past two decades the average portions of salty snacks such as chips have increased by 60% and soft drinks have grown by 50%. The average bag of chips grew from 1 ounce (28.3 g) in 1977 to 1.6 ounces (45.4 g) in 1996. During this same period, an average dispensed soft drink increased from 13.1 ounces (387.4 mL) to 19.9 ounces (588.5 mL). As a result, the average chips-and-soda snack contains 150 more calories than it did two decades before.

TABLE 1.5

Food away from home, total expenditures, selected years 1929–2008

Year	Eating and drinking places[a]	Hotels and motels[a]	Retail stores, direct selling[b]	Recreational places[c]	Schools and colleges[d]	All other[e]	Total[f]
			Million dollars				
1929	2,101	362	—	—	175	1,483	4,121
1933	1,235	250	—	—	105	869	2,459
1935	1,257	271	—	—	161	1,145	2,834
1936	1,430	320	—	—	175	1,236	3,161
1937	1,696	351	—	—	194	1,375	3,616
1938	1,626	312	—	—	191	1,260	3,389
1939	1,782	321	—	—	203	1,307	3,613
1940	1,938	353	—	—	219	1,385	3,895
1941	2,369	386	—	—	263	1,781	4,799
1942	2,992	453	—	—	310	2,539	6,294
1943	3,837	604	—	—	332	3,572	8,345
1944	4,471	681	—	—	326	4,415	9,893
1945	5,218	736	—	—	373	4,908	11,235
1946	5,859	846	—	—	525	3,802	11,032
1947	6,243	854	—	—	842	3,864	11,803
1948	6,338	846	—	—	983	4,069	12,236
1949	6,294	786	—	—	979	3,943	12,002
1950	6,472	774	—	—	1,051	4,172	12,469
1951	7,172	783	—	—	1,124	5,167	14,246
1952	7,549	805	—	—	1,138	5,435	14,927
1953	7,834	790	—	—	1,215	5,392	15,231
1954	8,008	752	1,416	274	1,311	3,676	15,437
1955	8,490	809	1,468	313	1,390	3,539	16,009
1956	8,992	875	1,534	354	1,530	3,506	16,791
1957	9,409	932	1,592	342	1,661	3,609	17,545
1958	9,447	922	1,599	356	1,809	3,756	17,889
1959	10,102	982	1,677	385	1,949	3,739	18,834
1960	10,505	1,028	1,716	421	2,082	3,855	19,607
1961	10,907	1,061	1,740	452	2,264	3,961	20,385
1962	11,624	1,134	1,812	472	2,463	4,090	21,595
1963	12,247	1,200	1,854	484	2,624	4,148	22,557
1964	13,156	1,289	1,988	496	2,814	4,279	24,022
1965	14,444	1,409	2,162	522	3,062	4,598	26,197
1966	15,768	1,541	2,346	544	3,329	5,173	28,701
1967	16,595	1,623	2,436	563	3,632	5,570	30,419
1968	18,695	1,703	2,713	616	3,903	5,830	33,460
1969	20,207	1,716	2,984	661	4,256	6,291	36,115
1970	22,617	1,894	3,325	721	4,475	6,551	39,583
1971	24,166	2,086	3,626	762	4,990	6,621	42,251
1972	27,167	2,390	3,811	832	5,370	7,017	46,587
1973	31,265	2,639	4,218	963	5,605	7,960	52,650
1974	34,029	2,864	4,520	1,167	6,287	9,178	58,045
1975	41,384	3,199	4,952	1,369	7,060	10,145	68,109
1976	47,536	3,769	5,341	1,511	7,854	10,822	76,833
1977	52,491	4,115	5,663	2,606	8,413	11,547	84,835
1978	60,042	4,863	6,323	2,810	9,034	13,012	96,084
1979	68,872	5,551	7,157	2,921	9,914	14,756	109,171
1980	75,883	5,906	8,158	3,040	11,115	16,194	120,296
1981	83,358	6,639	8,830	2,979	11,357	17,751	130,914
1982	90,390	6,888	9,256	2,887	11,692	18,663	139,776
1983	98,710	7,660	9,827	3,271	12,338	19,077	150,883
1984	105,836	8,409	10,315	3,489	12,950	20,047	161,046
1985	111,760	9,168	10,499	3,737	13,534	20,133	168,831
1986	121,699	9,665	11,116	4,059	14,401	20,755	181,695
1987	137,190	11,117	11,860	4,396	13,470	21,122	199,155
1988	150,724	11,905	12,972	5,082	13,889	22,471	217,044
1989	160,226	12,179	14,153	6,089	14,609	24,005	231,261
1990	171,616	12,508	15,763	7,206	15,299	25,744	248,136
1991	180,062	12,460	16,513	7,936	16,186	26,379	259,535
1992	184,860	13,204	13,595	8,513	17,666	27,128	264,966
1993	197,987	13,362	13,704	9,365	18,330	27,216	279,964
1994	207,545	13,880	14,008	10,107	19,271	27,655	292,466
1995	216,091	14,211	14,040	11,081	20,064	28,138	303,624
1996	223,546	14,553	14,056	11,515	20,867	28,602	313,139

The portion-size changes were observed with many fast-food offerings. During the 20 years studied, the size of the average hamburger grew by 23%, to 7 ounces (198.4 g), and servings of fries grew by 16%, to 3.5 ounces (99.2 g). A regular-sized burger-and-fries meal contained 155 calories more than it did in 1977. Worse still, Nielsen

TABLE 1.5

Food away from home, total expenditures, selected years 1929–2008 [CONTINUED]

Year	Eating and drinking places[a]	Hotels and motels[a]	Retail stores, direct selling[b]	Recreational places[c]	Schools and colleges[d]	All other[e]	Total[f]
			Million dollars				
1997	237,475	15,381	13,764	12,283	21,901	31,006	331,810
1998	250,495	16,069	14,872	13,048	23,053	32,053	349,590
1999	261,527	16,710	16,492	13,039	23,920	33,461	365,951
2000	282,236	18,003	16,932	14,662	24,468	35,157	391,457
2001	289,331	20,813	18,056	15,316	25,394	35,794	404,705
2002	300,753	21,812	19,753	16,235	26,735	36,169	421,283
2003	317,522	22,049	19,701	16,635	28,077	37,762	441,745
2004	338,147	22,543	20,012	16,797	29,287	39,368	466,153
2005	358,816	22,923	20,519	17,336	30,271	41,581	491,445
2006	382,193	23,093	24,257	18,163	30,897	43,153	521,758
2007	402,176	23,178	25,357	18,988	31,859	45,692	547,250
2008	417,064	23,772	24,198	19,691	33,130	47,429	565,284

—Not available.
[a]Includes tips.
[b]Includes vending machine operators but not vending machines operated by organizations.
[c]Motion picture theaters, bowling alleys, pool parlors, sports arenas, camps, amusement parks, golf and country clubs (includes concessions in 1977).
[d]Includes school food subsidies.
[e]Military exchanges and clubs; railroad dining cars; airlines; food service in manufacturing plants, institutions, hospitals, boarding houses, and sororities, and civic and social organizations; and food supplied to military forces, civilian employees and child day care centers.
[f]Computed from unrounded data.

SOURCE: "Table 3. Food away from Home: Total Expenditures," in *Food CPI and Expenditures: Food Expenditure Tables*, U.S. Department of Agriculture, Economic Research Service, June 17, 2008, http://www.ers.usda.gov/briefing/CPIFoodAndExpenditures/Data/table3.htm (accessed October 16, 2009)

FIGURE 1.7

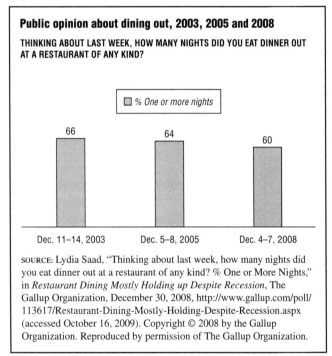

Public opinion about dining out, 2003, 2005 and 2008

THINKING ABOUT LAST WEEK, HOW MANY NIGHTS DID YOU EAT DINNER OUT AT A RESTAURANT OF ANY KIND?

☐ % One or more nights

66 — Dec. 11–14, 2003
64 — Dec. 5–8, 2005
60 — Dec. 4–7, 2008

SOURCE: Lydia Saad, "Thinking about last week, how many nights did you eat dinner out at a restaurant of any kind? % One or More Nights," in *Restaurant Dining Mostly Holding up Despite Recession*, The Gallup Organization, December 30, 2008, http://www.gallup.com/poll/113617/Restaurant-Dining-Mostly-Holding-Despite-Recession.aspx (accessed October 16, 2009). Copyright © 2008 by the Gallup Organization. Reproduced by permission of The Gallup Organization.

and Popkin find that portion size had also expanded in Americans' homes, indicating widespread ignorance about appropriate portion size. Interestingly, portion sizes were smallest in restaurants, although they, too, had increased during the study period. For example, the average restaurant portion of spaghetti with tomato sauce and meatballs doubled in size from 500 to 1,025 calories.

In "Increased Portion Size Leads to Increased Energy Intake in a Restaurant Meal" (*Obesity Research*, vol. 12, no. 3, March 2004), Nicole Diliberti et al. of Pennsylvania State University find that larger portions served in restaurants resulted in patrons consuming more calories. The investigators covertly recorded the food intake of patrons who selected a pasta entrée over a 10-day period of a cafeteria-style restaurant on a university campus. On five days the portion size of the entrée was the standard portion, and on five different days the size was increased to 150% of the standard portion. Subjects were also asked to complete a survey to determine perceptions of the portion size of the entrée and of the amount that they ate. The subjects who completed the survey were unaware that their intake was being monitored.

Diliberti et al. posited that when the portion size of an entrée was increased by 150%, the subjects would consume significantly more than when the standard portion was offered. They also sought to determine whether the subjects would compensate for the increased intake from the entrée by reducing their consumption of other foods at the meal and whether they could identify any characteristics of subjects that would predict how they would respond to the increased portion size.

When the larger portion size was offered, the subjects who purchased it consumed 43% more of the entrée than those who purchased the standard portion size. The subjects who purchased the larger portion also ate significantly more of the entrée accompaniments (tomato, roll, and butter) than those who purchased the standard portion, even though the portion size of the accompaniments was the same for all subjects.

FIGURE 1.8

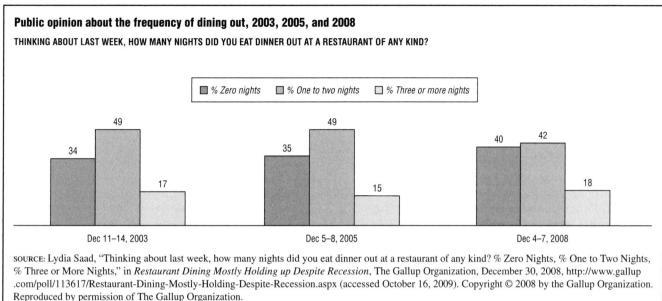

Public opinion about the frequency of dining out, 2003, 2005, and 2008

THINKING ABOUT LAST WEEK, HOW MANY NIGHTS DID YOU EAT DINNER OUT AT A RESTAURANT OF ANY KIND?

SOURCE: Lydia Saad, "Thinking about last week, how many nights did you eat dinner out at a restaurant of any kind? % Zero Nights, % One to Two Nights, % Three or More Nights," in *Restaurant Dining Mostly Holding up Despite Recession*, The Gallup Organization, December 30, 2008, http://www.gallup.com/poll/113617/Restaurant-Dining-Mostly-Holding-Despite-Recession.aspx (accessed October 16, 2009). Copyright © 2008 by the Gallup Organization. Reproduced by permission of The Gallup Organization.

Overall, ratings of the appropriateness of the portion size of the entrée did not differ between the subjects given the 150% portion and those who received the standard portion. There was, however, an effect of subject body size on this rating. Underweight and normal-weight subjects who purchased the 150% portion rated it as closer to the "too large" end of the seven-point scale than those who purchased the standard portion. In contrast, overweight and obese subjects did not rate the portion size as "too large." Diliberti et al. conclude that subjects ate significantly more when the portion size was increased, and their responses to the survey indicate that they were unaware that the portion was larger than normal or that they had consumed more food.

AND BIGGER PORTIONS AT HOME. Increased portion sizes at home are reflected in recipes and cookbooks. Lisa R. Young notes in *The Portion Teller: Smartsize Your Way to Permanent Weight Loss* (2005) that recipes call for bigger portions using the same ingredients than they did in past decades. For example, a brownie recipe from Irma S. Rombauer and Marion Rombauer Becker's *Joy of Cooking* (1964) recommended dividing it into 30 servings, whereas the same recipe in the 1997 edition of the book was divided into only 16 servings. Similarly, a 1987 recipe for Toll House cookies yielded 60 servings, whereas in earlier decades the same recipe yielded 100 servings. Other popular food items have increased in size and caloric content. In "Portion Distortion" (2010, http://hp2010.nhlbihin.net/portion/), the National Heart, Lung, and Blood Institute compares portion sizes and the corresponding calories of several popular foods from 1983 to 2003. Researchers find that two decades earlier a bagel measured 3 inches (7.6 cm) in diameter and contained 140 calories. In 2003 a 6-inch (15.2 cm) bagel contained 350 calories.

Nielsen and Popkin also note other changes in eating behavior. For example, they find that Americans obtain 19% of their total calories from snacks—double the amount of 1977—and 81% from meals. They conclude that "control of portion size must be systematically addressed both in general and as it relates to fast food pricing and marketing. The best way to encourage people to eat smaller portions is if food portions served inside and outside the home are smaller."

Even though the Nationwide Food Consumption Survey and the Continuing Survey of Food Intake by Individuals have not been repeated since 1996, there is no evidence that portion sizes have returned to their previous sizes or have even decreased in size. In a review of research about portion size, Ingrid H. M. Steenhuis and Willemijn M. Vermeer of Vrije Universiteit Amsterdam observe in "Portion Size: Review and Framework for Interventions" (*International Journal of Behavioral Nutrition and Physical Activity*, vol. 6, no. 58, August 21, 2009) that since the 1970s portion sizes, especially of high energy-dense (high calorie) foods eaten at home and in restaurants, have increased. The researchers confirm that "portion distortion," a term used to describe the phenomenon of people becoming acclimated to larger portions so that they not only do not view them as excessive but also have more difficulty selecting appropriate amounts of food, definitely increases consumption by at least 30%.

Technology Satisfies the Hunger for Quick, Inexpensive Food

In "Why Have Americans Become More Obese?" (*Journal of Economic Perspectives*, vol. 17, no. 3, summer 2003), David M. Cutler, Edward L. Glaeser, and Jesse M. Shapiro of Harvard University refute the notion that increased portion sizes, increasingly sedentary lifestyles, or restaurant dining are responsible for Americans' widening waistlines. After examining nearly 100 years of nutritional data, they determine that technological advances have increased the efficiency of food production and made food more varied, convenient, tastier, and cheaper.

Cutler, Glaeser, and Shapiro illustrate how efficiencies in food preparation have revolutionized Americans' eating habits. They compare the speed and ease of preparation of commercial French fries with the previously time-consuming, labor-intensive process of scrubbing, peeling, paring, and frying that was required to prepare French fries. They observe that during the 1960s women spent an average of two hours per day on meal preparation—twice as long as the time devoted to meal preparation in 2003 by the average American woman not working outside the home. It takes considerably less time in the 21st century to prepare food because of advances in food processing and packaging. Furthermore, technology improvements in the home, such as the microwave oven, have made it easier to eat quickly on demand.

According to Cutler, Glaeser, and Shapiro, increased food consumption is at least in part attributable to "a reduction in time costs of food preparation of about 20 minutes per person per day from 1965 to 1995." They also find that the average number of daily snacks between meals has risen by 60% since the late 1970s. Unable to resist the tempting, affordable variety of foods, Americans engage in more frequent snacking, consuming the excess calories that ultimately result in becoming overweight.

Is the Food Industry the Culprit?

Kelly D. Brownell and Katherine Battle Horgen cite in *Food Fight: The Inside Story of the Food Industry, America's Obesity Crisis, and What We Can Do about It* (2004) a "near-total surrender to a powerful food industry" as one of the main causes of the obesity epidemic in the United States. Brownell and Horgen contend that the obesity epidemic represents more than a failure of Americans to assume personal responsibility and exercise willpower over their appetite. They exhort consumers to agitate against a food industry intent on fattening them and to work to counteract a variety of unhealthy social trends. They lament the supersized meals and sedentary lifestyles, including Americans' "car-centric" culture that actively discourages walking and encourages children to sit in front of the television, video games, and computers while eliminating physical education classes from schools, but they insist that the food industry bears most of the responsibility for the rise in obesity. Brownell and Horgen argue that Americans feed their pets better than their children and that children are induced and manipulated by food industry media advertising to adopt poor eating habits and to consume high-caloric, low-nutrition junk food.

Brownell and Horgen cite toy giveaways, movie tie-ins, and in-school promotions as evidence of effective strategies employed by the politically powerful food industry to promote fast-food consumption. They feel that the battle against these pervasive influences is one that parents cannot win because even children receiving consistent, sound nutritional counseling from parents are not immune to the effects of multiple, powerful exposures to media advertising. Brownell and Horgen call for a nationwide, grassroots movement to reverse these trends and advocate specific measures such as junk-food taxes and banning advertisements that target children.

Greg Critser also indicts the food industry in *Fat Land: How Americans Became the Fattest People in the World* (2004). He presents a critical analysis of the many social and economic factors that make Americans among the most overweight people in the world. Critser believes that chief among these factors is high-fructose corn syrup, a low-cost sweetener that was developed in 1957 by Japanese scientists in response to an overabundance of inexpensive corn. Corn syrup does more than sweeten; it also acts as a preservative, giving sweet foods a longer shelf life. Since the 1970s high-fructose corn syrup has been used to sweeten nearly every product on supermarket shelves, from cereal to soda. Some researchers feel that because it is so ubiquitous, many Americans are unknowingly consuming excessive amounts of fructose. Table 1.6 shows the per capita consumption of high-fructose corn syrup, which peaked in 1999 and has since slowly declined.

Fructose also appears to trigger fat storage more efficiently than other sugars do. New studies show that the body does not metabolize high-fructose corn syrup well. Even though all sugars are stored in the body as fat, some researchers think that fructose is more readily converted into fat than other sugars. The fructose encourages the liver to promote fat by activating enzymes that create higher levels of cholesterol and triglycerides (fatty substances that are normally present in the bloodstream and all the cells of the body) and make muscles more insulin resistant. Elevated levels of cholesterol and triglycerides increase the risk of coronary heart disease. Insulin resistance can lead to diabetes.

Critser also explains that once the staples used to produce fast foods became cheaper, the industry intensified marketing efforts to induce consumers to buy and eat more. Table 1.7 shows that food expenditures have consistently decreased as a percent of disposable personal income, declining from 23.4% of personal disposable income in 1929 to just 9.6% in 2008. Critser observes that a serving of McDonald's French fries "ballooned from 200 calories (1960) ... to the present 610 calories" and that Americans' appetites grew to expect and demand the bigger servings. He notes that changing values and lifestyles conspired to fatten Americans. Furthermore, he

TABLE 1.6

Estimated number of per capita calories of high fructose corn syrup consumed daily, 1970–2008

Year	Primary weight (market level)[a]	Loss from primary to retail weight	Weight at retail level	Loss from retail/institutional to consumer level	Weight at consumer level	Loss at consumer level Nonedible share	Loss at consumer level Other (uneaten food, spoilage, etc.)	Per capita consumption (adjusted for loss)			Calories per serving	Serving weight	Calories consumed daily[b]	Servings (teaspoons) consumed daily[c]
	lb/yr	percent	lb/yr	percent	lb/yr	percent	percent	lbs/yr	oz/daily	g/daily	number	grams	number	teaspoons
1970	0.5	0.0	0.5	11.0	0.5	0.0	20.0	0.4	0.0	0.5	16.0	4.2	2	0.1
1971	0.8	0.0	0.8	11.0	0.7	0.0	20.0	0.6	0.0	0.7	16.0	4.2	3	0.2
1972	1.2	0.0	1.2	11.0	1.0	0.0	20.0	0.8	0.0	1.0	16.0	4.2	4	0.2
1973	2.1	0.0	2.1	11.0	1.8	0.0	20.0	1.5	0.1	1.8	16.0	4.2	7	0.4
1974	2.8	0.0	2.8	11.0	2.5	0.0	20.0	2.0	0.1	2.4	16.0	4.2	9	0.6
1975	4.9	0.0	4.9	11.0	4.3	0.0	20.0	3.5	0.2	4.3	16.0	4.2	16	1.0
1976	7.2	0.0	7.2	11.0	6.4	0.0	20.0	5.1	0.2	6.3	16.0	4.2	24	1.5
1977	9.6	0.0	9.6	11.0	8.5	0.0	20.0	6.8	0.3	8.5	16.0	4.2	32	2.0
1978	10.8	0.0	10.8	11.0	9.6	0.0	20.0	7.7	0.3	9.5	16.0	4.2	36	2.3
1979	14.8	0.0	14.8	11.0	13.1	0.0	20.0	10.5	0.5	13.1	16.0	4.2	50	3.1
1980	19.0	0.0	19.0	11.0	16.9	0.0	20.0	13.5	0.6	16.8	16.0	4.2	64	4.0
1981	22.8	0.0	22.8	11.0	20.3	0.0	20.0	16.3	0.7	20.2	16.0	4.2	77	4.8
1982	26.6	0.0	26.6	11.0	23.7	0.0	20.0	19.0	0.8	23.6	16.0	4.2	90	5.6
1983	31.2	0.0	31.2	11.0	27.8	0.0	20.0	22.2	1.0	27.6	16.0	4.2	105	6.6
1984	37.2	0.0	37.2	11.0	33.1	0.0	20.0	26.5	1.2	32.9	16.0	4.2	125	7.8
1985	45.2	0.0	45.2	11.0	40.2	0.0	20.0	32.2	1.4	40.0	16.0	4.2	152	9.5
1986	45.7	0.0	45.7	11.0	40.7	0.0	20.0	32.5	1.4	40.4	16.0	4.2	154	9.6
1987	47.7	0.0	47.7	11.0	42.5	0.0	20.0	34.0	1.5	42.2	16.0	4.2	161	10.1
1988	49.0	0.0	49.0	11.0	43.6	0.0	20.0	34.9	1.5	43.3	16.0	4.2	165	10.3
1989	48.2	0.0	48.2	11.0	42.9	0.0	20.0	34.3	1.5	42.6	16.0	4.2	162	10.2
1990	49.6	0.0	49.6	11.0	44.1	0.0	20.0	35.3	1.5	43.9	16.0	4.2	167	10.4
1991	50.3	0.0	50.3	11.0	44.8	0.0	20.0	35.8	1.6	44.5	16.0	4.2	170	10.6
1992	51.8	0.0	51.8	11.0	46.1	0.0	20.0	36.9	1.6	45.8	16.0	4.2	175	10.9
1993	54.5	0.0	54.5	11.0	48.5	0.0	20.0	38.8	1.7	48.2	16.0	4.2	184	11.5
1994	56.2	0.0	56.2	11.0	50.0	0.0	20.0	40.0	1.8	49.7	16.0	4.2	189	11.8
1995	57.6	0.0	57.6	11.0	51.3	0.0	20.0	41.0	1.8	51.0	16.0	4.2	194	12.1
1996	57.8	0.0	57.8	11.0	51.4	0.0	20.0	41.1	1.8	51.1	16.0	4.2	195	12.2
1997	60.4	0.0	60.4	11.0	53.7	0.0	20.0	43.0	1.9	53.4	16.0	4.2	204	12.7
1998	61.9	0.0	61.9	11.0	55.1	0.0	20.0	44.1	1.9	54.8	16.0	4.2	209	13.0
1999	63.7	0.0	63.7	11.0	56.7	0.0	20.0	45.4	2.0	56.4	16.0	4.2	215	13.4
2000	62.7	0.0	62.7	11.0	55.8	0.0	20.0	44.6	2.0	55.4	16.0	4.2	211	13.2
2001	62.6	0.0	62.6	11.0	55.7	0.0	20.0	44.6	2.0	55.4	16.0	4.2	211	13.2
2002	62.9	0.0	62.9	11.0	56.0	0.0	20.0	44.8	2.0	55.6	16.0	4.2	212	13.2
2003	61.0	0.0	61.0	11.0	54.2	0.0	20.0	43.4	1.9	53.9	16.0	4.2	205	12.8
2004	59.9	0.0	59.9	11.0	53.3	0.0	20.0	42.7	1.9	53.0	16.0	4.2	202	12.6
2005	59.2	0.0	59.2	11.0	52.7	0.0	20.0	42.2	1.8	52.4	16.0	4.2	200	12.5
2006	58.3	0.0	58.3	11.0	51.9	0.0	20.0	41.5	1.8	51.6	16.0	4.2	197	12.3
2007	56.3	0.0	56.3	11.0	50.1	0.0	20.0	40.1	1.8	49.8	16.0	4.2	190	11.9
2008	53.2	0.0	53.2	11.0	47.3	0.0	20.0	37.9	1.7	47.1	16.0	4.2	179	11.2

Note: Estimated number of daily per capita calories calculated by adjusting HFCS deliveries for domestic food and beverage use for food losses. HFCS = High fructose corn syrup.

[a]U.S. per capita HFCS estimated deliveries for domestic food and beverage use, calendar year.

[b]Number of daily teaspoons multiplied by calories per serving.

[c]Grams per day divided by serving weight.

SOURCE: "Table 52. High Fructose Corn Syrup: Estimated Number of per Capita Calories Consumed Daily, by Calendar Year," in *Sugar and Sweeteners: Recommended Data*, U.S. Department of Agriculture, Economic Research Service, May 28, 2009, http://www.ers.usda.gov/Briefing/Sugar/Data/Table52.xls (accessed October 18, 2009)

TABLE 1.7

Food expenditures by families and individuals as a share of disposable personal income, 1929–2008

Year	Disposable personal income Billion dollars	At home[a] Billion dollars	Percent	Away from home[b] Billion dollars	Percent	Total[c] Billion dollars	Percent
1929	83.4	16.9	20.3	2.6	3.1	19.5	23.4
1930	74.7	15.8	21.2	2.3	3.1	18.1	24.2
1931	64.3	12.7	19.8	2.1	3.3	14.8	23.0
1932	49.2	9.6	19.5	1.7	3.5	11.3	23.0
1933	46.1	10.1	21.9	1.5	3.3	11.6	25.2
1934	52.8	11.1	21.0	1.7	3.2	12.8	24.2
1935	59.3	12.1	20.4	1.8	3.0	13.9	23.4
1936	67.4	12.7	18.8	2.0	3.0	14.7	21.8
1937	72.2	13.3	18.4	2.2	3.0	15.5	21.5
1938	66.6	12.6	18.9	2.1	3.2	14.7	22.1
1939	71.4	13.0	18.1	2.3	3.2	15.2	21.3
1940	76.8	13.5	17.6	2.4	3.1	15.9	20.7
1941	93.8	15.3	16.3	2.9	3.1	18.2	19.4
1942	118.6	18.5	15.6	3.6	3.0	22.1	18.6
1943	135.4	20.7	15.3	4.5	3.3	25.2	18.6
1944	148.3	22.1	14.9	5.1	3.4	27.2	18.4
1945	152.2	23.6	15.5	5.7	3.7	29.3	19.2
1946	161.4	28.4	17.6	6.5	4.0	34.9	21.6
1947	171.2	32.8	19.2	7.4	4.3	40.2	23.5
1948	190.6	34.9	18.3	7.5	3.9	42.4	22.3
1949	190.4	34.3	18.0	7.8	4.1	42.0	22.1
1950	210.1	35.7	17.0	7.6	3.6	43.3	20.6
1951	231.0	40.0	17.3	8.4	3.6	48.4	20.9
1952	243.4	41.8	17.2	8.8	3.6	50.6	20.8
1953	258.6	42.3	16.4	9.0	3.5	51.3	19.9
1954	264.3	42.4	16.0	9.3	3.5	51.7	19.6
1955	283.3	42.9	15.1	9.8	3.5	52.7	18.6
1956	303.0	44.4	14.7	10.4	3.4	54.8	18.1
1957	319.8	48.1	15.0	10.9	3.4	59.0	18.4
1958	330.5	49.8	15.1	11.1	3.4	60.9	18.4
1959	350.5	50.1	14.3	12.1	3.5	62.3	17.8
1960	365.4	51.5	14.1	12.6	3.4	64.0	17.5
1961	381.8	52.0	13.6	13.1	3.4	65.1	17.1
1962	405.1	52.9	13.1	13.9	3.4	66.8	16.5
1963	425.1	53.3	12.5	14.5	3.4	67.9	16.0
1964	462.5	55.5	12.0	15.7	3.4	71.2	15.4
1965	498.1	58.4	11.7	16.9	3.4	75.4	15.1
1966	537.5	61.0	11.3	18.6	3.5	79.6	14.8
1967	575.3	61.4	10.7	19.8	3.4	81.1	14.1
1968	625.0	64.5	10.3	21.7	3.5	86.2	13.8
1969	674.0	69.0	10.2	23.4	3.5	92.3	13.7
1970	735.7	75.5	10.3	26.4	3.6	102.0	13.9
1971	801.8	79.5	9.9	28.1	3.5	107.6	13.4
1972	869.1	86.0	9.9	31.3	3.6	117.3	13.5
1973	978.3	94.9	9.7	34.9	3.6	129.8	13.3
1974	1,071.6	107.3	10.0	38.5	3.6	145.8	13.6
1975	1,187.4	117.4	9.9	45.9	3.9	163.3	13.8
1976	1,302.5	125.1	9.6	52.6	4.0	177.7	13.6
1977	1,435.7	133.8	9.3	58.5	4.1	192.3	13.4
1978	1,608.3	147.3	9.2	67.5	4.2	214.8	13.4
1979	1,793.5	164.0	9.1	76.9	4.3	240.9	13.4
1980	2,009.0	180.8	9.0	85.2	4.2	266.0	13.2
1981	2,246.1	195.5	8.7	95.8	4.3	291.3	13.0
1982	2,421.2	201.0	8.3	104.5	4.3	305.5	12.6
1983	2,608.4	211.4	8.1	113.7	4.4	325.1	12.5
1984	2,912.0	224.0	7.7	121.9	4.2	345.8	11.9
1985	3,109.3	234.0	7.5	128.6	4.1	362.6	11.7
1986	3,285.1	242.7	7.4	137.9	4.2	380.6	11.6
1987	3,458.1	252.7	7.3	146.4	4.2	399.0	11.5
1988	3,748.7	255.9	6.8	157.5	4.2	413.4	11.0
1989	4,021.7	274.8	6.8	165.4	4.1	440.2	10.9
1990	4,285.8	299.7	7.0	177.4	4.1	477.1	11.1
1991	4,464.3	313.5	7.0	186.3	4.2	499.8	11.2

describes the rise of a "new boundary-free culture" that promoted consumption of sugar- and fat-laden foods. Traditionally, families convened for home-cooked dinners, but Critser describes the rushed parents of the 1980s as preferring to eat out or take in prepared foods. Childcare experts popularized the theory that children instinctively

TABLE 1.7

Food expenditures by families and individuals as a share of disposable personal income, 1929–2008 [CONTINUED]

Year	Disposable personal income Billion dollars	Expenditures for food					
		At home[a]		Away from home[b]		Total[c]	
		Billion dollars	Percent	Billion dollars	Percent	Billion dollars	Percent
1992	4,751.4	313.6	6.6	191.9	4.0	505.5	10.6
1993	4,911.9	323.3	6.6	205.9	4.2	529.1	10.8
1994	5,151.8	337.1	6.5	216.5	4.2	553.5	10.7
1995	5,408.2	345.5	6.4	226.2	4.2	571.7	10.6
1996	5,688.5	360.6	6.3	233.2	4.1	593.8	10.4
1997	5,988.8	377.2	6.3	246.3	4.1	623.5	10.4
1998	6,395.9	387.1	6.1	259.7	4.1	646.8	10.1
1999	6,695.0	408.8	6.1	272.0	4.1	680.8	10.2
2000	7,194.0	420.1	5.8	291.3	4.0	711.4	9.9
2001	7,486.8	442.5	5.9	301.3	4.0	743.8	9.9
2002	7,830.1	455.0	5.8	313.9	4.0	768.9	9.8
2003	8,162.5	473.1	5.8	329.6	4.0	802.8	9.8
2004	8,680.9	491.1	5.7	347.9	4.0	839.1	9.7
2005	9,092.0	518.2	5.7	367.2	4.0	885.4	9.7
2006	9,640.7	550.9	5.7	390.3	4.0	941.2	9.8
2007	10,170.5	578.6	5.7	408.9	4.0	987.4	9.7
2008	10,637.0	598.2	5.6	422.1	4.0	1,020.3	9.6

[a]Food-at-home includes cash purchases from grocery stores and other retail outlets, including purchases with food stamps and WIC (Special Supplemental Nutrition Program for Women, Infants and Children) vouchers and food produced and consumed on farms (valued at farm prices), but excludes government-donated foods.
[b]Food-away-from-home includes meals and snacks purchased by families and individuals and food furnished to employees, but excludes food paid for by government and business, such as donated foods to schools, meals in prisons and other institutions, and expense-account meals.
[c]Total may not add due to rounding.

SOURCE: "Table 7. Food Expenditures by Families and Individuals as a Share of Disposable Personal Income," in *Food CPI and Expenditures: Food Expenditure Tables*, U.S. Department of Agriculture, Economic Research Service, June 17, 2008, http://www.ers.usda.gov/briefing/CPIFoodAndExpenditures/Data/table7.htm (accessed October 18, 2009)

knew when they were sated and encouraged busy parents to relinquish control over their children's food consumption. In some parts of the country, budget cuts prompted schools to allow fast-food franchises to sell lunches and snacks to students on the school campuses. Finally, Critser observes that to accommodate—or even camouflage—Americans' expanding bodies, clothing manufacturers marketed large, loose-fitting clothing.

CHAPTER 2
WEIGHT AND PHYSICAL HEALTH

If we could give every individual the right amount of nourishment and exercise, not too little and not too much, we would have found the safest way to health.
—Hippocrates

During the 20th century, advances in public health and medical care helped Americans lead longer, healthier lives. Two important measures of the health of the population are infant mortality (death) rates and life expectancy at birth rates. By the end of the last century, infant mortality rates had significantly decreased and life expectancy had increased by 29.4 years. Table 2.1 shows the long-term upward trend in life expectancy as well as recent gains. In 2005 life expectancy at birth for the total population reached a record high of 77.8 years, up from 75.4 years in 1990. The Central Intelligence Agency estimates in *World Factbook: United States* (November 27, 2009, https://www.cia.gov/library/publications/the-world-factbook/geos/us.html) that in 2009 life expectancy at birth increased to 78.1 years (80.7 years for females and 75.7 years for males).

As deaths from infectious diseases declined during the second half of the 20th century, mortality from chronic diseases, such as heart disease and cancer, increased. Table 2.2 displays the 10 leading causes of death in the United States in 1980 and 2005. Overweight and obesity are considered contributing factors to at least four of the 10 leading causes of death in 2005: diseases of the heart, malignant neoplasms (tumors), cerebrovascular diseases (diseases affecting the supply of blood to the brain), and diabetes mellitus. Obesity may also be implicated in some deaths attributable to another leading cause of death: nephritis, nephrotic syndrome, and nephrosis (kidney disease or chronic renal failure). Table 2.2 also reveals the rise of diabetes as a cause of death. In 1980 it was the seventh-leading cause of death, claiming 34,851 lives. By 2005 it rose to being the sixth-leading cause of death and was the underlying cause of 75,119 deaths. Epidemiologists

(scientists who study the occurrence and distribution of diseases and the factors that govern their spread) and medical researchers believe the increasing prevalence of diabetes in the U.S. population and the resultant rise in deaths attributable to diabetes are direct consequences of the obesity epidemic in the United States.

Figure 2.1 reveals the relatively stable prevalence rate of overweight and the increasing rate of obesity in people of all ages from 1971–74 to 2005–06. It also shows the steepest increase in overweight among young adults, aged 18 to 29. Even though young adults have a lower prevalence of obesity (24%) compared with people 30 years and older (31% to 41%), the proportion that is obese has more than tripled, from 8% in 1971–74 to 24% in 2005–06, while in most other adult age groups the prevalence doubled during the same years.

Overweight and obesity increase not only the risk of morbidity (illness or disease) and mortality but also the severity of diseases such as hypertension (high blood pressure), arthritis, and other musculoskeletal problems. Table 2.3 lists the health consequences that may result from overweight and obesity among adults and children. It also estimates the likelihood of these health consequences. For example, adults who are obese are twice as likely to suffer from high blood pressure than adults who have a healthy weight.

In the landmark study "A Potential Decline in Life Expectancy in the United States in the 21st Century" (*New England Journal of Medicine*, vol. 352, no. 11, March 17, 2005), S. Jay Olshansky et al. suggest that the steady rise in life expectancy the United States enjoyed during the past two centuries might soon come to an end. The researchers use obesity prevalence data and previously published estimates of years of life lost from obesity to project life expectancy. Instead of using historical trends to forecast life expectancy, they calculated in reverse, assessing the fall in death rates that

TABLE 2.1

Life expectancy at birth, at 65 years of age, and at 75 years of age, according to race and sex, selected years 1900–2005

[Data are based on death certificates]

Specified age and year	All races			White			Black or African American[a]		
	Both sexes	Male	Female	Both sexes	Male	Female	Both sexes	Male	Female
At birth				Remaining life expectancy in years					
1900[b,c]	47.3	46.3	48.3	47.6	46.6	48.7	33.0	32.5	33.5
1950[c]	68.2	65.6	71.1	69.1	66.5	72.2	60.8	59.1	62.9
1960[c]	69.7	66.6	73.1	70.6	67.4	74.1	63.6	61.1	66.3
1970	70.8	67.1	74.7	71.7	68.0	75.6	64.1	60.0	68.3
1980	73.7	70.0	77.4	74.4	70.7	78.1	68.1	63.8	72.5
1990	75.4	71.8	78.8	76.1	72.7	79.4	69.1	64.5	73.6
1995	75.8	72.5	78.9	76.5	73.4	79.6	69.6	65.2	73.9
1997	76.5	73.6	79.4	77.1	74.3	79.9	71.1	67.2	74.7
1998	76.7	73.8	79.5	77.3	74.5	80.0	71.3	67.6	74.8
1999	76.7	73.9	79.4	77.3	74.6	79.9	71.4	67.8	74.7
2000	77.0	74.3	79.7	77.6	74.9	80.1	71.9	68.3	75.2
2001	77.2	74.4	79.8	77.7	75.0	80.2	72.2	68.6	75.5
2002	77.3	74.5	79.9	77.7	75.1	80.3	72.3	68.8	75.6
2003	77.4	74.7	80.0	77.9	75.3	80.4	72.6	68.9	75.9
2004	77.8	75.2	80.4	78.3	75.7	80.8	73.1	69.5	76.3
2005	77.8	75.2	80.4	78.3	75.7	80.8	73.2	69.5	76.5
At 65 years									
1950[c]	13.9	12.8	15.0	—	12.8	15.1	13.9	12.9	14.9
1960[c]	14.3	12.8	15.8	14.4	12.9	15.9	13.9	12.7	15.1
1970	15.2	13.1	17.0	15.2	13.1	17.1	14.2	12.5	15.7
1980	16.4	14.1	18.3	16.5	14.2	18.4	15.1	13.0	16.8
1990	17.2	15.1	18.9	17.3	15.2	19.1	15.4	13.2	17.2
1995	17.4	15.6	18.9	17.6	15.7	19.1	15.6	13.6	17.1
1997	17.7	15.9	19.2	17.8	16.0	19.3	16.1	14.2	17.6
1998	17.8	16.0	19.2	17.8	16.1	19.3	16.1	14.3	17.4
1999	17.7	16.1	19.1	17.8	16.1	19.2	16.0	14.3	17.3
2000	18.0	16.2	19.3	18.0	16.3	19.4	16.2	14.2	17.7
2001	18.1	16.4	19.4	18.2	16.5	19.5	16.4	14.4	17.9
2002	18.2	16.6	19.5	18.2	16.6	19.5	16.6	14.6	18.0
2003	18.4	16.8	19.7	18.4	16.8	19.7	16.8	14.8	18.3
2004	18.7	17.1	20.0	18.7	17.2	20.0	17.1	15.2	18.6
2005	18.7	17.2	20.0	18.8	17.2	20.0	17.2	15.2	18.7
At 75 years									
1980	10.4	8.8	11.5	10.4	8.8	11.5	9.7	8.3	10.7
1990	10.9	9.4	12.0	11.0	9.4	12.0	10.2	8.6	11.2
1995	11.0	9.7	11.9	11.1	9.7	12.0	10.2	8.8	11.1
1997	11.2	9.9	12.1	11.2	9.9	12.1	10.7	9.3	11.5
1998	11.3	10.0	12.2	11.3	10.0	12.2	10.5	9.2	11.3
1999	11.2	10.0	12.1	11.2	10.0	12.1	10.4	9.2	11.1
2000	11.4	10.1	12.3	11.4	10.1	12.3	10.7	9.2	11.6
2001	11.5	10.2	12.4	11.5	10.2	12.3	10.8	9.3	11.7
2002	11.5	10.3	12.4	11.5	10.3	12.3	10.9	9.5	11.7
2003	11.7	10.5	12.5	11.6	10.4	12.5	11.1	9.6	12.1
2004	11.9	10.7	12.8	11.9	10.7	12.8	11.4	9.9	12.2
2005	12.0	10.8	12.8	11.9	10.7	12.8	11.4	10.0	12.3

—Data not available.

[a]Data shown for 1900–1960 are for the nonwhite population.

[b]Death registration area only. The death registration area increased from 10 states and the District of Columbia (DC) in 1900 to the coterminous United States in 1933.

[c]Includes deaths of persons who were not residents of the 50 states and DC.

Notes: Populations for computing life expectancy for 1991–1999 are 1990-based postcensal estimates of U.S. resident population. In 1997, life table methodology was revised to construct complete life tables by single years of age that extend to age 100 (Anderson RN. Method for constructing complete annual U.S. life tables. National Center for Health Statistics. Vital Health Stat 2(129). 1999).

Previously, abridged life tables were constructed for 5-year age groups ending with 85 years and over. Life table values for 2000 and later years were computed using a slight modification of the new life table method due to a change in the age detail of populations received from the U.S. Census Bureau. In 2003, seven states reported multiple-race data. In 2004, 15 states reported multiple-race data. In 2005, 21 states and the District of Columbia reported multiple-race data. The multiple-race data for these states were bridged to the single-race categories of the 1977 Office of Management and Budget Standards for comparability with other states. Some data have been revised. Data for additional years are available.

SOURCE: "Table 26. Life Expectancy at Birth, at 65 Years of Age, and at 75 Years of Age, by Race and Sex: United States, Selected Years 1900–2005," in *Health, United States, 2008*, Centers for Disease Control and Prevention, National Center for Health Statistics, 2008, http://www.cdc.gov/nchs/data/hus/hus08.pdf (accessed October 18, 2009)

would occur if all obese Americans had a normal weight. Olshansky et al.'s projections reveal that within 50 years obesity is likely to reduce the average life expectancy in the United States by at least two to five years. The impact of obesity and its health consequences on life expectancy was considered larger than cancer or heart disease.

TABLE 2.2

Leading causes of death and numbers of deaths, according to sex and race, 1980 and 2005

[Data are based on death certificates]

Sex, race, Hispanic origin, and rank order	1980		2005	
	Cause of death	Deaths	Cause of death	Deaths
All persons				
. . .	All causes	1,989,841	All causes	2,448,017
1	Diseases of heart	761,085	Diseases of heart	652,091
2	Malignant neoplasms	416,509	Malignant neoplasms	559,312
3	Cerebrovascular diseases	170,225	Cerebrovascular diseases	143,579
4	Unintentional injuries	105,718	Chronic lower respiratory diseases	130,933
5	Chronic obstructive pulmonary diseases	56,050	Unintentional injuries	117,809
6	Pneumonia and influenza	54,619	Diabetes mellitus	75,119
7	Diabetes mellitus	34,851	Alzheimer's disease	71,599
8	Chronic liver disease and cirrhosis	30,583	Influenza and pneumonia	63,001
9	Atherosclerosis	29,449	Nephritis, nephrotic syndrome and nephrosis	43,901
10	Suicide	26,869	Septicemia	34,136
Male				
. . .	All causes	1,075,078	All causes	1,207,675
1	Diseases of heart	405,661	Diseases of heart	322,841
2	Malignant neoplasms	225,948	Malignant neoplasms	290,422
3	Unintentional injuries	74,180	Unintentional injuries	76,375
4	Cerebrovascular diseases	69,973	Chronic lower respiratory diseases	62,435
5	Chronic obstructive pulmonary diseases	38,625	Cerebrovascular diseases	56,586
6	Pneumonia and influenza	27,574	Diabetes mellitus	36,538
7	Suicide	20,505	Influenza and pneumonia	28,052
8	Chronic liver disease and cirrhosis	19,768	Suicide	25,907
9	Homicide	18,779	Nephritis, nephrotic syndrome and nephrosis	21,268
10	Diabetes mellitus	14,325	Alzheimer's disease	20,559
Female				
. . .	All causes	914,763	All causes	1,240,342
1	Diseases of heart	355,424	Diseases of heart	329,250
2	Malignant neoplasms	190,561	Malignant neoplasms	268,890
3	Cerebrovascular diseases	100,252	Cerebrovascular diseases	86,993
4	Unintentional injuries	31,538	Chronic lower respiratory diseases	68,498
5	Pneumonia and influenza	27,045	Alzheimer's disease	51,040
6	Diabetes mellitus	20,526	Unintentional injuries	41,434
7	Atherosclerosis	17,848	Diabetes mellitus	38,581
8	Chronic obstructive pulmonary diseases	17,425	Influenza and pneumonia	34,949
9	Chronic liver disease and cirrhosis	10,815	Nephritis, nephrotic syndrome and nephrosis	22,633
10	Certain conditions originating in the perinatal period	9,815	Septicemia	18,814
White				
. . .	All causes	1,738,607	All causes	2,098,097
1	Diseases of heart	683,347	Diseases of heart	564,796
2	Malignant neoplasms	368,162	Malignant neoplasms	482,132
3	Cerebrovascular diseases	148,734	Cerebrovascular diseases	121,868
4	Unintentional injuries	90,122	Chronic lower respiratory diseases	120,884
5	Chronic obstructive pulmonary diseases	52,375	Unintentional injuries	100,406
6	Pneumonia and influenza	48,369	Alzheimer's disease	66,191
7	Diabetes mellitus	28,868	Diabetes mellitus	59,755
8	Atherosclerosis	27,069	Influenza and pneumonia	55,540
9	Chronic liver disease and cirrhosis	25,240	Nephritis, nephrotic syndrome and nephrosis	34,806
10	Suicide	24,829	Suicide	29,527

In 2009 researchers for the Prospective Studies Collaboration assessed more than 900,000 people over more than a decade to determine how obesity affects longevity and mortality and then published their results in "Body-Mass Index and Cause-Specific Mortality in 900,000 Adults: Collaborative Analyses of 57 Prospective Studies" (*Lancet*, vol. 373, no. 9669, March 28, 2009). The researchers indicate that moderate obesity reduces life expectancy by about three years and that severe obesity can reduce life expectancy by 10 years, which is comparable to the reduced life expectancy associated with lifelong smoking. They conclude, "BMI is in itself a strong predictor of overall mortality both above and below the apparent optimum of about 22.5–25 kg/m2."

IS OBESITY A DISEASE?

Researchers now recognize that obesity does not simply result from willful overeating and laziness, but from a complex combination of genetic, metabolic, behavioral, and environmental factors. Rather than viewing it as a lifestyle choice or personal failing, several groups favor declaring obesity a disease. Proponents assert that many public health benefits would result from designating obesity as a disease including:

TABLE 2.2

Leading causes of death and numbers of deaths, according to sex and race, 1980 and 2005 [CONTINUED]

[Data are based on death certificates]

Sex, race, Hispanic origin, and rank order	1980		2005	
	Cause of death	Deaths	Cause of death	Deaths
Black or African American				
...	All causes	233,135	All causes	292,808
1	Diseases of heart	72,956	Diseases of heart	74,159
2	Malignant neoplasms	45,037	Malignant neoplasms	63,165
3	Cerebrovascular diseases	20,135	Cerebrovascular diseases	17,541
4	Unintentional injuries	13,480	Unintentional injuries	13,652
5	Homicide	10,172	Diabetes mellitus	12,970
6	Certain conditions originating in the perinatal period	6,961	Homicide	8,669
7	Pneumonia and influenza	5,648	Chronic lower respiratory diseases	8,229
8	Diabetes mellitus	5,544	Nephritis, nephrotic syndrome and nephrosis	8,075
9	Chronic liver disease and cirrhosis	4,790	Human immunodeficiency virus (HIV) disease	7,022
10	Nephritis, nephrotic syndrome, and nephrosis	3,416	Septicemia	6,221

Notes: For cause of death codes based on the International Classification of Diseases, 9th Revision (ICD–9) in 1980 and ICD–10 in 2005.
In 2005, 21 states and the District of Columbia reported multiple-race data. The multiple-race data for these states were bridged to the single-race categories of the 1977 Office of Management and Budget standards for comparability with other states.

SOURCE: Adapted from "Table 30. Leading Causes of Death and Numbers of Deaths, by Sex, Race, and Hispanic Origin: United States, 1980 and 2005," in *Health, United States, 2008*, Centers for Disease Control and Prevention, National Center for Health Statistics, 2008, http://www.cdc.gov/nchs/data/hus/hus08.pdf (accessed October 18, 2009)

- Reducing the social stigma and prejudice associated with obesity, and promoting attitudinal changes to reduce weight-based discrimination

- Enabling more people to seek treatment for obesity by providing health insurance coverage for treatment

- Increasing public awareness of the severity of obesity as a threat to health and longevity

- Stimulating scientific and medical research about the prevention and treatment of the condition and speeding approval of new antiobesity drugs

Advocates of classifying obesity as a disease, including the World Health Organization, the National Institutes of Health, the National Academy of Sciences, the Federal Trade Commission, the Maternal and Child Health Bureau, the American Heart Association, the American Academy of Family Physicians, the American Society for Bariatric Surgery, the American Society of Bariatric Physicians, and the American Obesity Association (AOA), observe that not long ago in U.S. history alcoholism was viewed as a personal choice or moral weakness, whereas in the 21st century it is considered a disease. They also note that eating disorders such as anorexia and bulimia are classified as diseases. In view of the size and scope of the obesity epidemic, proponents argue that the social and financial costs of allowing it to go unchecked will far exceed the costs associated with extending health care coverage for weight-reduction programs.

The AOA contends that obesity meets the criteria for disease because according to *Stedman's Medical Dictionary* (2009) a disease should have at least two of the following three features:

- Recognized etiologic (causative) agents

- Identifiable signs and symptoms

- Consistent anatomical alterations

The AOA describes etiologic agents for obesity as social, behavioral, cultural, physiological, metabolic, and genetic factors. The identifiable signs and symptoms of obesity include an excess accumulation of adipose tissue (fat), an increase in the size or number of fat cells, insulin resistance, decreased levels of high-density lipoprotein (HDL) and norepinephrine, alterations in the activity of the sympathetic and parasympathetic nervous system, and elevated blood pressure, blood glucose, cholesterol, and triglyceride levels. The consistent anatomical alteration of obesity is the increase in body mass.

Opponents contend that even though obesity increases the risk of developing many diseases, it is not an ailment in itself but an unhealthy consequence of poor lifestyle choices. They liken it to cigarette smoking, a risk factor that predisposes people to disease, and they dispute the notion that labeling obesity as a disease will have a beneficial effect on the ability of public health organizations to alter the course of the obesity epidemic. They maintain the public tends to view diseases as conditions that are contracted or contagious; and with disease comes a victim mentality, rather than an assumption of personal responsibility. Because many health professionals consider the assumption of personal responsibility as being crucial for the long-term success of obesity treatment, any action that releases people from assuming personal responsibility is counterproductive.

FIGURE 2.1

Overweight and obese, by age, 1971–74 through 2005–06

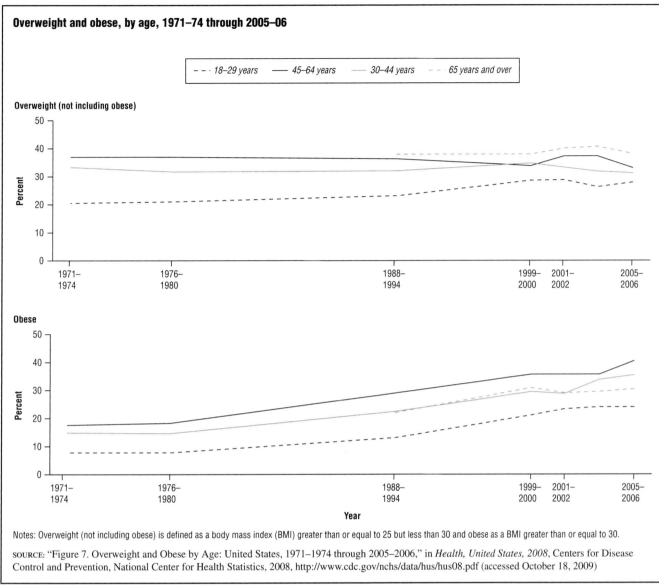

Notes: Overweight (not including obese) is defined as a body mass index (BMI) greater than or equal to 25 but less than 30 and obese as a BMI greater than or equal to 30.

SOURCE: "Figure 7. Overweight and Obese by Age: United States, 1971–1974 through 2005–2006," in *Health, United States, 2008*, Centers for Disease Control and Prevention, National Center for Health Statistics, 2008, http://www.cdc.gov/nchs/data/hus/hus08.pdf (accessed October 18, 2009)

Opponents to granting disease status to obesity predict that the financial ramifications would be devastating for taxpayers and the health insurance industry. Health care costs, which increase every year, would skyrocket. Anti-obesity programs would drive insurance premiums even higher and place unreasonable burdens on the already overburdened Medicare and Medicaid programs. Employers, especially small businesses, might be forced by high health care costs to drop employee coverage altogether.

A related concern is the lack of universally accepted, effective treatment for obesity. If obesity is classified as a disease, which treatment or therapies should be covered? For example, if exercise is deemed beneficial, then health insurers might be required to pay for gym memberships.

Furthermore, some opponents believe it is not necessary to designate obesity as a disease to encourage Americans to seek treatment. They cite the more than $50 billion

spent annually on weight-loss programs and services as evidence that Americans are not reluctant to seek treatment.

Even though the debate has not been fully resolved, obesity is rapidly acquiring recognition as a disease. In 2002 the Internal Revenue Service ruled that for tax purposes obesity is a disease, allowing Americans for the first time to claim a deduction for some health care expenses related to obesity, just as they can for expenditures related to heart disease, cancer, diabetes, and other illnesses.

In 2004 the federal Medicare program discarded its long-standing position that obesity is not a disease, which effectively removed a major roadblock for people seeking coverage for treatment of obesity. After years of review, the Centers for Medicare and Medicaid Services, which administers the health program for older adults and people who are disabled, announced in *CMS Manual System: Pub. 100-03 Medicare National Coverage Determinations*

TABLE 2.3

Health consequences of overweight and obesity

Premature death

- An estimated 300,000 deaths per year may be attributable to obesity.
- The risk of death rises with increasing weight.
- Even moderate weight excess (10 to 20 pounds for a person of average height) increases the risk of death, particularly among adults aged 30 to 64 years.
- Individuals who are obese (body mass index (BMI) > 30) have a 50 to 100% increased risk of premature death from all causes, compared to individuals with a healthy weight.

Heart disease

- The incidence of heart disease (heart attack, congestive heart failure, sudden cardiac death, angina or chest pain, and abnormal heart rhythm) is increased in persons who are overweight or obese (BMI > 25).
- High blood pressure is twice as common in adults who are obese than in those who are at a healthy weight.
- Obesity is associated with elevated triglycerides (blood fat) and decreased high density lipoprotein (HDL) cholesterol ("good cholesterol").

Diabetes

- A weight gain of 11 to 18 pounds increases a person's risk of developing type 2 diabetes to twice that of individuals who have not gained weight.
- Over 80% of people with diabetes are overweight or obese.

Cancer

- Overweight and obesity are associated with an increased risk for some types of cancer including endometrial (cancer of the lining of the uterus), colon, gall bladder, prostate, kidney, and postmenopausal breast cancer.
- Women gaining more than 20 pounds from age 18 to midlife double their risk of postmenopausal breast cancer, compared to women whose weight remains stable.

Breathing problems

- Sleep apnea (interrupted breathing while sleeping) is more common in obese persons.
- Obesity is associated with a higher prevalence of asthma.

Arthritis

- For every 2-pound increase in weight, the risk of developing arthritis is increased by 9 to 13%.
- Symptoms of arthritis can improve with weight loss.

Reproductive complications

Complications of pregnancy
- Obesity during pregnancy is associated with increased risk of death in both the baby and the mother and increases the risk of maternal high blood pressure by 10 times.
- In addition to many other complications, women who are obese during pregnancy are more likely to have gestational diabetes and problems with labor and delivery.
- Infants born to women who are obese during pregnancy are more likely to be high birthweight and, therefore, may face a higher rate of Cesarean section delivery and low blood sugar (which can be associated with brain damage and seizures).
- Obesity during pregnancy is associated with an increased risk of birth defects, particularly neural tube defects, such as spina bifida.
- Obesity in premenopausal women is associated with irregular menstrual cycles and infertility.

Additional health consequences

- Overweight and obesity are associated with increased risks of gall bladder disease, incontinence, increased surgical risk, and depression.
- Obesity can affect the quality of life through limited mobility and decreased physical endurance as well as through social, academic, and job discrimination.

Children and adolescents

- Risk factors for heart disease, such as high cholesterol and high blood pressure, occur with increased frequency in overweight children and adolescents compared to those with a healthy weight.
- Type 2 diabetes, previously considered an adult disease, has increased dramatically in children and adolescents. Overweight and obesity are closely linked to type 2 diabetes.
- Overweight adolescents have a 70% chance of becoming overweight or obese adults. This increases to 80% if one or more parent is overweight or obese.
- The most immediate consequence of overweight, as perceived by children themselves, is social discrimination.

SOURCE: "Overweight and Obesity: Health Consequences," in *The Surgeon General's Call to Action to Prevent and Decrease Overweight and Obesity*, U.S. Department of Health and Human Services, Office of the Surgeon General, 2001, http://www.surgeongeneral.gov/topics/obesity/calltoaction/fact_consequences .htm (accessed October 19, 2009)

(October 1, 2004, http://www.cms.hhs.gov/transmittals/downloads/R23NCD.pdf) that it eliminated the phrase "obesity itself cannot be considered an illness" from its policy that had been used to deny coverage for weight-loss treatment. Even though the decision stopped short of declaring obesity a disease and does not automatically imply coverage for any specific treatment, it enables individuals, physicians, and companies to apply to Medicare for reimbursement for a variety of weight-loss therapies. Because private insurance companies often use Medicare as a model for their coverage and benefits, the Medicare decision has pressured them to expand coverage for weight-loss treatments. Ironically, the Medicare decision was announced at the same time that many private insurers intended to eliminate or sharply curtail coverage of weight-loss surgery.

THE GENETICS OF BODY WEIGHT AND OBESITY

Genetics, the study of single genes and their effects, explains how and why traits such as hair color and blood types run in families. In the early 21st century the scientific community agreed that body shape and body weight are also regulated traits, that genes govern much of this regulation, and that altering genetically predetermined set points for body weight is often difficult. Genomics, a discipline that emerged during the 1980s, is the study of more than single genes; it considers the functions and interactions of all the genes in the genome. In terms of understanding genetics as a risk factor for obesity, genomics has broader applicability than does genetics because it is likely that humans carry dozens of genes that are directly related to body size and that most obesity

TABLE 2.4

Obesity and genetics

What we know:	What we don't know:
Biological relatives tend to resemble each other in many ways, including body weight. Individuals with a family history of obesity may be predisposed to gain weight and interventions that prevent obesity are especially important.	Why are biological relatives more similar in body weight? What genes are associated with this observation? Are the same genetic associations seen in every family? How do these genes affect energy metabolism and regulation?
In an environment made constant for food intake and physical activity, individuals respond differently. Some people store more energy as fat in an environment of excess; others lose less fat in an environment of scarcity. The different responses are largely due to genetic variation between individuals.	Why are interventions based on diet and exercise more effective for some people than others? What are the biological differences between these high and low responders? How do we use these insights to tailor interventions to specific needs?
Fat stores are regulated over long periods of time by complex systems that involve input and feedback from fatty tissues, the brain, and endocrine glands like the pancreas and the thyroid. Overweight and obesity can result from only a very small positive energy input imbalance over a long period of time.	What elements of energy regulation feedback systems are different in individuals? How do these differences affect energy metabolism and regulation?
Rarely, people have mutations in single genes that result in severe obesity that starts in infancy. Studying these individuals is providing insight into the complex biological pathways that regulate the balance between energy input and energy expenditure.	Do additional obesity syndromes exist that are caused by mutations in single genes? If so, what are they? What are the natural history, management strategy, and outcome for affected individuals?
Obese individuals have genetic similarities that may shed light on the biological differences that predispose to gain weight. This knowledge may be useful in preventing or treating obesity in predisposed people.	How do genetic variations that are shared by obese people affect gene expression and function? How do genetic variation and environmental factors interact to produce obesity? What are the biological features associated with the tendency to gain weight? What environmental factors are helpful in countering these tendencies?
Pharmaceutical companies are using genetic approaches (pharmacogenomics) to develop new drug strategies to treat obesity	Will pharmacologic approaches benefit most people affected with obesity? Will these drugs be accessible to most people?
The tendency to store energy in the form of fat is believed to result from thousands of years of evolution in an environment characterized by tenuous food supplies. In other words, those who could store energy in times of plenty, were more likely to survive periods of famine and to pass this tendency to their offspring.	How can thousands of years of evolutionary pressure be countered? Can specific factors in the modern environment (other than the obvious) be identified and controlled to more effectively counter these tendencies?

SOURCE: "Obesity and Genetics: What We Know, What We Don't Know and What It Means," in *Public Health Genomics*, Centers for Disease Control and Prevention, National Office of Public Health Genomics, July 21, 2009, http://www.cdc.gov/genomics/resources/diseases/obesity/obesknow.htm (accessed December 8, 2009)

is multifactorial—resulting from the complex interactions of multiple genes and environmental factors.

Because genomics is a relatively new discipline, many questions are still unanswered about how genes influence the ability to balance energy input and energy expenditure, and why individuals vary in their abilities to perform this critical body function. Table 2.4 summarizes what is known and what remains to be learned about variations in body weight, energy metabolism, and inherited obesity syndromes.

Single Mutant Genes Cause Obesity

Even though most obesity in humans is not due to mutations (alterations or changes) in single genes, there are obesity syndromes caused by variations in single genes. These account for approximately 1% to 5% of all obesity, according to Astrid Newell et al. of the Centers for Disease Control and Prevention (CDC), in "Addressing the Obesity Epidemic: A Genomics Perspective" (*Preventing Chronic Disease*, April 2007). In rare cases of severe obesity that begin during childhood, a single gene has a major effect in determining the occurrence of obesity, with environmental factors playing a lesser role. The mutations occur in genes that encode proteins related to the regulation of food intake. One example is mutations of the leptin gene (on chromosome 7) and its receptor. The circulating hormone leptin (leptos means thin) sends the brain a satiety signal to decrease

appetite. Obese mice of the ob/ob strain produce no leptin and tend to overeat; when given leptin, the mice stop eating and lose weight. However, experiments have failed to replicate these findings in humans. Blood concentrations of leptin are usually elevated in obese people, suggesting that they may be insensitive or resistant to leptin, rather than leptin deficient. Most obese individuals appear to have normal genetic sequences for leptin and its receptor, although people with a demonstrable genetic leptin deficiency suffer from extreme obesity.

Melanocortin 4 receptor (MC4R) deficiency is the most commonly occurring monogenic (single gene) form of obesity. Inheriting one copy of certain variants of the gene causes obesity in some families. In "Melanocortin-4 Receptor Mutations in Obesity" (*Advances in Clinical Chemistry*, vol. 48, 2009), Ferruccio Santini et al. report that mutations in MC4R produce a distinct obesity syndrome that is inherited. The researchers observe that these mutant receptors play a pivotal role in the control of eating behavior—that the regulation of body weight in humans is sensitive to variations in the amount of functional MC4R and are present in about 6% of people who are obese.

Timothy M. Frayling et al. identify in "A Common Variant in the *FTO* Gene Is Associated with Body Mass Index and Predisposes to Childhood and Adult Obesity" (*Science*, vol. 316, no. 5826, May 2007) a variant of a gene called *FTO*, located on chromosome 16, that is linked to obesity. The researchers indicate that people with one or two copies of the gene's variant were more likely to be overweight than those who had no copies at all.

In "Pediatric Obesity: Etiology and Treatment" (*Endocrinology and Metabolism Clinics*, vol. 38, no. 3, September 2009), Melissa K. Crocker and Jack A. Yanovski of the U.S. Public Health Service summarize what is known about the genetic underpinnings of obesity. They observe that "single nucleotide polymorphisms (SNPs) of many genes and chromosomal regions have been found to be associated with body weight or body composition. The mechanisms explaining how such SNPs might change energy balance are often not fully understood." The researchers reiterate one of the challenges of clinical genetic research: "Even in studies including thousands of genotyped people, such SNPs can be linked to body weight only when they are relatively common in the population."

Multiple Gene Variants Involved in Body Weight and Obesity

Heritability studies seek to determine the proportion of variance of a particular trait that is attributable to genetic factors and the proportion that is attributable to environmental factors. Such studies indicate that genetic factors may account for as much as 75% of the variability in human body weight and approximately 33% of the variation in the overall body mass index (BMI; body weight in kilograms divided by height in meters squared). Genetic factors affect the variations in resting metabolic rate, body fat distribution, and weight gain related to overfeeding, which explains in part why some individuals are more susceptible than others to weight gain or weight loss. To ensure survival in times of scarce food supplies, the human body has evolved to resist any loss of body fat. This biological drive to maintain weight is coordinated through central nervous system pathways, with the involvement of many neuropeptides. (Peptides are released by neurons as intercellular messengers. Many neuropeptides are also hormones outside of the nervous system.) Evidence from twin, adoption, and family studies reveals that biological relatives exhibit similarities in the maintenance of body weight. First-degree relatives of moderately obese people are at three to four times the risk of obesity relative to the general population. First-degree relatives of severely obese people are at five times greater risk. Genetic predisposition to obesity does not mean that developing the condition is inevitable; however, research indicates that inherited genetic variation is an important risk factor for obesity.

Genetic factors have been implicated in the development of eating disorders such as anorexia and bulimia and appear to be involved in the extent to which diet and exercise are effective strategies for weight reduction. Furthermore, genetic variations among individuals may promote different food preferences and eating patterns that interact with environmental conditions to maintain healthy body weight or promote obesity.

These genetic risk factors tend to be familial but are not inherited in a simple manner; they may reflect many genetic variations, and each variation may contribute a small amount of risk and may interact with environmental elements to produce obesity. Tuomo Rankinen et al. present in "The Human Obesity Gene Map: The 2005 Update" (*Obesity*, vol. 14, no. 4, April 2006) the 12th update of the human obesity gene map by the Pennington Biomedical Research Center, which was completed in October 2005. This map contains over 600 genes, markers, and chromosomal regions that are associated with or linked to human obesity. Besides offering direction for future efforts to prevent and treat obesity, mounting genetic evidence offers a compelling argument that obesity is not a personal failing and that in most cases obesity involves multiple genetic and environmental components that affect endocrine, metabolic, and regulatory mechanisms.

Genetic Susceptibility and Environmental Influences

Even though genetics may largely predetermine adult body weight absent specific environmental triggers or influences, genetic destiny in terms of body weight may not necessarily be realized. For example, an individual with a strong genetic predisposition for obesity will not become obese in the absence of sufficient food (caloric) intake. Similarly, when people genetically predisposed to normal body weight consume a largely high-fat diet, they may become overweight or obese because they may be more inclined to overeat. This is in part because the brain has difficulty conveying the satiety signal—the message to stop eating—when fatty foods are being consumed.

Besides caloric intake and physical activity, both of which are able to modify body weight, environmental influences before birth also significantly influence adult health and body weight. Research demonstrates that the pregnant mother's nutritional status affects the metabolism of her unborn child. Women who are severely malnourished during pregnancy stimulate the fetus to modify its metabolism to conserve and store energy, a survival practice that can promote overweight when the food supply is ample.

Societal and cultural norms can also cause environmental influences such as lifestyle and behavior to override genetic programming. For example, in the United States many young women with genetic predisposition to normal body weight or even overweight sharply limit their caloric intake and exercise vigorously to achieve "model thin" bodies. Similarly, in cultures where overweight is perceived as an indication of prosperity and is admired and coveted, people may override genetic tendencies to be normal weight by increasing caloric intake in an effort to achieve the culturally established ideal.

HEALTH RISKS AND CONSEQUENCES OF OVERWEIGHT AND OBESITY

The *Surgeon General's Call to Action to Prevent and Decrease Overweight and Obesity, 2001* (2001, http://www.surgeongeneral.gov/topics/obesity/calltoaction/CalltoAction.pdf) predicted that "overweight and obesity may soon cause as much preventable disease and death as cigarette smoking" and that failure to address these conditions "could wipe out the gains we have made in areas such as heart disease, diabetes, several forms of cancer, and other chronic health problems." By 2009 the scientific community acknowledged that the health consequences of overweight and obesity threatened to erode Americans' life span.

People who are overweight or obese are at higher risk of developing one or more serious medical conditions, and obesity is associated with increases in deaths from all causes. Overweight and obesity significantly increase the risk for hypercholesterolemia (high cholesterol), hypertension, heart disease, and stroke; Type 2 diabetes; osteoarthritis and chronic joint pain; gallbladder disease; fatty liver disease; several types of cancers; and sleep apnea (interrupted breathing while sleeping) and sleep disorders. According to James A. Greenberg of the City University of New York, in "Correcting Biases in Estimates of Mortality Attributable to Obesity" (*Obesity*, vol. 14, no. 11, 2006), obesity is a contributing cause in at least 400,000 deaths per year.

The CDC observes in "Frequently Asked Questions about Calculating Obesity-Related Risk" (May 25, 2005, http://www.cdc.gov/PDF/Frequently_Asked_Questions_About_Calculating_Obesity-Related_Risk.pdf) that "because obesity has so many different effects on so many diseases, it is extremely difficult for doctors to identify obesity-related deaths reliably on death certificates. So, instead, scientists use complex modeling techniques to estimate deaths related to obesity," which in turn produce varying estimates of the annual number of obesity-related deaths.

Hypercholesterolemia, Hypertension, Heart Disease, and Stroke

Overweight, obesity, and excess abdominal fat are directly related to cardiovascular risk factors, including high levels of total serum cholesterol, LDL-cholesterol (low-density lipoprotein; a fatlike substance often called bad cholesterol because high levels increase the risk for heart disease), triglycerides, blood pressure, fibrinogen, and insulin, and low levels of HDL-cholesterol (often called good cholesterol because high levels appear to protect against heart disease). The association between total serum cholesterol and coronary heart disease is largely due to LDL. A high-risk LDL-cholesterol is greater than or equal to 160 milligrams per deciliter (mg/dL) with a 10 mg/dL rise in LDL-cholesterol corresponding to approximately a 10% increase in risk. A high-risk total serum cholesterol is greater than or equal to 240 mg/dL. The percent of the population suffering from high serum cholesterol levels fell from 19.7% in 1988–94 to 16.3% in 2003–06. (See Table 2.5.) The overall decline in high total serum cholesterol occurred in response to the increasing use of effective cholesterol-lowering statin drugs.

The percent of the population suffering from hypertension (people with elevated blood pressure and those taking antihypertensive medication) increased between the periods 1988–1994 and 2003–2006, from 25.5% to 31.3% of the population. (See Table 2.6.) The highest rates for those aged 20 to 74 during the 2003–2006 period were reported among African-American females (44.1%). Both men and women were increasingly likely to have hypertension as they aged. Hypertension is approximately three times more common in obese than in normal-weight people, and the relationship between weight and blood pressure is clearly one of cause and effect, because when weight increases, so does blood pressure, and when weight decreases, blood pressure falls.

The physiological processes that produce the hypertension associated with obesity include sodium retention and increases in vascular resistance, blood volume, and cardiac output (the volume of blood pumped, measured in liters per minute). Even though it is not known precisely how weight loss results in a decrease in blood pressure, it is known that weight loss is associated with a reduction in vascular resistance and total blood volume and cardiac output. Weight loss also results in an improvement in insulin resistance, a reduction in sympathetic nervous system activity, and the suppression of the renin-angiotensin-aldosterone system, a group of hormones that are responsible for the opening and narrowing of blood vessels and the retention of fluids.

Obesity increases the risk for coronary artery disease, which in turn increases the risk for future heart failure. Congestive heart failure is not a disease but a condition that occurs when the heart is unable to pump enough blood to meet the needs of the body's tissues. When the heart fails, it is unable to pump out all the blood that enters its chambers. Congestive heart failure is a frequent complication of severe obesity and a major cause of death. The duration of obesity is a strong predictor of congestive heart failure because over time elevated total blood volume and high cardiac output cause the left ventricle of the heart to increase in size (known as left ventricular hypertrophy) beyond that expected from normal growth. Left ventricular

TABLE 2.5

Serum cholesterol levels among persons 20 years of age and over, by demographic characteristics, selected years 1960–2006

[Data are based on interviews and laboratory work of a sample of the civilian noninstitutionalized population]

Sex, age, race and Hispanic origin[a], and percent of poverty level	1960–1962	1971–1974	1976–1980[b]	1988–1994	1999–2002	2003–2006
20–74 years, age-adjusted[c]		Percent of population with high serum total cholesterol (greater than or equal to 240 mg/dL)				
Both sexes[d]	33.3	28.6	27.8	19.7	17.0	16.3
Male	30.6	27.9	26.4	18.8	16.9	15.6
Female	35.6	29.1	28.8	20.5	17.0	16.9
Not Hispanic or Latino:						
White only, male	—	—	26.4	18.7	17.0	16.0
White only, female	—	—	29.6	20.7	17.4	17.9
Black or African American only, male	—	—	25.5	16.4	12.5	11.2
Black or African American only, female	—	—	26.3	19.9	16.6	13.0
Mexican male	—	—	20.3	18.7	17.6	17.7
Mexican female	—	—	20.5	17.7	12.7	13.8
Percent of poverty level:[e]						
Below 100%	—	24.4	23.5	19.3	17.8	18.2
100%–less than 200%	—	28.9	26.5	19.4	18.8	16.5
200% or more	—	28.9	29.0	19.6	16.5	16.2
20 years and over, age-adjusted[c]						
Both sexes[d]	—	—	—	20.8	17.3	16.3
Male	—	—	—	19.0	16.4	15.1
Female	—	—	—	22.0	17.8	17.1
Not Hispanic or Latino:						
White only, male	—	—	—	18.8	16.5	15.5
White only, female	—	—	—	22.2	18.1	18.0
Black or African American only, male	—	—	—	16.9	12.4	10.9
Black or African American only, female	—	—	—	21.4	17.7	13.3
Mexican male	—	—	—	18.5	17.4	17.6
Mexican female	—	—	—	18.7	13.8	14.4
Percent of poverty level:[e]						
Below 100%	—	—	—	20.6	18.3	18.1
100%–less than 200%	—	—	—	20.6	19.1	16.7
200% or more	—	—	—	20.4	16.5	16.0
20 years and over, crude						
Both sexes[d]	—	—	—	19.6	17.3	16.4
Male	—	—	—	17.7	16.6	15.2
Female	—	—	—	21.3	18.0	17.5
Not Hispanic or Latino:						
White only, male	—	—	—	18.0	16.9	15.7
White only, female	—	—	—	22.5	19.1	18.9
Black or African American only, male	—	—	—	14.7	12.2	10.8
Black or African American only, female	—	—	—	18.2	16.1	12.5
Mexican male	—	—	—	15.4	15.0	15.7
Mexican female	—	—	—	14.3	10.7	12.6
Percent of poverty level:[e]						
Below 100%	—	—	—	17.6	16.4	16.8
100%–less than 200%	—	—	—	19.8	18.2	16.0
200% or more	—	—	—	19.5	16.9	16.5
Male						
20–34 years	15.1	12.4	11.9	8.2	9.8	9.5
35–44 years	33.9	31.8	27.9	19.4	19.8	20.5
45–54 years	39.2	37.5	36.9	26.6	23.6	20.8
55–64 years	41.6	36.2	36.8	28.0	19.9	16.0
65–74 years	38.0	34.7	31.7	21.9	13.7	10.9
75 years and over	—	—	—	20.4	10.2	9.6
Female						
20–34 years	12.4	10.9	9.8	7.3	8.9	10.3
35–44 years	23.1	19.3	20.7	12.3	12.4	12.7
45–54 years	46.9	38.7	40.5	26.7	21.4	19.7
55–64 years	70.1	53.1	52.9	40.9	25.6	30.5
65–74 years	68.5	57.7	51.6	41.3	32.3	24.2
75 years and over	—	—	—	38.2	26.5	18.6

hypertrophy is frequently identified in cardiac patients with obesity and in part results from hypertension, but abnormalities in left ventricular mass and function also occur in the absence of hypertension and may be related to the severity of obesity.

Inflammation in blood vessels and throughout the body is thought to increase the risk for heart disease and stroke (sudden injury to the brain due to a compromised blood and oxygen supply). People with more body fat have higher blood levels of substances such as plasminogen

TABLE 2.5

Serum cholesterol levels among persons 20 years of age and over, by demographic characteristics, selected years 1960–2006 [CONTINUED]

[Data are based on interviews and laboratory work of a sample of the civilian noninstitutionalized population]

Sex, age, race and Hispanic origin[a], and percent of poverty level	1960–1962	1971–1974	1976–1980[b]	1988–1994	1999–2002	2003–2006
20–74 years, age-adjusted[c]			Mean serum cholesterol level, mg/dL			
Both sexes[d]	222	216	215	205	203	200
Male	220	216	213	204	203	199
Female	224	217	216	205	202	201
Not Hispanic or Latino:						
White only, male	—	—	213	204	202	199
White only, female	—	—	216	206	204	203
Black or African American only, male	—	—	211	201	195	193
Black or African American only, female	—	—	216	204	200	194
Mexican male	—	—	209	206	205	203
Mexican female	—	—	209	204	198	199
Percent of poverty level:[e]						
Below 100%	—	211	211	203	200	203
100%–less than 200%	—	217	213	203	203	201
200% or more	—	217	216	206	203	200
20 years and over, age-adjusted[c]						
Both sexes[d]	—	—	—	206	203	200
Male	—	—	—	204	202	198
Female	—	—	—	207	204	202
Not Hispanic or Latino:						
White only, male	—	—	—	205	202	198
White only, female	—	—	—	208	205	203
Black or African American only, male	—	—	—	202	195	193
Black or African American only, female	—	—	—	207	202	195
Mexican male	—	—	—	206	204	203
Mexican female	—	—	—	206	199	200
Percent of poverty level:[e]						
Below 100%	—	—	—	205	201	203
100%–less than 200%	—	—	—	205	204	201
200% or more	—	—	—	207	203	200
20 years and over, crude						
Both sexes[d]	—	—	—	204	203	200
Male	—	—	—	202	202	198
Female	—	—	—	206	204	202
Not Hispanic or Latino:						
White only, male	—	—	—	203	203	198
White only, female	—	—	—	208	206	205
Black or African American only, male	—	—	—	198	194	192
Black or African American only, female	—	—	—	201	199	194
Mexican male	—	—	—	199	200	200
Mexican female	—	—	—	198	194	196
Percent of poverty level:[e]						
Below 100%	—	—	—	200	198	200
100%–less than 200%	—	—	—	202	202	199
200% or more	—	—	—	205	204	201

activator inhibitor-1—an enzyme produced in the kidneys that inhibits the conversion of plasminogen to plasmin and initiates fibrinolysis. Fibrinolysis leads to the breakdown of fibrin, which is responsible for the semisolid character of a blood clot that can occlude (block) blood vessels. This is the mechanism believed to account for the finding that obesity is associated with an increased risk of blood clot formation. Occluded arteries may produce myocardial infarction (heart attack) or stroke. Overweight increases the risk for ischemic stroke—resulting from a clot or blockage—but does not appear to increase the risk for hemorrhagic stroke (bleeding inside the brain), which, in general, is associated with more fatality. According to the National Heart, Lung, and Blood Institute (NHLBI), in *Guidelines on Overweight and Obesity: Electronic Textbook* (June 1998, http://www.nhlbi.nih.gov/guidelines/obesity/e_txtbk/index.htm), the risk of stroke increases as BMI rises. For example, the risk of ischemic stroke is 75% higher in women with a BMI greater than 27 and 137% higher in women with a BMI greater than 32, compared with women having a BMI less than 21.

In "Association of Overweight with Increased Risk of Coronary Heart Disease Partly Independent of Blood Pressure and Cholesterol Levels: A Meta-analysis of 21 Cohort Studies Including More Than 300,000 Persons" (*Archives of Internal Medicine*, vol. 167, no. 16, September 2007), Rik P. Bogers et al. reveal that even moderately overweight people have an increased risk of heart disease, independent of the impact of their weight on blood pressure and cholesterol levels. The results of this

TABLE 2.5

Serum cholesterol levels among persons 20 years of age and over, by demographic characteristics, selected years 1960–2006 [CONTINUED]

[Data are based on interviews and laboratory work of a sample of the civilian noninstitutionalized population]

Sex, age, race and Hispanic origin[a], and percent of poverty level	1960–1962	1971–1974	1976–1980[b]	1988–1994	1999–2002	2003–2006
Male			Mean serum cholesterol level, mg/dL			
20–34 years	198	194	192	186	188	186
35–44 years	227	221	217	206	207	209
45–54 years	231	229	227	216	215	208
55–64 years	233	229	229	216	212	202
65–74 years	230	226	221	212	202	191
75 years and over	—	—	—	205	195	187
Female						
20–34 years	194	191	189	184	185	188
35–44 years	214	207	207	195	198	197
45–54 years	237	232	232	217	211	208
55–64 years	262	245	249	235	221	219
65–74 years	266	250	246	233	224	214
75 years and over	—	—	—	229	217	206

—Data not available.

[a]Persons of Mexican origin may be of any race. Starting with 1999 data, race-specific estimates are tabulated according to the 1997 Revisions to the Standards for the Classification of Federal Data on Race and Ethnicity and are not strictly comparable with estimates for earlier years. The two non-Hispanic race categories shown in the table conform to the 1997 Standards. Starting with 1999 data, race-specific estimates are for persons who reported only one racial group. Prior to data year 1999, estimates were tabulated according to the 1977 Standards. Estimates for single-race categories prior to 1999 included persons who reported one race or, if they reported more than one race, identified one race as best representing their race.

[b]Data for Mexicans are for 1982–1984.

[c]Age-adjusted to the 2000 standard population using five age groups: 20–34 years, 35–44 years, 45–54 years, 55–64 years, and 65 years and over (65–74 years for estimates for 20–74 years). Age-adjusted estimates may differ from other age-adjusted estimates based on the same data and presented elsewhere if different age groups are used in the adjustment procedure.

[d]Includes persons of all races and Hispanic origins, not just those shown separately.

[e]Percent of poverty level is based on family income and family size. Persons with unknown percent of poverty level are excluded (4% in 2003–2006).

Notes: High serum cholesterol is defined as greater than or equal to 240 mg/dL (6.20 mmol/L). Borderline high serum cholesterol is defined as greater than or equal to 200 mg/dL and less than 240 mg/dL. Risk levels have been defined by the Third Report of the National Cholesterol Education Program Expert Panel on Detection, Evaluation, and Treatment of High Blood Cholesterol in Adults. National Heart, Lung, and Blood Institute, National Institutes of Health. September 2002. Individuals who take medicine to lower their serum cholesterol levels and whose measured total serum cholesterol levels are below the cut-offs for high and borderline high cholesterol are not defined as having high or borderline high cholesterol, respectively.

SOURCE: "Table 72. Serum Total Cholesterol Levels among Persons 20 Years of Age and over, by Sex, Age, Race and Hispanic Origin, and Poverty Level: United States, 1960–1962 through 2003–2006," in *Health, United States, 2008*, Centers for Disease Control and Prevention, National Center for Health Statistics, 2008, http://www.cdc.gov/nchs/data/hus/hus08.pdf (accessed October 18, 2009)

study are important because they show that even when overweight people are treated for high blood pressure and high cholesterol, they are still at increased risk for heart disease.

In "Contribution of Obesity and Abdominal Fat Mass to Risk of Stroke and Transient Ischemic Attacks" (*Stroke*, vol. 39, no. 12, December 2008) Yaroslav Winter et al. confirm that abdominal obesity in particular is related to increased risk of stroke, independent of other risk factors. The researchers find that waist-to-hip ratios, which are better measures of abdominal obesity than BMI alone, are the best predictive markers of stroke risk.

Figure 2.2 shows the process, known as a treatment algorithm, that is used to assess and treat overweight individuals, based on their body weight, abdominal fat, and the risk factors for cardiovascular morbidity and mortality.

Type 2 Diabetes

Diabetes is a disease that affects the body's use of food, causing blood glucose (sugar levels in the blood) to become too high. Normally, the body converts sugars, starches, and proteins into a form of sugar called glucose.

The blood then carries glucose to all the cells throughout the body. In the cells, with the help of the hormone insulin, the glucose is either converted into energy for use immediately or stored for the future. Beta cells of the pancreas, a small organ located behind the stomach, manufacture the insulin. The process of turning food into energy via glucose (blood sugar) is important because the body depends on glucose for every function.

With diabetes, the body can convert food to glucose, but there is a problem with insulin. In one type of diabetes (insulin-dependent diabetes or Type 1), the pancreas does not manufacture enough insulin, and in another type (noninsulin dependent or Type 2), the body has insulin but cannot use the insulin effectively (this latter condition is called insulin resistance). When insulin is either absent or ineffective, glucose cannot get into the cells to be used for energy. Instead, the unused glucose builds up in the bloodstream and circulates through the kidneys. If a person's blood-glucose level rises high enough, the excess glucose "spills" over into the urine, causing frequent urination. This, in turn, leads to an increased feeling of thirst as the body tries to compensate for the fluid lost through urination.

TABLE 2.6

Hypertension and elevated blood pressure among persons 20 years of age and over, by demographic characteristics, selected years 1988–2006

[Data are based on interviews and physical examinations of a sample of the civilian noninstitutionalized population]

Sex, age, race and Hispanic origin,[b] and percent of poverty level	Hypertension[c, d] (elevated blood pressure and/or taking antihypertensive medication)			Elevated blood pressure[c]		
	1988–1994	1999–2002	2003–2006	1988–1994	1999–2002	2003–2006
20 years and over, age-adjusted[e]	Percent of population					
Both sexes[f]	25.5	30.0	31.3	18.5	19.9	17.9
Male	26.4	28.8	31.8	20.6	19.1	18.2
Female	24.4	30.6	30.3	16.4	20.2	17.3
Not Hispanic or Latino:						
White only, male	25.6	27.6	31.2	19.7	17.6	17.4
White only, female	23.0	28.5	28.3	15.1	18.5	15.9
Black or African American only, male	37.5	40.6	42.2	30.3	28.2	26.5
Black or African American only, female	38.3	43.5	44.1	26.4	28.8	23.9
Mexican male	26.9	26.8	24.8	22.2	21.5	15.3
Mexican female	25.0	27.9	28.6	20.4	21.2	19.2
Percent of poverty level:[g]						
Below 100%	31.7	33.9	35.0	22.5	23.3	22.6
100%–less than 200%	26.6	33.5	34.1	19.3	23.0	21.1
200% or more	23.9	28.2	30.3	17.5	18.2	16.6
20 years and over, crude						
Both sexes[f]	24.1	30.2	32.1	17.6	19.9	18.2
Male	23.8	27.6	31.3	18.7	18.2	17.9
Female	24.4	32.7	32.9	16.5	21.6	18.6
Not Hispanic or Latino:						
White only, male	24.3	28.3	32.4	18.7	17.8	17.9
White only, female	24.6	32.8	33.4	16.4	21.6	18.8
Black or African American only, male	31.1	35.9	38.8	25.5	25.2	24.8
Black or African American only, female	32.5	41.9	42.8	22.2	27.2	22.4
Mexican male	16.4	16.5	16.6	13.9	14.1	10.9
Mexican female	15.9	18.8	20.0	12.7	13.8	13.0
Percent of poverty level:[g]						
Below 100%	25.7	30.3	28.8	18.7	21.1	18.3
100%–less than 200%	26.7	34.8	36.8	19.8	24.1	22.5
200% or more	22.2	28.2	31.1	16.2	17.8	16.8
Male						
20–34 years	7.1	8.1[a]	9.2	6.6	*7.3	7.6
35–44 years	17.1	17.1	21.1	15.2	12.1	13.2
45–54 years	29.2	31.0	36.2	21.9	20.4	21.0
55–64 years	40.6	45.0	50.2	28.4	24.8	26.4
65–74 years	54.4	59.6	64.1	39.9	34.9	29.2
75 years and over	60.4	69.0	65.0	49.7	50.6	38.2

Type 2 diabetes is most often seen in adults and is the most common type of diabetes in the United States. In this type, the pancreas produces insulin, but it is not used effectively because the body resists responding to it. Heredity may be a predisposing factor in the genesis of Type 2 diabetes, but because the pancreas continues to produce insulin, the disease is considered more of a problem of insulin resistance, in which the body is not using the hormone efficiently.

Because diabetes deprives body cells of the glucose needed to function properly, several complications can develop to threaten the lives of diabetics further. The healing process of the body is slowed or impaired and the risk of infection increases. Complications of diabetes include higher risk and rates of heart disease; circulatory problems, especially in the legs, are often severe enough to require surgery or even amputation; diabetic retinopathy, a condition that can cause blindness; kidney disease that may require dialysis; dental problems; and problems with pregnancy.

The National Institutes of Health's Weight-Control Information Network (WIN) observes in *Do You Know the Health Risks of Being Overweight?* (December 2007, http://win.niddk.nih.gov/Publications/health_risks.htm) that over 85% of people with Type 2 diabetes are overweight, and in people prone to Type 2 diabetes, becoming overweight can trigger the onset of the disease. It is not known precisely how overweight contributes to the causation of this disease. One hypothesis is that being overweight causes cells to change, making them less effective at using glucose. This then stresses the cells that produce insulin, causing them to fail gradually. Maintaining a healthy weight and keeping physically fit can usually prevent or delay the onset of Type 2 diabetes.

TABLE 2.6

Hypertension and elevated blood pressure among persons 20 years of age and over, by demographic characteristics, selected years 1988–2006 [CONTINUED]

[Data are based on interviews and physical examinations of a sample of the civilian noninstitutionalized population]

Sex, age, race and Hispanic origin,[b] and percent of poverty level	Hypertension[c, d] (elevated blood pressure and/or taking antihypertensive medication)			Elevated blood pressure[e]		
	1988–1994	1999–2002	2003–2006	1988–1994	1999–2002	2003–2006
Female						
20–34 years	2.9	2.7[a]	2.2[a]	2.4[a]	1.4[a]	[a]
35–44 years	11.2	15.1	12.6	6.4	8.5	5.8
45–54 years	23.9	31.8	36.2	13.7	19.1	20.0
55–64 years	42.6	53.9	54.4	27.0	31.9	28.6
65–74 years	56.2	72.7	70.8	38.2	53.0	40.8
75 years and over	73.6	83.1	80.2	59.9	64.4	55.4

[a]Estimates are considered unreliable.

[b]Persons of Mexican origin may be of any race. Starting with 1999 data, race-specific estimates are tabulated according to the 1997 Revisions to the Standards for the Classification of Federal Data on Race and Ethnicity and are not strictly comparable with estimates for earlier years. The two non-Hispanic race categories shown in the table conform to the 1997 Standards. Starting with 1999 data, race-specific estimates are for persons who reported only one racial group. Prior to data year 1999, estimates were tabulated according to the 1977 Standards. Estimates for single-race categories prior to 1999 included persons who reported one race or, if they reported more than one race, identified one race as best representing their race.

[c]Hypertension is defined as having measured elevated blood pressure and/or taking antihypertensive medication. Elevated blood pressure is defined as having a measured systolic pressure of at least 140 mmHg or diastolic pressure of at least 90 mmHg. Those with elevated blood pressure also may be taking prescribed medicine for high blood pressure. Those taking antihypertensive medication may not have measured elevated blood pressure but are still classified as having hypertension.

[d]Respondents were asked, "Are you now taking prescribed medicine for your high blood pressure?"

[e]Age-adjusted to the 2000 standard population using five age groups: 20–34 years, 35–44 years, 45–54 years, 55–64 years, and 65 years and over (65–74 years for estimates for 20–74 years). Age-adjusted estimates may differ from other age-adjusted estimates based on the same data and presented elsewhere if different age groups are used in the adjustment procedure.

[f]Includes persons of all races and Hispanic origins, not just those shown separately.

[g]Percent of poverty level is based on family income and family size. Persons with unknown percent of poverty level are excluded (5% in 2003–2006).

Notes: Percents are based on the average of blood pressure measurements taken. In 2003–2006, 81% of participants had three blood pressure readings. Excludes pregnant women. Estimates for persons 20 years and over are used for setting and tracking *Healthy People 2010* objectives. Data have been revised. Data for additional years are available.

SOURCE: "Table 71. Hypertension and Elevated Blood Pressure among Persons 20 Years of Age and over, by Selected Characteristics: United States, 1988–1994, 1999–2002, and 2003–2006," in *Health, United States, 2008*, Centers for Disease Control and Prevention, National Center for Health Statistics, 2008, http://www.cdc.gov/nchs/data/hus/hus08.pdf (accessed October 18, 2009)

From 1997 to March 2009 the percent of Americans diagnosed with diabetes rose from 5.1% to 10.1% of the population. (See Figure 2.3.) These numbers may significantly underestimate the true prevalence of diabetes in the United States in view of National Health and Nutrition Examination Survey findings that show sizable numbers of adults have undiagnosed diabetes.

"DIABESITY" AND "DOUBLE DIABETES." The recognition of obesity-dependent diabetes prompted scientists and physicians to coin a new term to describe this condition: diabesity. The term was first used in the 1990s and has gained widespread acceptance. Even though diabesity is attributed to the same causes as Type 2 diabetes—insulin resistance and pancreatic cell dysfunction—researchers are beginning to link the inflammation associated with obesity to the development of diabetes and cardiovascular disease.

Francine Ratner Kaufman contends in *Diabesity: The Obesity-Diabetes Epidemic That Threatens America—And What We Must Do to Stop It* (2005) that the diabesity epidemic "imperils human existence as we now know it" and observes that more than one-third of American children born in 2000 will develop diabetes in their lifetime. Kaufman warns that unless drastic measures are taken, by 2020 there will be a 72% increase in the number of

diabetics in the United States. The increasing prevalence of diabesity has prompted the development of new treatment strategies to address both problems. In "New Therapies for Diabesity" (*Current Diabetes Report*, vol. 9, no. 5, October 2009), Christopher J. Bailey of Aston University explains that "the two conditions together impose a particularly complex therapeutic challenge."

Another recent phenomenon is the growing number of patients diagnosed with both Type 1 and Type 2 diabetes simultaneously. Dubbed "double diabetes," it has been reported in both children and adults. Dennis Thompson Jr. explains in "The Double Diabetes Epidemic" (May 5, 2009, http://www.everydayhealth.com/type-1-diabetes/double-diabetes.aspx) that it often results when people with Type 1 diabetes who rely on insulin injections to control their diabetes gain weight and develop the insulin resistance that characterizes Type 2 diabetes.

Osteoarthritis and Joint Injury

Being only 10 pounds overweight increases the force on the knee by 30–60 pounds with each step.... Even small amounts of weight loss reduce the risk of developing knee OA [osteoarthritis]. Preliminary studies suggest weight loss decreases pain substantially in those with knee OA. —Susan Bartlett, "Osteoarthritis Weight Management" (2010)

FIGURE 2.2

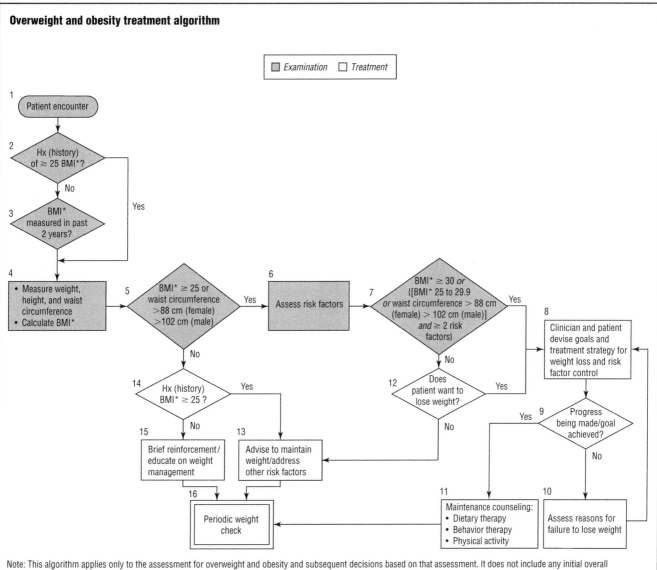

Overweight and obesity treatment algorithm

☐ Examination   ☐ Treatment

1 — Patient encounter

2 — Hx (history) of ≥ 25 BMI*?
— No
— Yes

3 — BMI* measured in past 2 years?
— No

4 — • Measure weight, height, and waist circumference • Calculate BMI*

5 — BMI* ≥ 25 or waist circumference >88 cm (female) >102 cm (male)
— Yes
— No

6 — Assess risk factors

7 — BMI* ≥ 30 or {[BMI* 25 to 29.9 or waist circumference > 88 cm (female) > 102 cm (male)] and ≥ 2 risk factors}
— Yes
— No

8 — Clinician and patient devise goals and treatment strategy for weight loss and risk factor control

9 — Progress being made/goal achieved?
— Yes
— No

10 — Assess reasons for failure to lose weight

11 — Maintenance counseling: • Dietary therapy • Behavior therapy • Physical activity

12 — Does patient want to lose weight?
— Yes
— No

13 — Advise to maintain weight/address other risk factors

14 — Hx (history) BMI* ≥ 25 ?
— Yes
— No

15 — Brief reinforcement/ educate on weight management

16 — Periodic weight check

Note: This algorithm applies only to the assessment for overweight and obesity and subsequent decisions based on that assessment. It does not include any initial overall assessment for cardiovascular risk factors or diseases that are indicated.
*BMI=body mass index.

SOURCE: "Treatment Algorithm," in *Clinical Guidelines on the Identification, Evaluation, and Treatment of Overweight and Obesity in Adults: The Evidence Report*, National Institutes of Health, National Heart, Lung, and Blood Institute in cooperation with The National Institute of Diabetes and Digestive and Kidney Diseases, 2005, http://hp2010.nhlbihin.net/oei_ss/download/pdf/CORESET2.pdf, (accessed October 18, 2009)

The word *arthritis* literally means joint inflammation. The name applies to more than 100 related diseases known as rheumatic diseases. A joint is any point where two bones meet. When a joint becomes inflamed, swelling, redness, pain, and loss of motion occur. In the most serious forms of the disease, the loss of motion can be physically disabling. Arthritis is the leading cause of disability and the leading cause of limitation of activity among working-age adults (aged 18 to 64) in the United States. (See Figure 2.4.)

People who are overweight or obese are at increased risk for osteoarthritis, which is not an inflammatory arthritis. Osteoarthritis, sometimes called degenerative arthritis, causes the breakdown of bones and

cartilage (connective tissue attached to bones), and usually causes pain and stiffness in the fingers, knees, feet, hips, and back. Extra weight places extra pressure on joints and cartilage, causing them to erode. Furthermore, people with more body fat may have higher blood levels of substances that cause inflammation. Inflammation at the joints may increase the risk for osteoarthritis.

According to the CDC, in "Arthritis Related Statistics: Prevalence of Specific Types of Arthritis" (August 1, 2009, http://www.cdc.gov/arthritis/data_statistics/arthritis _related_stats.htm), in 2005 osteoarthritis affected approximately 27 million Americans, usually after the age of 45 years. In "Osteoarthritis Weight Management"

FIGURE 2.3

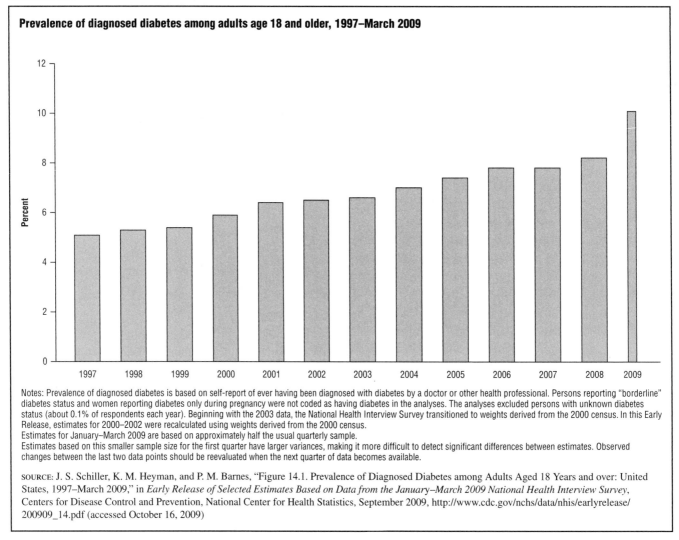

Prevalence of diagnosed diabetes among adults age 18 and older, 1997–March 2009

Notes: Prevalence of diagnosed diabetes is based on self-report of ever having been diagnosed with diabetes by a doctor or other health professional. Persons reporting "borderline" diabetes status and women reporting diabetes only during pregnancy were not coded as having diabetes in the analyses. The analyses excluded persons with unknown diabetes status (about 0.1% of respondents each year). Beginning with the 2003 data, the National Health Interview Survey transitioned to weights derived from the 2000 census. In this Early Release, estimates for 2000–2002 were recalculated using weights derived from the 2000 census.
Estimates for January–March 2009 are based on approximately half the usual quarterly sample.
Estimates based on this smaller sample size for the first quarter have larger variances, making it more difficult to detect significant differences between estimates. Observed changes between the last two data points should be reevaluated when the next quarter of data becomes available.

SOURCE: J. S. Schiller, K. M. Heyman, and P. M. Barnes, "Figure 14.1. Prevalence of Diagnosed Diabetes among Adults Aged 18 Years and over: United States, 1997–March 2009," in *Early Release of Selected Estimates Based on Data from the January–March 2009 National Health Interview Survey*, Centers for Disease Control and Prevention, National Center for Health Statistics, September 2009, http://www.cdc.gov/nchs/data/nhis/earlyrelease/200909_14.pdf (accessed October 16, 2009)

(2010, http://www.hopkins-arthritis.org/patient-corner/disease-management/osteoandweight.html), Susan Bartlett of Johns Hopkins University indicates that obese women have about four times the risk of knee osteoarthritis, compared with women of healthy weight, and for obese men the risk is five times greater. According to Jingbo Niu et al., in "Is Obesity a Risk Factor for Progressive Radiographic Knee Osteoarthritis?" (*Arthritis Care and Research*, vol. 61, no. 3, March 2009), people with clinically severe obesity—those in the highest fifth quintile of body weight—have a 10-fold risk of developing knee osteoarthritis, compared with those in the lowest fifth quintile. The researchers confirm that obesity is associated with an increased risk of developing knee arthritis but that it does not increase the risk of progression, or worsening, of the condition.

Weight loss may decrease the likelihood of developing osteoarthritis in the knees, hips, and lower back and has been shown to relieve the symptoms of osteoarthritis. Marlene Fransen reports in "Dietary Weight Loss and Exercise for Obese Adults with Knee Osteoarthritis: Mod-

est Weight Loss Targets, Mild Exercise, Modest Effects" (*Arthritis and Rheumatism*, vol. 50, no. 5, May 2004) that a decrease in BMI of two points or greater during a 10-year period decreases the risk of developing knee osteoarthritis by more than 50%. In another study, Louise Murphy et al. find in "Lifetime Risk of Symptomatic Knee Osteoarthritis" (*Arthritis Care and Research*, vol. 59, no. 9, September 15, 2008) that along with aging, obesity is associated with an increased risk of developing osteoarthritis. The researchers opine that this finding "underscores the immediate need for greater use of clinical and public health interventions, especially those that address weight loss."

In "Associations of Body Mass Index with Meniscal Tears" (*American Journal of Preventive Medicine*, vol. 28, no. 4, May 2005), Gregory M. Ford et al. of the University of Utah School of Medicine state that overweight is also linked to cartilage tears in the knee. The study's subjects were men and women aged 50 to 79 who had surgery to repair the meniscus, the shock-absorbing cartilage in the knee. Ford et al. find that people with a BMI even slightly over the healthy range were three

FIGURE 2.4

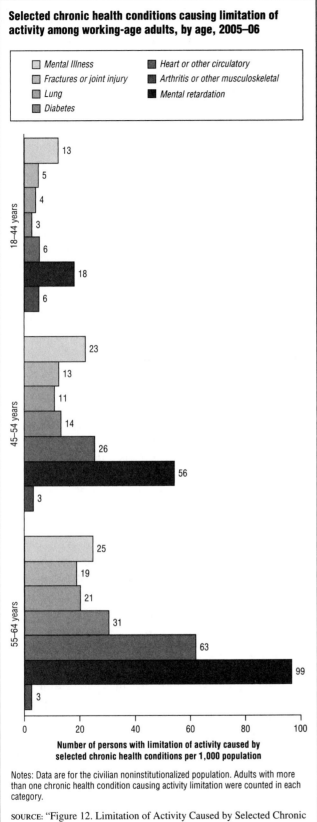

Selected chronic health conditions causing limitation of activity among working-age adults, by age, 2005–06

Legend:
- Mental Illness
- Fractures or joint injury
- Lung
- Diabetes
- Heart or other circulatory
- Arthritis or other musculoskeletal
- Mental retardation

18–44 years: 13, 5, 4, 3, 6, 18, 6

45–54 years: 23, 13, 11, 14, 26, 56, 3

55–64 years: 25, 19, 21, 31, 63, 99, 3

Number of persons with limitation of activity caused by selected chronic health conditions per 1,000 population

Notes: Data are for the civilian noninstitutionalized population. Adults with more than one chronic health condition causing activity limitation were counted in each category.

SOURCE: "Figure 12. Limitation of Activity Caused by Selected Chronic Health Conditions among Working-Age Adults, by Age: United States, 2005–2006," in *Health, United States, 2008*, Centers for Disease Control and Prevention, National Center for Health Statistics, 2008, http://www.cdc.gov/nchs/data/hus/hus08.pdf (accessed October 18, 2009)

times more likely to have a cartilage tear. The heaviest men were 15 times more likely to have torn knee cartilage and the heaviest women were 25 times more likely to have torn cartilage than those in the healthy-weight ranges. One possible explanation for this finding may be that obese people have circulation problems that reduce the blood supply to the cartilage. Ford et al. conclude that overweight probably accounts for more than half of the nation's 850,000 annual operations to repair cartilage tears in the knee.

By 2009 the relationship between weight loss and improvements in the symptoms of knee pain due to arthritis was clear and definitive enough to warrant classifying it as an effective treatment for this condition. According to John Richmond et al., in "Treatment of Osteoarthritis of the Knee (Nonarthroplasty)" (*Journal of the American Academy of Orthopedic Surgeons*, vol. 17, no. 9, September 2009), the American Academy of Orthopedic Surgeons considers weight loss one of the standard nonsurgical treatments for overweight patients suffering from osteoarthritis of the knee.

Gallbladder Disease

Gallstones are small, hard pellets that can form when bile in the gallbladder (a muscular saclike organ that lies under the liver in the right side of the abdomen) precipitates (becomes solid out of the bile solution). Bile contains water, cholesterol, fats, bile salts, proteins, and bilirubin. The gallbladder stores and concentrates the bile produced in the liver that is not needed immediately for digestion. Bile is released from the gallbladder into the small intestine in response to food. The pancreatic duct joins the common bile duct at the small intestine, adding enzymes to aid in digestion. (See Figure 2.5.) If bile contains too much cholesterol, bile salts, or bilirubin, under certain conditions it can harden into stones. Most gallstones are formed primarily from cholesterol.

The National Institute of Diabetes and Digestive and Kidney Diseases' National Digestive Diseases Information Clearinghouse (NDDIC) explains in "Gallstones" (July 2007, http://digestive.niddk.nih.gov/ddiseases/pubs/gallstones/) that when gallstones block the flow of bile they can produce inflammation in the gallbladder, liver, and pancreas. When blockage persists, the consequences may be severe infection, which untreated, may not only be painful but also deadly. When gallstones produce such symptoms, the treatment is generally a surgical procedure, called cholecystectomy, in which the gallbladder is removed. People who are not candidates for surgery may be given prescription drugs to dissolve gallstones; however, it is likely that gallstones will recur in people treated with drugs.

People who are overweight are at a higher risk for developing gallstones because the liver overproduces

FIGURE 2.5

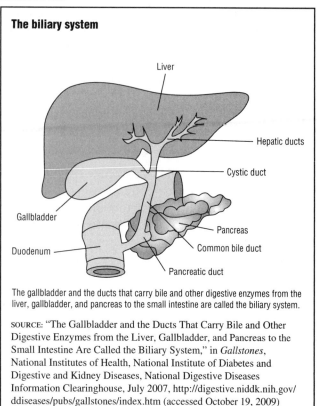

The biliary system

The gallbladder and the ducts that carry bile and other digestive enzymes from the liver, gallbladder, and pancreas to the small intestine are called the biliary system.

SOURCE: "The Gallbladder and the Ducts That Carry Bile and Other Digestive Enzymes from the Liver, Gallbladder, and Pancreas to the Small Intestine Are Called the Biliary System," in *Gallstones*, National Institutes of Health, National Institute of Diabetes and Digestive and Kidney Diseases, National Digestive Diseases Information Clearinghouse, July 2007, http://digestive.niddk.nih.gov/ddiseases/pubs/gallstones/index.htm (accessed October 19, 2009)

cholesterol and deposits it in the bile, which then becomes supersaturated. The NDDIC indicates that the risk of gallstones is higher among people who are overweight or obese and among people who fast or lose a large amount of weight very quickly.

Rapid weight loss or weight cycling (the repeated loss and regain of body weight) further increases cholesterol production in the liver, with resulting supersaturation and risk for gallstone formation. Olga N. Tucker et al. of the Bariatric and Metabolic Institute in Weston, Florida, indicate in "Is Concomitant Cholecystectomy Necessary in Obese Patients Undergoing Laparoscopic Gastric Bypass Surgery?" (*Surgical Endoscopy*, vol. 22, no. 11, November 2008) that gallstones develop in approximately 25% of obese patients who undergo strict dietary restriction and within six months in as many as 50% of patients who undergo gastric bypass surgery (one of several surgical weight-loss treatments that may be prescribed for people with clinically severe obesity).

Fatty Liver Disease

Fatty liver is defined as an excess accumulation of fat in the liver, usually exceeding 5% of the total liver weight. More than 50% of the excess fat deposit in the liver is triglyceride. The enlargement of the liver is caused by the reduction of fatty acid oxidation (fat metabolism) in the liver, resulting in an excess accumulation of fat. It causes injury and inflammation in the liver

and may lead to severe liver damage, cirrhosis (buildup of scar tissue that blocks proper blood flow in the liver), or liver failure. Heiner Wedemeyer and Michael P. Manns of the Hannover Medical School in Hannover, Germany, report in "Fatty Liver Disease—It's More Than Alcohol and Obesity" (*Medscape Gastroenterology*, vol. 5, no. 2, 2003) that an estimated 9 million individuals in the United States suffer from nonalcoholic fatty liver disease.

People with diabetes or with higher than normal blood sugar levels (but not yet in the diabetic range) are more likely to have fatty liver disease than those with normal blood sugar levels. It is not known why some people who are overweight or diabetic get fatty liver and others do not. Losing weight reduces the buildup of fat in the liver and prevents further injury; however, weight loss should not exceed 2.2 pounds (0.9 kg) per week because more rapid weight loss may exacerbate the disease.

Interestingly, Hong Ji and Mark I. Friedman of the Monell Chemical Senses Center in Philadelphia, Pennsylvania, assert in "Reduced Capacity for Fatty Acid Oxidation in Rats with Inherited Susceptibility to Diet-Induced Obesity" (*Metabolism: Clinical and Experimental*, vol. 56, no. 8, August 2007) that a genetic defect that impairs fatty acid oxidation may be a factor in obesity. Animal studies suggest that it may be harder for people prone to obesity to use energy from the fats they eat and to burn their own body fat for energy than their healthy-weight counterparts. This in turn prompts them to overeat in an effort to get enough energy.

Cancer

Cancer encompasses a large group of diseases characterized by the uncontrolled growth and spread of abnormal cells. These cells may grow into masses of tissue called malignant tumors. The dangerous aspect of cancer is that cancer cells invade and destroy normal tissue.

The spread of cancer cells occurs either by local growth of the tumor or by some of the cells becoming detached and traveling through the blood and lymph systems to start additional tumors in other parts of the body. Metastasis (the spread of cancer cells) may be confined to a region of the body, but if left untreated (and often despite treatment), the cancer cells can spread throughout the entire body, eventually causing death. It is perhaps the rapid, invasive, and destructive nature of cancer that makes it, arguably, the most feared of all diseases, even though it is second to heart disease as the leading cause of death in the United States. (See Table 2.2.)

Maria Cheng reports in "Obesity Could Become Top Cancer Cause" (Associated Press, September 24, 2009) that overweight and obesity are responsible for as many as 8% of cancers in Europe. Cheng notes that researchers at a joint meeting of the European Cancer Organisation and the European Society for Medical Oncology in Berlin, Germany, asserted in September 2009 that cancer may become the leading cause of cancer in women in western countries in the foreseeable future.

Overweight increases the risk of developing several types of cancer, including cancers of the colon, esophagus, gallbladder, kidney, pancreas, liver, and prostate, as well as uterine (specifically cancer of the lining of the uterus) and postmenopausal breast cancer. Excessive weight gain during adult life increases the risk for several of these cancers. For example, according to the American Cancer Society, in *Cancer Prevention and Early Detection: Facts and Figures, 2009* (June 2009, http://www.cancer.org/downloads/STT/860009web_6-4-09.pdf), 14% to 20% of all cancer-related deaths are attributed to overweight and obesity. In "Obesity and Cancer: Pathophysiological and Biological Mechanisms" *Archives of Physiology and Biochemistry* vol. 114, no. 1, February 2008), Andrew G. Renehan, Darren L. Roberts, and Caroline Dive of the Christie NHS Foundation Trust in Manchester, England, report that an increase of 5 kilograms per square meter in BMI raised the risk of esophageal adenocarcinoma by 52%, thyroid cancer by 33%, and colon and kidney cancers each by 24%. In women, a BMI increase of 5 kilograms per square meter increased the risk of endometrial (59%), gallbladder (59%), esophageal adenocarcinoma (51%), and kidney (34%) cancers. The researchers also find associations between increased BMI and rectal cancer and malignant melanoma in men and postmenopausal breast, pancreatic, thyroid, and colon cancers in women. Furthermore, there is a relationship between BMI and an increased risk of other cancers including leukemia, multiple myeloma (cancer involving different sites within bone marrow), and non-Hodgkin's lymphoma (cancer of lymphocytes, a type of white blood cell).

In "Obesity, Recreational Physical Activity, and Risk of Pancreatic Cancer in a Large U.S. Cohort" (*Cancer Epidemiology Biomarkers and Prevention*, vol. 14, no. 2, February 2005), Alpa V. Patel et al. find a relationship between obesity and pancreatic cancer. The researchers obtained information on current weight and weight at age 18, location of weight gain, and recreational physical activity to obtain a baseline using a self-administered questionnaire for 145,627 men and women who were cancer-free at the start of the study. During the seven years of follow-up, 242 cases of pancreatic cancer were diagnosed in the research subjects. Analysis of these data revealed an increased risk of pancreatic cancer among obese men and women, compared with men and women of normal weight. The risk of pancreatic cancer was also higher among men and women who reported a tendency for central (abdominal) weight gain, compared with subjects who reported a tendency for peripheral weight gain.

Susanna C. Larsson and Alicja Wolk of the National Institute of Environmental Medicine in Stockholm, Sweden, observe in "Overweight and Obesity and Incidence of Leukemia: A Meta-analysis of Cohort Studies" (*International Journal of Cancer*, vol. 122, no. 6, March 15, 2008) that nine studies comparing healthy-weight individuals (a BMI less than 25) with people who were overweight or obese found that overweight and obese people were at increased risk of developing four types of leukemia. Specifically, an increase in BMI was associated with a 13% increased risk of leukemia.

Overweight may also increase the risk of dying from some cancers. In "Influence of Obesity on Breast Cancer Receptor Status and Prognosis" (*Expert Review of Anticancer Therapy*, vol. 9, no. 8, August 2009), David P. Rose and Linda Vona-Davis conclude that "pre-existing obesity and postoperative weight gain are related to a poor prognosis in breast cancer. Weight control is important, not only to target breast cancer progression, but also to reduce the risk of nonbreast cancer mortality risk associated with excess adiposity."

It is not known exactly how being overweight increases cancer risk, recurrence, or mortality. It may be that fat cells make or influence hormones that affect cell growth and lead to cancer. It is also possible that eating habits—such as a high-fat, high-caloric diet—or physical inactivity that promote overweight contribute to cancer risk.

Sleep Apnea and Sleep Disorders

Sleep apnea is a condition in which breathing becomes shallow or stops completely for short periods during sleep. A pause in breathing can last about 10 to 20 seconds or longer, and pauses can occur 20 times or more an hour. Sleep apnea can increase the risk of developing high blood pressure, heart attack, or stroke. Untreated sleep apnea can increase the risk of diabetes and daytime sleepiness, which can increase the risk for work-related accidents and automobile accidents.

The most common type of sleep apnea, and the type that is linked to overweight and obesity, is obstructive sleep apnea (OSA). During sleep there is insufficient airflow into the lungs through the mouth and nose, and the amount of oxygen in the blood may drop because the airway is transiently occluded. The NHLBI notes in "Who Is at Risk for Sleep Apnea?" (January 14, 2010, http://www.nhlbi.nih.gov/health/dci/Diseases/SleepApnea/SleepApnea_WhoIsAtRisk.html) that over 12 million Americans have OSA and that "more than half of the people who have this condition are overweight." One out of 25 men and one out of 50 women over the age of 40 have debilitating sleep apnea that causes them to be sleepy during the day.

Obesity, particularly upper-body obesity, is a risk factor for sleep apnea and is related to its severity. Most people with sleep apnea have a BMI greater than 30. In general, men whose neck circumference is 17 inches (43 cm) or greater and women with neck circumference of 16 inches (41 cm) or greater are at higher risk for sleep apnea. Large neck girth in both men and women who snore is highly predictive of sleep apnea because people with large neck girth store more fat around their necks, which may compromise their airway. A smaller airway can make breathing difficult or stop it altogether. In addition, fat stored in the neck and throughout the body can produce substances that cause inflammation, and inflammation in the neck may be a risk factor for sleep apnea. Weight loss usually resolves or significantly improves sleep apnea by decreasing neck size and reducing inflammation.

Too little sleep is also linked to obesity. Robert D. Vorona et al. of the Eastern Virginia Medical School find in "Overweight and Obese Patients in a Primary Care Population Report Less Sleep than Patients with a Normal Body Mass Index" (*Archives of Internal Medicine*, vol. 165, no. 1, January 10, 2005) that people who were overweight or obese reported that they slept less per week than their normal-weight counterparts. Total sleep time decreased as BMI increased except in the extremely obese group. The difference averaged 16 minutes per day between normal-weight and overweight subjects, totaling nearly two hours per week. Vorona et al. speculate that lost sleep might have metabolic and hormonal consequences. For example, sleep restriction may reduce levels of leptin, a hormone involved in appetite regulation, which could account for the relationship between diminished sleep and obesity. They observe that their findings do not establish a cause-and-effect relationship between sleep and obesity; however, they "suggest that an extra twenty minutes of sleep per night seems to be associated with a lower BMI."

More recent research confirms the relationship between disordered sleep and BMI and reveals that besides too little sleep, interrupted or discontinuous sleep is also associated with obesity. In "Sleep Discontinuity and Impaired Sleep Continuity Affect Transition to and from Obesity over Time: Results from the Alameda County Study" (*Scandinavian Journal of Public Health*, January 11, 2010), Maria E. Nordin and Robert M. Kaplan examined self-reported changes in sleep and BMI over time—from 1965 through 1994. The researchers find that discontinuous sleep is not only associated with an increased risk for obesity but also lowers the chance for weight loss among people who are obese.

Women's Reproductive Health

Besides increased risk of breast and endometrial cancers (the endometrium is the lining of the uterus), women who are overweight or obese may suffer from infertility (difficulty or inability to conceive a child) and other gynecological or pregnancy-related medical problems. Obesity is associated with menstrual irregularities such as abnormally heavy menstrual periods and amenorrhea (cessation of menstruation), and has been found to affect ovulation, response to fertility treatment, pregnancy rates, and pregnancy outcomes.

In "The Importance of Diagnosing the Polycystic Ovary Syndrome" (*Annals of Internal Medicine*, vol. 132, no. 12, June 20, 2000), Rogerio A. Lobo and Enrico Carmina of Columbia University note that abdominal obesity in women is linked to polycystic ovarian syndrome (PCOS), an endocrine condition that afflicts approximately 6% to 10% of premenopausal women. PCOS is characterized by the accumulation of cysts (fluid-filled sacs) on the ovaries, chronic anovulation (absent ovulation), and other metabolic disturbances. Symptoms include excess facial and body hair, acne, obesity, irregular menstrual cycles, insulin resistance, and infertility. A key characteristic of PCOS is hyperandrogenism—excessive production of male hormones (androgens), particularly testosterone, by the ovaries—which is responsible for the acne, male-pattern hair growth, and baldness seen in women with PCOS. Hyperandrogenism has been linked to insulin resistance and hyperinsulinemia (high blood insulin levels), both of which are common in PCOS. Women with PCOS have an increased risk of early-onset heart disease, hypertension, diabetes, and reproductive cancers and a higher incidence of miscarriage and infertility. In overweight women, modest weight loss (as little as 5%) through diet and exercise may correct hyperandrogenism and restore ovulation and fertility.

According to Gabriella G. Gosman et al., in "Reproductive Health of Women Electing Bariatric Surgery" (*Fertility and Sterility*, October 6, 2009), a study of 1,538 women undergoing weight-loss surgery, women who become obese by age 18 are at greater risk of developing PCOS and infertility than their healthy-weight peers. This finding is of increased significance in view of the growing number of overweight young adults.

Obesity during pregnancy is associated with increased morbidity for both the expectant mother and the unborn child. Obese pregnant women are significantly more likely to suffer from hypertension and gestational diabetes (glucose intolerance of variable severity that starts or is first recognized during pregnancy) than normal-weight expectant mothers. Obesity is also associated with difficulties in managing labor and delivery, leading to premature births and higher rates of cesarean section (delivery of a fetus by surgical incision through the abdominal wall and uterus). Risks associated with anesthesia are higher in obese women, as there is a greater tendency toward hypoxemia (abnormal lack of oxygen in the blood) and greater difficulty administering local or general anesthesia.

The children of women who are obese during pregnancy are at increased risk of birth defects—congenital malformations, particularly of neural tube defects. Neural tube defects are abnormalities of the brain and spinal cord resulting from the failure of the neural tube to develop properly during early pregnancy. The neural tube is the embryonic nerve tissue that eventually develops into the brain and the spinal cord.

Research indicates that boys born to higher-weight mothers may be more likely to develop testicular cancer. In "Is There an Association between Maternal Weight and the Risk of Testicular Cancer? An Epidemiologic Study of Norwegian Data with an Emphasis on World War II" (*International Journal of Cancer*, vol. 116, no. 2, August 20, 2005), Elin L. Aschim et al. indicate that exposure of unborn males to high levels of estrogen is believed to be involved in the subsequent development of testicular cancer. Boys born to higher-weight mothers are more likely to have been exposed to high estrogen levels than boys born to lower-weight mothers because higher weight results in higher insulin levels and lower levels of the protein that normally binds estrogen. As a result, higher levels of estrogen are able to cross the placenta and affect the male fetus.

Furthermore, women who are obese before pregnancy appear to have a higher risk of stillbirth and of having an infant die soon after birth. Janni Kristensen et al. find in "Pre-pregnancy Weight and the Risk of Stillbirth and Neonatal Death" (*British Journal of Gynecology*, vol. 112, no. 4, April 2005) that compared with normal-weight women, those who were obese before pregnancy had twice the risk of stillbirth and newborn deaths. Previous researchers reported comparable risks attributed in part to the higher rates of diabetes and high blood pressure observed in overweight pregnant women. Nevertheless, Kristensen et al. note that diabetes and high blood pressure were not responsible for their findings. When women with diabetes or high blood pressure were excluded from their analysis, the risks of stillbirth and newborn death linked to obesity were still significantly higher than the risks for normal-weight or overweight women. It is not yet known how obesity increases the risk of stillbirth and early infant death, but Kristensen et al. posit that obesity influences the hormonal system and the metabolism of blood fats that in turn may compromise blood flow to the placenta (an organ that forms during pregnancy and functions as a filter between the mother and fetus).

Babies born to overweight and obese women are at greater risk of having heart defects. Suzanne M. Gilboa et al. report in "Association between Prepregnancy Body Mass Index and Congenital Heart Defects" (*American Journal of Obstetrics and Gynecology*, vol. 202, no. 1, January 2010) the results of a study of 6,440 infants born with congenital heart defects and 5,673 infants without birth defects. The researchers find that when compared with babies born to normal-weight women, there was a significant increase in many types of heart defects in babies born to overweight and obese women. Gilboa et al. looked at 25 types of heart defects and found associations with obesity for 10 of them. Five of these 10 types were also associated with overweight prior to pregnancy. Women who were overweight but not obese had approximately a 15% increased risk of delivering a baby with certain heart defects.

WEIGHT GAIN DURING PREGNANCY. Weight gain during pregnancy is expected and beneficial. The fetus, expanded blood volume, the enlarged uterus, breast tissue growth, and other products of conception generate approximately 13 to 17 pounds (5.9 to 7.7 kg) of extra weight. Weight gain beyond this anticipated amount is largely maternal adipose tissue that is often retained after pregnancy. The challenge health professionals face when developing recommendations about weight gain during pregnancy is achieving a balance between gains intended to produce high-birth-weight infants, who may then require delivery by cesarean section, and low-birth-weight infants with a higher infant mortality rate. Analysis of data from the CDC's Pregnancy Nutrition Surveillance System shows that extremely overweight women benefit from reduced weight gain during pregnancy to help decrease the risk for high-birth-weight infants. Table 2.7 shows the recommended amount of weight gain during pregnancy based on prepregnancy BMI.

In "Gestational Weight Gain and Pregnancy Outcomes in Obese Women" (*Obstetrics and Gynecology*, vol. 110, no. 4, October 2007), a study that analyzed the pregnancies of 120,251 obese women to see how weight gain affected pregnancy-related high blood pressure, cesarean delivery, and birth weight, Deborah W. Kiel et al. conclude that obese women who gained little or no weight during pregnancy as well as those who lost weight fared best. By not gaining weight during pregnancy, they

TABLE 2.7

Recommended weight gain during pregnancy

BMI	Kilograms	Pounds
<19.8	12.5 to 18	28 to 40
>19.8 to 26	11.5 to 16	25 to 35
>26 to 29	7 to 11.5	15 to 25
>29	≤6	≤13

SOURCE: "Weight Gain during Pregnancy," in *Guidelines on Overweight and Obesity: Electronic Textbook*, National Institutes of Health, National Heart, Lung, and Blood Institute in cooperation with The National Institute of Diabetes and Digestive and Kidney Diseases, 1998, http://www.nhlbi.nih.gov/guidelines/obesity/e_txtbk/ratnl/22111.htm (accessed October 19, 2009)

reduced their risk for high blood pressure, had fewer cesarean deliveries, and were more likely to have babies of normal weight.

Metabolic Syndrome

Phillip D. Levin and Charles Weissman of the Hebrew University–Hadassah School of Medicine observe in "Obesity, Metabolic Syndrome, and the Surgical Patient" (*Anesthesiology Clinics*, vol. 27, no. 4, December 2009) that between 35% and 40% of Americans exhibit a cluster of medical conditions characterized by insulin resistance and the presence of obesity, abdominal fat, high blood sugar and triglycerides, high blood cholesterol, and high blood pressure. This constellation of symptoms, called metabolic syndrome, was first defined in *Third Report of the National Cholesterol Education Program (NCEP) Expert Panel on Detection, Evaluation, and Treatment of High Blood Cholesterol in Adults (Adult Treatment Panel III)* (September 2002, http://www.nhlbi.nih.gov/guidelines/cholesterol/atp3full.pdf). The report concludes that for most affected people, metabolic syndrome results from poor diet and insufficient physical activity.

The diagnosis of metabolic syndrome, which is also known as syndrome X, requires that people meet at least three of the following criteria:

- Waistline measurement (waist circumference) of 40 inches (102 cm) or more for men and 35 inches (88 cm) or more for women

- Blood pressure of 130/85 millimeters of mercury (mmHg) or higher

- Fasting blood glucose level greater than 100 mg/dL

- Serum triglyceride level above 150 mg/dL

- HDL level less than 40 mg/dL for men or under 50 mg/dL for women

According to the American Heart Association, three groups of people are the most likely to be diagnosed with metabolic syndrome: diabetics, people with hypertension and hyperinsulinemia, and people who have suffered heart attacks and have hyperinsulinemia without glucose intolerance. Table 2.8 shows the prevalence of individual risk factors for metabolic syndrome in adults aged 20 and older from 2003 to 2006.

Even though research shows that the signs of metabolic syndrome are common among family members, until recently a definitive genetic link had not been identified. Ruth J. F. Loos et al. demonstrate in "Genome-Wide Linkage Scan for the Metabolic Syndrome in the HERITAGE Family Study" (*Journal of Clinical Endocrinology and Metabolism*, vol. 88, no. 12, December 2003) the existence of genetic regions that may signal a predisposition to metabolic syndrome. The researchers find evidence of genetic linkages to metabolic syndrome in both African-American and white patients.

In "High Prevalence of Metabolic Syndrome in First-Degree Male Relatives of Women with Polycystic Ovary Syndrome Is Related to High Rates of Obesity" (*Journal of Clinical Endocrinology and Metabolism*, vol. 94, no. 11, November 2009), Andrea D. Coviello et al. find additional evidence of heritability of the metabolic syndrome. The researchers indicate that women with PCOS have twice the risk for metabolic syndrome compared with women from the general population, and that mothers and sisters of women with PCOS are also at increased risk for metabolic syndrome.

The exact origins and mechanism of metabolic syndrome are not fully known; regardless, affected individuals experience a series of biochemical changes that, in time, lead to the development of potentially harmful medical conditions. The biochemical changes begin when insulin loses its ability to cause cells to absorb glucose from the blood (insulin resistance). As a result, glucose levels remain high after food is consumed and the pancreas, sensing a high glucose level in the blood, continues to secrete insulin. The loss of insulin sensitivity may be genetic or may be in response to high fat levels with fatty deposits in the pancreas.

Moderate weight loss, in the range of 5% to 10% of body weight, can help restore the body's sensitivity to insulin and greatly reduce the chance that the syndrome will progress into a more serious illness. Increased activity alone has also been shown to improve insulin sensitivity.

Giovanni de Simone et al. investigated the relationship between increased prevalence of left ventricular hypertrophy (which is associated with an increased risk for cardiovascular disease) and metabolic syndrome–associated cardiovascular risk and reported their findings in "Metabolic Syndrome and Left Ventricular Hypertrophy in the Prediction of Cardiovascular Events: The Strong Heart Study" (*Nutrition, Metabolism, and Cardiovascular Diseases*, vol. 19, no. 2, February 2009). Using data from the Strong Heart Study, a population-based longitudinal cohort study of cardiovascular risk factors and disease in Native Americans living in communities in Arizona, in southwestern Oklahoma, and in South and North Dakota, the researchers find metabolic syndrome in 60% of the subjects. Of this group, 25% had left ventricular hypertrophy, compared with 13% of subjects in a control group. About half of the subjects were obese and had diabetes and high blood pressure and low HDL cholesterol.

After adjusting for age, sex, LDL cholesterol, smoking, and diabetes, subjects with metabolic syndrome were twice as likely to have left ventricular hypertrophy as those without metabolic syndrome. De Simone et al.

TABLE 2.8

Prevalence of risk factors for metabolic syndrome in adults age 20 and older, 2003–06

Characteristic	Number of subjects	Abdominal obesity	Hypertriglyceridemia	Low HDL cholesterol	High blood pressure or medication use[a]	High fasting glucose or medication use
		Percent	Percent	Percent	Percent	Percent
Total, crude[b]	3,423	53.2	31.4	24.7	40.0	39.0
Total, age-adjusted[b,c]	3,423	52.8	31.2	24.7	39.5	38.6
Sex[c]						
Male	1,794	44.8	35.6	21.6	43.4	45.8
Female	1,629	60.7	26.5	27.8	35.2	31.3
			Male			
Age						
20–39 years	607	32.0	29.6	21.4	24.1	28.8
40–59 years	546	52.1	41.5	23.0	44.5	50.3
60 years and over	641	55.2	36.7	19.5	74.4	67.8
Race and ethnicity[c]						
Non-Hispanic white	967	47.4	36.6	22.6	43.5	44.8
Non-Hispanic black	346	36.0	21.2	11.5	51.3	40.9
Mexican American	364	37.6	43.7	26.0	35.5	49.8
Body mass index (BMI)[c]						
Underweight and normal weight	532	*	18.0	**9.4	32.0	35.0
Overweight	701	35.1	37.7	22.6	40.3	45.0
Obese and extremely obese	557	94.4	48.6	31.3	57.5	55.5
			Female			
Age						
20–39 years	488	49.8	17.8	29.4	6.8	13.4
40–59 years	542	64.1	27.3	29.4	43.2	35.5
60 years and over	599	74.0	40.1	22.7	71.0	55.1
Race and ethnicity[c]						
Non-Hispanic white	846	58.0	27.3	27.6	33.0	28.7
Non-Hispanic black	348	76.3	14.4	26.8	53.4	38.7
Mexican American	306	74.9	34.6	39.6	32.1	41.7
Body mass index (BMI)[c]						
Underweight and normal weight	519	13.6	12.9	12.9	26.4	15.8
Overweight	474	77.7	32.3	30.5	31.7	31.2
Obese and extremely obese	634	99.6	36.8	43.1	46.8	46.9

*Indicates a relative standard error of 30% or more. These estimates are considered highly unreliable and are not shown.
**Indicates a relative standard error greater than 20% but less than 30%. These estimates may be unreliable and should be interpreted with caution.
[a]Blood pressure measurement is the average of up to three blood pressure readings.
[b]Total includes racial and ethnic groups not shown separately plus respondents with missing BMI values.
[c]Age-adjusted estimates. Age adjustment was performed using the direct method of adjustment to the 2000 U.S. Census figures.
HDL = High Density Lipoprotein (so-called "good" cholesterol)

SOURCE: Adapted from R. Bethane Ervin, "Table 2. Prevalence of Individual Risk Factors for Metabolic Syndrome among Adults 20 Years of Age and over by Selected Characteristics: United States, 2003–2006," in "Prevalence of Metabolic Syndrome among Adults 20 Years of Age and over, by Sex, Age, Race and Ethnicity, and Body Mass Index: United States, 2003–2006," in *National Health Statistics Reports*, no. 13, May 5, 2009, http://www.cdc.gov/nchs/data/nhsr/nhsr013.pdf (accessed October 23, 2009).

conclude, "In this study we demonstrate that a substantial part of the metabolic syndrome–related cardiovascular risk is mediated by the metabolic syndrome–associated left ventricular hypertrophy."

Metabolic syndrome is also a risk factor for cognitive decline (loss of memory, thinking, and reasoning skills). In "The Metabolic Syndrome, Inflammation, and Risk of Cognitive Decline" (*Journal of the American Medical Association*, vol. 292, no. 18, November 10, 2004), Kristine Yaffe et al. analyze data from 2,632 nondemented (cognitively normal) participants in the Health, Aging, and Body Composition study. The subjects were aged 70 to 79 and were followed from 1997 through 2002. The subjects with metabolic syndrome were more likely than those without to exhibit cognitive decline. Yaffe et al. hypothesize that metabolic syndrome hastened atherosclerosis (a hardening of the walls of the arteries caused by the buildup of fatty deposits on the inner walls of the arteries that interferes with blood flow) or inflammation, which led to cognitive decline.

By 2009 it was widely accepted that metabolic syndrome included vascular risk factors that were associated to cognitive decline and even the development of dementia. In "Mental Slowness and Executive Dysfunctions in Patients with Metabolic Syndrome" (*Neuroscience Letters*, vol. 462, no. 1, October 2, 2009), Barbara Segura et al. compare specific cognitive functions such as memory, language, and speed of processing in patients with and without metabolic syndrome and find significant differences, suggesting that metabolic syndrome is related to the development of these changes.

REDEFINING THE METABOLIC SYNDROME. In an effort to standardize diagnosis, prevention, screening, and treatment, the International Diabetes Federation presents in *The IDF Consensus Worldwide Definition of the Metabolic Syndrome* (2006, http://www.idf.org/webdata/docs/IDF_Meta_def_final.pdf) a new worldwide definition of metabolic syndrome. The diagnostic criteria are central obesity, defined as a waist equal to or more than 37 inches (94 cm) for males and 31.5 inches (80 cm) for females of European descent, and ethnic-specific levels for Chinese, Japanese, and South Asians; along with two of the following: triglycerides of at least 150 mg/dL; low HDL-cholesterol, defined as less than 40 mg/dL in males and less than 50 mg/dL in females; blood pressure of at least 130/85 mmHg; fasting hyperglycemia, defined as glucose equal to or greater than 100 mg/dL; previous diagnosis of diabetes; or impaired glucose tolerance. The new definition of metabolic syndrome, which includes diabetes or prediabetes, abdominal obesity, unfavorable lipid profile, and hypertension, triples the risk of myocardial infarction and stroke and doubles mortality from these conditions. It also increases the risk of developing Type 2 diabetes, if not already present, fivefold. Using this definition, Earl S. Ford of the CDC calculates in "Prevalence of the Metabolic Syndrome Defined by the International Diabetes Federation among Adults in the U.S." (*Diabetes Care*, vol. 28, no. 11, November 2005) that about one-quarter of the U.S. adult population may be diagnosed as having the metabolic syndrome.

SOME QUESTION THE DIAGNOSIS OF METABOLIC SYNDROME. Two leading diabetes organizations, the American Diabetes Association and the European Association for the Study of Diabetes, question the utility of the diagnosis of metabolic syndrome. Representatives of these organizations say they feel the syndrome is neither a distinct disease nor well established by scientific research. In

"The Metabolic Syndrome: Time for a Critical Appraisal" (*Diabetes Care*, vol. 28, no. 9, September 2005), Richard Kahn et al. state, "While there is no question that certain CVD [cardiovascular disease] risk factors are prone to cluster, we found that the metabolic syndrome has been imprecisely defined, there is a lack of certainty regarding its pathogenesis, and there is considerable doubt regarding its value as a CVD risk marker. Our analysis indicates that too much critically important information is missing to warrant its designation as a 'syndrome.'"

Kahn et al. advise physicians against classifying metabolic syndrome as a disease. Instead, they encourage them to screen for and treat high triglyceride levels, high blood pressure, low levels of HDL cholesterol, and high blood glucose as separate conditions to reduce the risk of heart disease. Their specific recommendations are that:

1. Adults with any major cardiovascular disease risk factor should be evaluated for the presence of other cardiovascular disease risk factors.

2. Patients with cardiovascular disease risk variables above the cut point for normal should receive counseling for lifestyle modification, and at cut points indicative of frank disease, treatment should correspond to established guidelines.

3. Providers should avoid labeling patients with the term *metabolic syndrome*, as this might create the impression that the metabolic syndrome denotes a greater risk than its components, that it is more serious than other cardiovascular disease risk factors, or that the underlying pathophysiology is clear.

4. All cardiovascular disease risk factors should be individually and aggressively treated.

5. Until randomized controlled trials have been completed, there is no appropriate pharmacological treatment for the metabolic syndrome, nor should it be assumed that pharmacological therapy to reduce insulin resistance will be beneficial to patients with the metabolic syndrome.

CHAPTER 3

THE INFLUENCES OF MENTAL HEALTH AND CULTURE ON WEIGHT AND EATING DISORDERS

That diet and appetite are closely linked to psychological health and emotional well-being is widely recognized. Psychological factors often influence eating habits. Many people overeat when they are bored, stressed, angry, depressed, or anxious. Psychological distress can aggravate weight problems by triggering impulses to overeat. Emotional discomfort drives many people to overeat as a way to relieve anxiety and improve mood. Some people revert to the "comfort foods of their youth"—the meals or treats offered to them when they were sick or foods that evoke memories of the carefree days of childhood. Others rely on chocolate and other sweets, which actually contain chemicals known to have a soothing effect on mood. Over time, the associations between emotions, food, and eating can become firmly fixed.

Emotional arousal may also sabotage healthy self-care efforts such as resolutions to diet and exercise. Anxiety and depression can produce feelings of helplessness and hopelessness about efforts to lose weight that undermine the best intentions, prompt detrimental food choices and inactivity, and over time cause many people to give up trying entirely. Because overweight and obesity often contribute to emotional stress and psychological disorders, a cycle develops that couples increasing weight gain with progressively more severe emotional difficulties.

Emotional disturbance alone is rarely the causative factor of overweight or obesity. However, for people with a genetic susceptibility or predisposition to obesity and exposure to environmental factors that promote obesity, emotional and psychological stress can trigger or exacerbate the problem. Even efforts to lose weight can backfire—serving to increase rather than to alleviate emotional stress. For example, people who fail to lose weight or those who succeed in losing weight only to regain it may suffer from frustration and diminished feelings of competence and self-worth. Similarly, being overweight or obese and feeling self-conscious about it or suffering from weight-based discrimination or prejudice can be ongoing sources of stress and frustration. Feelings of helplessness, frustration, and continuous emotional stress can cause or worsen mental health problems such as anxiety and depression.

Many mental health and medical professionals view overweight as both a cause and a consequence of disturbances in physical and mental health. Even though it may be important to determine whether a metabolic disturbance caused an individual to become overweight or resulted from excessive weight gain, or whether depression triggered behaviors leading to obesity or resulted from problems associated with obesity, it is often impossible to distinguish whether overweight is a symptom of another disorder or the causative factor.

THE ORIGINS OF EATING DISORDERS

Despite the challenges of compromised self-esteem and societal prejudice, the National Institute of Diabetes and Digestive and Kidney Diseases indicates that most overweight people have about the same number of psychological problems as people of average weight. However, the Weight-Control Information Network explains in *Binge Eating Disorder* (June 2008, http://win.niddk.nih.gov/publications/binge.htm) that even though eating disorders affect normal-weight individuals, people who are mildly obese and try to lose weight repetitively may suffer from eating disorders such as binge eating, and most people with binge-eating disorders are overweight or obese. People with the most severe eating disorders are more likely to have symptoms of depression and low self-esteem. Binge eaters have lost control of their eating behaviors and consume abnormal quantities of food in short periods of time. Binge-eating disorders are thought to be even more common in people who are severely obese.

Even though depression and stress may contribute to a substantial percent of cases of obesity, they are considered the leading causes of eating disorders. Most mental health professionals concur that the origins of eating disorders can be traced to behavioral or psychological difficulties. Anger and impulsive behavior have been associated with binge-eating disorders, but even mild mental health or social problems such as shyness or lack of self-confidence can lead to social withdrawal, isolation, and a sedentary lifestyle that promotes weight gain and ultimately obesity. James I. Hudson et al. explain in "The Prevalence and Correlates of Eating Disorders in the National Comorbidity Survey Replication" (*Biological Psychiatry*, vol. 61, no. 3, February 1, 2007) that eating disorders frequently coexist with other mental disorders, including depression, substance abuse, and anxiety disorders.

At first glance, eating disorders appear to center on preoccupations with food and weight; however, mental health professionals believe these disorders are often about more than simply food. Besides psychological factors that may predispose people to eating disorders, including diminished self-esteem, depression, anxiety, loneliness, or feelings of lack of control, a variety of interpersonal and social factors have been implicated as causal factors for these disorders. Interpersonal issues that may increase the risk for developing eating disorders include troubled family and personal relationships; difficulty expressing emotions; a history of physical or sexual abuse; or the experience of being teased, taunted, or ridiculed about body size, shape, or weight.

In "A 30-Year Follow-up of the Effects of Child Abuse and Neglect on Obesity in Adulthood" (*Obesity*, vol. 17, no. 10, October 2009), Tyrone Bentley and Cathy S. Widom report the results of research considering the relationship between mistreatment of children (physical and sexual abuse and neglect) and the risk for obesity in adulthood. The researchers matched 410 children with court-substantiated cases of physical and sexual abuse and neglect with 303 children of similar ages, sex, race, ethnicity, and social class who had not suffered abuse or neglect. Thirty years later the body mass index (BMI; body weight in kilograms divided by height in meters squared) of each subject was compared with the other subjects. Bentley and Widom find that a history of physical abuse predicted higher adult BMI scores but that histories of sexual abuse or neglect were not predictive of having a higher BMI as an adult. The researchers posit that physical abuse may have activated a hormonal response that resulted in increasing peripheral cortisol, a hormone that is pivotal in mediating responses to stress and metabolism. Alternatively, or in addition to the hormonal imbalance, the subjects may have developed disordered eating as a way to cope with the trauma of physical abuse.

Social factors that may contribute to eating disorders include sharply restricted, rigid definitions of beauty that exclude people who do not conform to a particular body weight and shape; cultures that glorify thinness and overemphasize the importance of obtaining a "perfect body"; and cultures that judge and value people based on external physical appearance rather than on internal qualities such as character, intellect, generosity, and kindness. Appearance-driven concerns, rather than health needs, continue to motivate many obese individuals to lose weight. Societal pressures reinforce these appearance-driven concerns by portraying obese individuals in a negative manner.

A related consideration that further complicates pinpointing the origins of eating disorders is the extent to which temperament interacts with interpersonal and social factors to promote eating disorders. Researchers and mental health professionals observe that temperamental tendencies such as perfectionism, compulsivity, impulsivity, and other behavioral, cognitive, and emotional leanings seem to predispose to eating disorders.

Binge-Eating Disorders

Binge eating is a common problem among people who are overweight and obese. Besides consuming unusually large amounts of food in a single sitting, binge eaters generally suffer from low mood and low alertness, and experience uncontrollable compulsions to eat. They experience food cravings before binge episodes and feelings of discontent, dissatisfaction, and restlessness following binges.

Hudson et al. report that 3.5% of women and 2% of men report having a binge-eating disorder at some point in their life. In *BodyWise Handbook* (2005), the U.S. Department of Health and Human Services (HHS) cites research suggesting that binge-eating disorder is the most common eating disorder, affecting about one-third of obese participants in weight-loss programs.

Even though the disorder is more common in people who are severely obese, normal-weight people also develop the disorder. People who suffer from binge eating often:

- Feel that eating is out of their ability to control

- Eat amounts of food most people would think are unusually large

- Eat much more quickly than usual during binge episodes

- Eat until the point of physical discomfort

- Consume large amounts of food, even when they are not hungry

- Eat alone because they feel embarrassed about the amount of food they eat

- Feel disgusted, depressed, or guilty after overeating

In an effort to identify the risk factors for binge-eating disorder, Ruth H. Striegel-Moore et al. compared women diagnosed with binge-eating disorder to those with no history of an eating disorder and reported their findings in "Toward an Understanding of Risk Factors for Binge-Eating Disorder in Black and White Women: A Community-Based Case-Control Study" (*Psychological Medicine*, vol. 35, no. 6, June 2005). The researchers conclude that childhood obesity and the presence of eating problems in other family members are reliable, specific risk factors for binge-eating disorder. Subjects with binge-eating disorder also reported more family discord and felt they had more parental demands placed on them than the subjects with no history of an eating disorder.

Some Dieters Are Consumed by Eating Disorders

In the 21st century Americans are preoccupied with body image. They are constantly bombarded with images of thin, beautiful young women and lean, muscular men in magazines, on billboards, on the Internet, on television, and in movies. Advertising implies that to be thin and beautiful is to be happy. Many prominent weight-loss programs reinforce this suggestion. Well-balanced, low-fat food plans or other diets that restrict carbohydrates or calories combined with exercise can help many overweight people achieve a healthier weight and lifestyle. Dieting to achieve a healthy weight is quite different from dieting obsessively to become "model thin," which can have consequences ranging from mildly harmful to life-threatening. Table 3.1 enumerates the health consequences of eating disorders.

According to the National Institute of Mental Health (NIMH), dieting plays a role in the onset of two serious eating disorders: anorexia nervosa and bulimia. Preteens, teens, and college-age women are at special risk. In fact, the National Women's Health Resource Center states in "Eating Disorders" (2010, http://www.healthywomen .org/condition/eating-disorders) that more than 90% of those who develop an eating disorder are women, although researchers are beginning to report rising rates of anorexia and bulimia among men. Studies suggest that for every 10 women with an eating disorder, one male is afflicted. According to the NIMH, in *Eating Disorders* (October 2007, http://www.nimh.nih.gov/health/publications/ eating-disorders/nimheatingdisorders.pdf), 5% to 15% of people with anorexia or bulimia and 35% of people with binge-eating disorders are male.

Hudson et al. report that of the 2,980 adults they surveyed about eating disorders, 0.9% of women and 0.3% of men suffered from anorexia and 1.5% of women and 0.5% of men had bulimia. A 2007 survey of high school students found that 16.3% of teenaged girls and 7.3% of teenaged boys said they had not eaten for 24 or more hours or reported other behaviors that may be

TABLE 3.1

Health consequences of eating disorders

- Eating disorders are serious, potentially life-threatening conditions that affect a person's emotional and physical health.
- Eating disorders are not just a "fad" or a "phase." People do not just "catch" an eating disorder for a period of time. They are real, complex, and devastating conditions that can have serious consequences for health, productivity, and relationships.
- People struggling with an eating disorder need to seek professional help. The earlier a person with an eating disorder seeks treatment, the greater the likelihood of physical and emotional recovery.

Health consequences of anorexia nervosa: In anorexia nervosa's cycle of self-starvation, the body is denied the essential nutrients it needs to function normally. Thus, the body is forced to slow down all of its processes to conserve energy, resulting in serious medical consequences:

– Abnormally slow heart rate and low blood pressure, which mean that the heart muscle is changing. The risk for heart failure rises as the heart rate and blood pressure level sink lower and lower.
– Reduction of bone density (osteoporosis), which results in dry, brittle bones.
– Muscle loss and weakness.
– Severe dehydration, which can result in kidney failure.
– Fainting, fatigue, and overall weakness.
– Dry hair and skin; hair loss is common.
– Growth of a downy layer of hair called lanugo all over the body, including the face, in an effort to keep the body warm.

Health consequences of bulimia nervosa: The recurrent binge-and-purge cycles of bulimia can affect the entire digestive system and can lead to electrolyte and chemical imbalances in the body that affect the heart and other major organ functions. Some of the health consequences of bulimia nervosa include:

– Electrolyte imbalances that can lead to irregular heartbeats and possibly heart failure and death. Electrolyte imbalance is caused by dehydration and loss of potassium and sodium from the body as a result of purging behaviors.
– Potential for gastric rupture during periods of bingeing.
– Inflammation and possible rupture of the esophagus from frequent vomiting.
– Tooth decay and staining from stomach acids released during frequent vomiting.
– Chronic irregular bowel movements and constipation as a result of laxative abuse.
– Peptic ulcers and pancreatitis.

Health consequences of binge eating disorder: Binge eating disorder often results in many of the same health risks associated with clinical obesity. Some of the potential health consequences of binge eating disorder include:

– High blood pressure.
– High cholesterol levels.
– Heart disease as a result of elevated triglyceride levels.
– Secondary diabetes.
– Gallbladder disease.

SOURCE: "Health Consequences of Eating Disorders," National Eating Disorders Association, 2002, http://www.nationaleatingdisorders.org/ nedaDir/files/documents/handouts/HlthCnsq.pdf (accessed October 26, 2009)

symptoms of eating disorders, such as vomiting or taking laxatives to lose weight or keep from gaining weight. (See Figure 3.1.)

Anorexia Nervosa

Anorexia nervosa involves severe weight loss—a minimum of 15% below normal body weight. Anorexic people literally starve themselves, even though they may be very hungry. For reasons that researchers do not yet fully understand, anorexics become terrified of gaining weight. Both food and weight become obsessions. They often develop strange eating habits, refuse to eat with other people, and exercise strenuously to burn calories and prevent weight gain. Anorexic individuals continue to believe they are overweight even when they are dangerously thin.

This condition often begins when a young woman who is slightly overweight or normal weight starts to diet

FIGURE 3.1

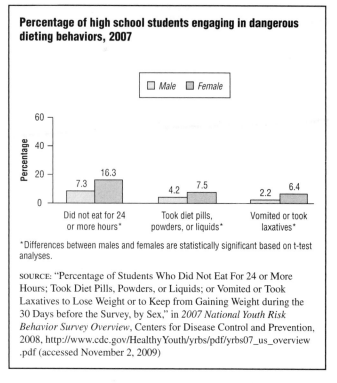

Percentage of high school students engaging in dangerous dieting behaviors, 2007

*Differences between males and females are statistically significant based on t-test analyses.

SOURCE: "Percentage of Students Who Did Not Eat For 24 or More Hours; Took Diet Pills, Powders, or Liquids; or Vomited or Took Laxatives to Lose Weight or to Keep from Gaining Weight during the 30 Days before the Survey, by Sex," in *2007 National Youth Risk Behavior Survey Overview*, Centers for Disease Control and Prevention, 2008, http://www.cdc.gov/HealthyYouth/yrbs/pdf/yrbs07_us_overview .pdf (accessed November 2, 2009)

to lose weight. After achieving the desired weight loss, she redoubles her efforts to lose weight, and dieting becomes an obsession that may eclipse other interests. Affected individuals take pleasure in how well they can avoid food consumption and measure their self-worth by their ability to lose weight. Eating and weight gain are perceived as weaknesses and personal failures.

The medical complications of anorexia are similar to starvation. When the body attempts to protect its most vital organs, the heart and the brain, it goes into "slow gear." Menstrual periods stop, and breathing, pulse, blood pressure, and thyroid function slow down. The nails and hair become brittle, the skin dries, and the lack of body fat produces an inability to withstand cold temperatures. Depression, weakness, and a constant obsession with food are also symptoms of the disease. In addition, personality changes may occur. The person suffering from anorexia may have outbursts of anger and hostility or may withdraw socially. In the most serious cases, death can result.

Scientists often describe eating disorders as addictions, and Alexandra Jean et al. support this notion in "Anorexia Induced by Activation of Serotonin 5-HT4 Receptors Is Mediated by Increases in CART in the Nucleus Accumbens" (*Proceedings of the National Academy of Sciences*, vol. 104, no, 41, October 9, 2007). The researchers find that anorexia and MDMA, a psychoactive drug known as ecstasy, share a common signaling pathway in the brain. Jean et al. also note that by stimulating serotonin 5-HT4 receptors, which are involved in addictive behavior, they could decrease the amount of food mice consumed and diminish the urge to eat in food-deprived mice.

Bulimia

People who suffer from bulimia eat compulsively and then purge (get rid of the food) through self-induced vomiting, use of laxatives, diuretics, strict diets, fasts, exercise, or a combination of several of these compensatory behaviors. Bulimia often begins when a person is disgusted with the excessive amount of "bad" food consumed and vomits to rid the body of the calories.

Many bulimics are at a normal body weight or above because of their frequent binge-purge behavior, which can occur from once or twice a week to several times per day. Those bulimics who maintain normal weight may manage to keep their eating disorder a secret for years. As with anorexia, bulimia usually begins during adolescence, but many bulimics do not seek help until they are in their 30s or 40s.

Binge eating and purging are dangerous. In rare cases bingeing can cause esophageal ruptures, and purging can result in life-threatening cardiac (heart) conditions because the body loses vital minerals. The acid in vomit wears down tooth enamel and the lining of the esophagus, throat, and mouth and can cause scarring on the hands when fingers are pushed down the throat to induce vomiting. The esophagus may become inflamed, and glands in the neck may become swollen.

Bulimics often talk of being "hooked" on certain foods and needing to feed their "habits." This addictive behavior carries over into other areas of their life, including the likelihood of alcohol and drug abuse. Many bulimics suffer from coexisting medical or mental health problems, such as severe depression, which increases their risk of committing suicide.

CAUSES OF EATING DISORDERS

Evidence suggests a genetic component to susceptibility to eating disorders. For example, in the general population the chance of developing anorexia is about one out of 200, but when a family member has the disorder, the risk increases to one out of 30. Twin studies demonstrate that when one twin is affected, there is a 50% chance the other will develop an eating disorder. Cynthia M. Bulik et al. calculated heritability estimates for anorexia nervosa and bulimia nervosa and published the estimates of their genetic correlation in "Understanding the Relation between Anorexia Nervosa and Bulimia Nervosa in a Swedish National Twin Sample" (*Biological Psychiatry*, vol. 67, no. 1, January 1, 2010). They find an overlap of genetic and unique environmental factors that influence the development of both eating disorders.

Kelly L. Klump et al. indicate in "Puberty Moderates Genetic Influences on Disordered Eating" (*Psychological Medicine*, vol. 37, no. 5, May 2007) that during puberty there is an increased risk of developing eating disorders. The researchers find that before the onset of puberty, environmental factors made the strongest contribution to the risk of developing eating disorders; however, during and after puberty genetic factors predominated, accounting for more than half of the risk. These findings suggest that puberty influences the expression of genes for disordered eating.

Besides a genetic predisposition, bulimics and anorexics seem to have different temperaments. Bulimics are likely to be impulsive (acting without thought of the consequences) and are more likely to abuse alcohol and drugs. Anorexics tend to be perfectionists, good students, and competitive athletes. They usually keep their feelings to themselves and rarely disobey their parents. However, bulimics and anorexics do share certain traits: they lack self-esteem, have feelings of helplessness, and fear gaining weight. In both disorders the eating problems appear to develop as a way of handling stress and anxiety.

Bulimics consume huge amounts of food (often junk food) in a search for comfort and stress relief. The bingeing, however, brings only guilt and depression. By contrast, anorexics restrict food to gain a sense of control and mastery over some aspect of their life. Controlling their weight seems to offer two advantages: they can take control of their body, and they can gain approval from others.

Psychological theories that explain the origins of bulimia include conflicted relationships between mothers and daughters, attempts to control one's own body in the face of seemingly uncontrollable family or other interpersonal relationships, or ambivalence about sexual development and attention. The latter theory has also been used to explain overweight and obesity in teenaged girls and young women—as protection from or defense against attention from males who make them fearful or uncomfortable.

In "Childhood Anxiety Associated with Low BMI in Women with Anorexia Nervosa" (*Behaviour Research and Therapy*, vol. 48, no. 1, January 2010), Jocilyn E. Dellava et al. look at risk factors for developing anorexia nervosa and low BMI after they interviewed 326 women and their mothers who participated in the Genetics of Anorexia Nervosa Study. The researchers find that women with anorexia nervosa who had been especially fearful or anxious as children were at greater risk for dangerously low BMI and that childhood anxiety was associated with caloric restriction. Dellava et al. posit that "measures of anxiety and factors associated with anxiety-proneness in childhood may index children at risk for restrictive behaviors and extremely low BMIs

in [anorexia nervosa]." In another study, Tamar B. Rubinstein et al. consider risk factors for developing eating disorders and report their findings in "Disordered Eating in Adulthood Is Associated with Reported Weight Loss Attempts in Childhood" (*International Journal of Eating Disorders*, October 2009). The researchers indicate that adults who had made efforts to lose weight when they were children (aged 12 and younger) were at increased risk of unhealthy eating behaviors, especially binge-eating disorder.

OCCURRENCE OF EATING DISORDERS

Lillian Huang Cummins and Janice Lehman of Alliant International University note in "Eating Disorders and Body Image Concerns in Asian American Women: Assessment and Treatment from a Multicultural and Feminist Perspective" (*Eating Disorders*, vol. 15, no. 3, May–June 2007) that the global prevalence of eating disorders appears to be increasing. However, thinness is not necessarily admired among all people throughout the world, especially in countries where hunger is not a matter of choice.

The NIMH states in "The Numbers Count: Mental Disorders in America" (2008, http://www.nimh.nih.gov/health/publications/the-numbers-count-mental-disorders-in-america.shtml) that in their lifetime, an estimated 0.5% to 3.7% of women suffer from anorexia and 1.1% to 4.2% suffer from bulimia. The National Women's Health Information Center observes that eating disorders often coexist with other high-risk health behaviors such as tobacco, alcohol and drug use, delinquency, unprotected sexual activity, and suicide attempts.

In "Pathological Dieting and Alcohol Use in College Women—A Continuum of Behaviors" (*Eating Behaviors*, vol. 6, no. 1, January 2005), Dean D. Krahn et al. examine the relationship between dieting, binge-eating disorder, and alcohol use in female college students. They find a relationship between dieting and bingeing severity and the frequency, intensity, and negative consequences of alcohol use in the students. Dieting and bingeing were more closely associated with alcohol use than were factors such as depression, age at which drinking began, or parents' drinking history. Furthermore, the severity of the eating disorder behavior was linked to the occurrence of negative consequences of alcohol use, including blackouts and unintended sexual activity. Krahn et al. conclude that destructive eating behaviors are often associated with harmful alcohol use.

Ana Calvero-Elvira et al. find in "Meta-analysis on Drugs in People with Eating Disorders" (*European Eating Disorders Review*, vol. 17, no. 4, July 2009) that drug use was highest in people suffering from bulimia and slightly higher in people suffering from binge eating than their healthy counterparts. There was no difference, however, in the frequency of drug use between the healthy subjects and those with anorexia nervosa.

The Eating Disorders Coalition for Research, Policy, and Action notes in the fact sheet "Facts about Eating Disorders: What the Research Shows" (May 2009, http://www.eatingdisorderscoalition.org/documents/Talking pointsEatingDisordersFactSheetUpdated5-20-09.pdf) that about 11 million Americans are affected by eating disorders and that anorexia is the third most common illness among adolescents. The coalition observes that the incidence of eating disorders is increasing in younger age groups and is becoming more common in diverse ethnic and sociocultural groups. Eating disorders have been diagnosed in children as young as seven years old, 40% of nine-year-old girls have dieted, and even five-year-old girls express concern about weight. About 40% to 60% of high school age girls diet and 13% engage in purging.

TREATMENT OF EATING DISORDERS

Generally, physicians treat the medical complications of the disorder, whereas nutritionists advise the affected individuals about specific diet and eating plans. To help people with eating disorders face their underlying problems and emotional issues, psychotherapy is usually necessary. For people with eating disorders, the initial challenge is to convince them to seek and obtain treatment; after they start treatment, the challenge then becomes helping them to stay in the program. Many anorexics deny their illness, and getting and keeping anorexic patients in treatment can be difficult. Treating bulimia is also difficult. Many bulimics are easily frustrated and want to leave treatment if their symptoms are not quickly relieved.

Several approaches are used to treat eating disorders. Cognitive-behavioral therapy (CBT) teaches people how to monitor their eating and change unhealthy eating habits. It also teaches them how to change the way they respond to stressful situations. CBT is based on the premise that thinking influences emotions and behavior—that feelings and actions originate with thoughts. CBT posits that it is possible to change the way people feel and act even if their circumstances do not change. It teaches the advantages of feeling calm when faced with undesirable situations. CBT clients learn that they will confront undesirable events and circumstances whether they become troubled about them or not. When they are troubled about events or circumstances, they have two problems: the troubling event or circumstance, and the troubling feelings about the event or circumstance. Clients learn that when they do not become troubled about trying events and circumstances, they can reduce the number of problems they face by half.

Interpersonal psychotherapy (IPT) helps people look at their relationships with friends and family and make changes to resolve problems. IPT is short-term therapy that has demonstrated effectiveness for the treatment of depression. According to the International Society for Interpersonal Psychotherapy, IPT emphasizes that mental health and emotional problems occur within an interpersonal context. For this reason the therapy aims to intervene specifically in social functioning to relieve symptoms.

Group therapy has been found helpful for bulimics, who are relieved to find that they are not alone or unique in their eating behavior. A combination of behavioral therapy and family systems therapy is often the most effective with anorexics. Family systems therapy considers the family as the unit of treatment and focuses on relationships and communication patterns within the family rather than on the personality traits or symptoms displayed by individual family members. Problems are addressed by modifying the system rather than by trying to change an individual family member. People with eating disorders who also suffer from depression may benefit from antidepressant and antianxiety medications to help relieve coexisting mental health problems.

Recovery from eating disorders is uneven. The Eating Disorders Coalition for Research, Policy, and Action characterizes recovery as a process that frequently entails multiple rehospitalizations, limited ability to work or attend school, and limited capacity for interpersonal relationships. Carlos M. Grilo et al. report in "Natural Course of Bulimia Nervosa and of Eating Disorder Not Otherwise Specified: 5-Year Prospective Study of Remissions, Relapses, and the Effects of Personality Disorder Psychopathology" (*Journal of Clinical Psychiatry*, vol. 68, no. 5, May 2007) that about one-third of sufferers recover after an initial episode and treatment, another one-third fluctuate between recovery and relapse, and the remaining one-third suffer chronic decline and deterioration.

In part, eating disorders are difficult to treat effectively because many sufferers resist entering treatment and/or fail to complete treatment programs. In "Eating Behavior among Women with Anorexia Nervosa" (*American Journal of Clinical Nutrition*, vol. 82, no. 2, August 2005), Robin Sysko et al. try to determine whether current treatment for anorexia successfully addresses severe caloric restriction and other characteristic features of anorexia nervosa. To do this, they scrutinized eating behavior among people with anorexia nervosa before and immediately after treatment that restored their weight and compared these behaviors to those of control subjects.

Sysko et al. observed 12 anorexic patients and 12 individuals without eating disorders who were asked to consume a strawberry yogurt shake, which they were told would be their lunch for the day. They were also told to consume as much as they wanted. The yogurt shake was in an opaque container and was drunk with a straw so that the subjects could not see the shake. They were also not told the contents of the shake or how many calories it contained. The anorexic patients were tested when they were admitted for treatment and retested after they had reached 90% of their ideal body weight.

Before treatment, anorexic patients consumed an average of 3.7 ounces (104 g) of the shake, which increased to an average of 6.3 ounces (178 g) after treatment. However, in both instances control subjects consumed significantly more than anorexic patients, at an average of 17.3 ounces (489.6 g). The researchers observe that subjects with anorexia found the experiment difficult and anxiety provoking because they were unable to see the shake and control their calorie intake. This was despite the fact that subjects treated for anorexia displayed significant decreases in psychological and eating-disordered symptoms after they had regained weight. Sysko et al. believe their findings underscore the need to intervene with anorexics who leave an intensive treatment program. They hope to devise strategies to help normalize patients' eating behavior outside the hospital, such as by helping reduce their anxiety and fear about eating unknown quantities of food.

New Directions in Research and Treatment

According to the NIMH, in *Eating Disorders*, the results of its research are aiding both the understanding of eating disorders and their treatment. Research on intervening in the binge-eating cycle demonstrates that initiating structured patterns of eating enables people with eating disorders to experience less hunger, less deprivation, and fewer negative feelings about food and eating. When the two key predictors of bingeing—hunger and negative feelings—are reduced, the frequency of binges declines.

Continued study of the human genome promises the identification of susceptibility genes (genes that indicate an individual's increased risk for developing eating disorders) that will help develop more effective treatments for these disorders. Other research is investigating the relationship between brain functions and emotional and social behavior related to eating disorders and the role of the brain in feeding behavior. Scientists have learned that both appetite and energy expenditure are regulated by a highly complex network of nerve cells and intercellular messengers called neuropeptides. The role of sex hormones, known as gonadal steroids, in the development of eating disorders is suggested by gender and the onset of puberty as a risk for these disorders. These discoveries provide insight into the biochemical mechanisms of eating disorders and offer potential direction for the development of new drugs and treatments for these disorders.

In "A Review and Primer of Molecular Genetic Studies of Anorexia Nervosa" (*International Journal of Eating Disorders*, vol. 37, supplement S43–48, July 2005), Kelly L. Klump and Kyle L. Gobrogge summarize

recent findings about the genetic underpinnings of eating disorders. They report that research reveals some role for the brain system that involves the chemical serotonin in the development of anorexia nervosa. Serotonin is a neurotransmitter involved in the regulation of mood and certain mental disorders, such as depression and anxiety. Genomic regions on chromosomes 1 and 10 are likely to harbor susceptibility genes for anorexia as well as for other eating disorders. The findings from these genetic studies support those of neurobiologic studies indicating that alterations in serotonin functioning may contribute to the development of eating disorders.

Christian Hammer et al. examine in "Functional Variants of the Serotonin Receptor Type 3A and B Gene Are Associated with Eating Disorders" (*Pharmacogenetic Genomics*, vol. 19, no. 10, October 2009) the genes of 265 subjects with anorexia nervosa, 91 with bulimia, and 191 without a eating disorder. The results of these analyses indicate that variants in the 5-HT3 receptor genes, HTR3A and HTR3B, which govern serotonin (5-hydroxytryptamine, 5-HT), are likely implicated in increased susceptibility to eating disorders, specifically anorexia nervosa and bulimia.

PREVENTING EATING DISORDERS

Conventional public health definitions describe primary prevention as the prevention of new cases and secondary prevention as the prevention of recurrence of a disease or prevention of its progression. Primary prevention measures fall into two categories: actions to protect against disease and disability and actions to promote health such as good nutrition and hygiene, adequate exercise and rest, and avoidance of environmental and health risks. Health promotion also includes education about other interdependent dimensions of health known as wellness. Examples of health promotion programs aimed at preventing eating disorders include programs to enhance self-esteem, nutrition education classes, and programs that support children and teens to resist unhealthy pressures to conform to unrealistic body weight.

Secondary prevention programs are intended to identify and detect disease in its earliest stages, when it is most likely to be successfully treated. With early detection and diagnosis, it may be possible to cure the disease, slow its progression, prevent or minimize complications, and limit disability. Secondary prevention of eating disorders includes efforts to identify affected individuals to intervene early and prevent the development of serious and potentially life-threatening consequences.

Tertiary prevention programs aim to improve the quality of life for people with various diseases by limiting complications and disabilities, reducing the severity and progression of the disease, and providing rehabilitation (therapy to restore function and self-sufficiency). Unlike primary and secondary prevention, tertiary prevention involves actual treatment for the disease, and in the case of eating disorders it is conducted primarily by medical and mental health practitioners rather than by public health or social service agencies. An example of tertiary prevention is a program that monitors people with eating disorders to ensure that they maintain appropriate body weight and adhere to healthy diets and other prescribed medication or treatment. Because the treatment of eating disorders is not always effective or lasting, many health professionals contend that initiatives directed at controlling or eliminating the disorders by treating each affected individual or by training enough professionals as interventionists are ill advised. Instead, they advocate redirecting time, energy, and resources to primary and secondary prevention efforts.

Table 3.2 lists the basic principles for the prevention of eating disorders prepared by the National Eating Disorders Association (NEDA). These principles underscore the

TABLE 3.2

Eating disorders prevention

What is eating disorders prevention?

Prevention is any systematic attempt to change the circumstances that promote, initiate, sustain, or intensify problems like eating disorders.

- **Primary prevention** refers to programs or efforts that are designed to prevent the occurrence of eating disorders before they begin. Primary prevention is intended to help promote healthy development.
- **Secondary prevention** (sometimes called "targeted prevention") refers to programs or efforts that are designed to promote the early identification of an eating disorder—to recognize and treat an eating disorder before it spirals out of control. The earlier an eating disorder is discovered and addressed, the better the chance for recovery.

Basic principles for the prevention of eating disorders

1. Eating disorders are serious and complex problems. We need to be careful to avoid thinking of them in simplistic terms, like "anorexia is just a plea for attention," or "bulimia is just an addiction to food." Eating disorders arise from a variety of physical, emotional, social, and familial issues, all of which need to be addressed for effective prevention and treatment.
2. Eating disorders are not just a "woman's problem" or "something for the girls." Males who are preoccupied with shape and weight can also develop eating disorders as well as dangerous shape control practices like steroid use. In addition, males play an important role in prevention. The objectification and other forms of mistreatment of women by others contribute directly to two underlying features of an eating disorder: obsession with appearance and shame about one's body.
3. Prevention efforts will fail, or worse, inadvertently encourage disordered eating, if they concentrate solely on warning the public about the signs, symptoms, and dangers of eating disorders. Effective prevention programs must also address:
   - Our cultural obsession with slenderness as a physical, psychological, and moral issue.
   - The roles of men and women in our society.
   - The development of people's self-esteem and self-respect in a variety of areas (school, work, community service, hobbies) that transcend physical appearance.
4. Whenever possible, prevention programs for schools, community organizations, etc., should be coordinated with opportunities for participants to speak confidentially with a trained professional with expertise in the field of eating disorders, and, when appropriate, receive referrals to sources of competent, specialized care.

SOURCE: Michael Levine and Margo Maine, "Eating Disorders Can Be Prevented!" National Eating Disorders Association, 2006, http://www.nationaleatingdisorders.org/p.asp?WebPage_ID=286&Profile_ID=41169 (accessed October 26, 2009)

TABLE 3.3

Ten things parents can do to prevent eating disorders

1. Consider your thoughts, attitudes, and behaviors toward your own body and the way that these beliefs have been shaped by the forces of weightism and sexism. Then educate your children about
   (a) the genetic basis for the natural diversity of human body shapes and sizes, and
   (b) the nature and ugliness of prejudice.
   - Make an effort to maintain positive, healthy attitudes & behaviors. Children learn from the things you say and do!
2. Examine closely your dreams and goals for your children and other loved ones. Are you overemphasizing beauty and body shape, particularly for girls?
   - Avoid conveying an attitude which says in effect, "I will like you more if you lose weight, don't eat so much, look more like the slender models in ads, fit into smaller clothes, etc."
   - Decide what you can do and what you can stop doing to reduce the teasing, criticism, blaming, staring, etc. that reinforce the idea that larger or fatter is "bad" and smaller or thinner is "good."
3. Learn about and discuss with your sons and daughters (a) the dangers of trying to alter one's body shape through dieting, (b) the value of moderate exercise for health, and (c) the importance of eating a variety of foods in well-balanced meals consumed at least three times a day.
   - Avoid categorizing foods into "good/safe /no-fat or low-fat" vs."bad/dangerous/ fattening."
   - Be a good role model in regard to sensible eating, exercise, and self-acceptance.
4. Make a commitment not to avoid activities (such as swimming, sunbathing, dancing, etc.) simply because they call attention to your weight and shape. Refuse to wear clothes that are uncomfortable or that you don't like but wear simply because they divert attention from your weight or shape.
5. Make a commitment to exercise for the joy of feeling your body move and grow stronger, not to purge fat from your body or to compensate for calories eaten.
6. Practice taking people seriously for what they say, feel, and do, not for how slender or "well put together" they appear.
7. Help children appreciate and resist the ways in which television, magazines, and other media distort the true diversity of human body types and imply that a slender body means power, excitement, popularity, or perfection.
8. Educate boys and girls about various forms of prejudice, including weightism, and help them understand their responsibilities for preventing them.
9. Encourage your children to be active and to enjoy what their bodies can do and feel like. Do not limit their caloric intake unless a physician requests that you do this because of a medical problem.
10. Do whatever you can to promote the self-esteem and self-respect of all of your children in intellectual, athletic, and social endeavors. Give boys and girls the same opportunities and encouragement. Be careful not to suggest that females are less important than males, e.g., by exempting males from housework or child care. A well-rounded sense of self and solid self-esteem are perhaps the best antidotes to dieting and disordered eating.

SOURCE: Michael Levine and Linda Smolak, "Ten Things Parents Can Do to Prevent Eating Disorders," National Eating Disorders Association, 2006, http://www.nationaleatingdisorders.org/p.asp?WebPage_ID=286&Profile_ID=41171 (accessed October 26, 2009)

complexity of addressing the problem and the need for comprehensive, community-wide prevention programs that address the social and cultural issues promoting the rise of these disorders. NEDA also urges parents to spearhead efforts to prevent eating disorders by practicing positive, healthy attitudes and behaviors and encouraging children to resist media stereotypes about body shape and weight. Furthermore, it outlines the philosophies and actions parents can adopt and the behaviors they can model to help their children cultivate healthy attitudes about food, eating, exercise, and body weight. Table 3.3 outlines steps parents can take to help prevent eating disorders.

Changing Social and Cultural Norms

The cultural idealization of thinness as a standard of female beauty and worth and the societal acceptance of dieting as a female ritual have been widely cited as sociocultural causes of eating disorders. The widespread misperception that the body is readily reshaped and that one can, and should, strive to change its size and form to correspond with aesthetic preferences also contributes to distorted perceptions and unrealistic expectations.

Media images that create, reflect, communicate, and reinforce cultural definitions of attractiveness, especially female beauty, are often acknowledged as factors that contribute to the rise of eating disorders. They exert powerful influences on values, attitudes, and practices for body image, diet, and activity. The role of the media, in conjunction with the fashion and entertainment industries, especially those targeting women and girls, in promoting unrealistic standards of female beauty and unhealthy eating habits has been named as a causative factor for body dissatisfaction, unhealthy dieting behavior, and the rise of eating disorders.

Even though media messages portraying thinness as a desirable attribute do not directly cause eating disorders, they help create the context in which people learn to place a value on the size and shape of their body. To the extent that media advertising defines cultural values about that which is beautiful and desirable, the media have potent power over the development of self-esteem and body image. Even if the media were to present more diverse and realistic images of people, this change would be unlikely to immediately reduce or eliminate eating disorders. However, many observers do believe it would reduce the pressures to conform to one ideal, lessen feelings of body dissatisfaction, and ultimately decrease the potential for eating disorders.

According to many health professionals and media observers, besides promoting unrealistic and unattainable body weight, media coverage of health, nutrition, diet, overweight, and inactivity does not fulfill its potential to educate people about how to make healthful changes in their life. The *Surgeon General's Call to Action to Prevent and Decrease Overweight and Obesity, 2001* (December 2001, http://www.surgeongeneral.gov/topics/obesity/calltoaction/CalltoAction.pdf), a landmark report that outlines strategies to address the increasing prevalence of overweight and obesity in the United States, identifies the media as having a key role in prevention efforts. The surgeon general's report recommends a range of proactive interventions intended to educate the public and change Americans' eating behavior and exercise patterns. It takes direct aim at preventing eating disorders by calling for media actions to "promote the recognition of inappropriate weight change" and enumerates the efforts necessary to reorient the media, including:

- Communicating to media professionals that the primary concern of overweight and obesity is one of health rather than appearance.

- Informing media professionals about the prevalence of overweight and obesity in low-income and racial and ethnic minority populations and the need for culturally sensitive health messages.

- Communicating the importance of prevention of overweight by paying attention to the caloric intake and being physically active at all ages.

- Building awareness of the social and environmental influences on making healthy decisions regarding diet and physical activity.

- Providing professional education for media professionals on policy areas related to diet and physical activity.

- Emphasizing to media professionals the need to develop uniform health messages about physical activity and nutrition that are consistent with the *Dietary Guidelines for Americans, 2005* (January 2005, http://www.health.gov/dietaryguidelines/dga2005/document/pdf/DGA2005.pdf), which is published jointly by the HHS and the U.S. Department of Agriculture.

The surgeon general's report also describes specific actions the media can take to help Americans change their attitudes and behaviors, including:

- Launching a national campaign to increase public awareness of the health benefits of regular physical activity, healthful dietary choices, and maintaining a healthy weight, based on the *Dietary Guidelines for Americans, 2005.*

- Educating consumers about realistic and reasonable goals for weight-loss programs and weight-management products.

- Incorporating messages about proper nutrition, including eating at least five servings of fruits and vegetables per day, and regular physical activity in youth-oriented television programming.

- Training nutrition and exercise scientists and specialists in media advocacy skills that will enable them to disseminate their knowledge to a broad audience.

- Encouraging a balance between advertising campaigns that endorse the consumption of excess calories and inactivity with messages promoting the benefits of healthy diet and exercise.

- Advocating that media celebrities use their influence as role models to demonstrate eating and physical activity lifestyles for health rather than for appearance.

- Encouraging the media to employ actors of diverse sizes.

ADVERTISING CAMPAIGN EMPHASIZING REALISTIC BODIES DRAWS PRAISE AND CRITICISM. In June 2005 Dove, a skin and hair care division of the Unilever company, launched the "Campaign for Real Beauty," which featured a purportedly unretouched photo of six smiling women of various sizes and ethnicities posing in plain white underwear to promote a skin-firming cream. The women, who were not models, ranged from a slim size 6 to a curvy size 14 and graced print advertisements and billboards. The campaign generated considerable discussion and debate in the media.

Dove claimed that it developed the campaign in response to the results of its "Real Truth about Beauty" survey, which was published in *"The Real Truth about Beauty: A Global Report": Findings of the Global Study on Women, Beauty, and Well-Being* (September 2004, http://www.campaignforrealbeauty.com/uploadedfiles/ dove_white_paper_final.pdf). Conducted by researchers from Harvard University and the London School of Economics, the study interviewed 3,200 women aged 18 to 64 in 10 countries. A scant 2% of the women surveyed considered themselves "beautiful" and only 13% were "very satisfied" with their body weight and shape.

According to the article "Dove Ads with 'Real' Women Get Attention" (Associated Press, July 29, 2005), Philippe Harousseau, the Dove marketing director, described the campaign as responsive to "our belief that beauty comes in different shapes, sizes and ages. Our mission is to make more women feel beautiful every day by broadening the definition of beauty." Industry observers wondered whether the company was in fact broadening the definition of beauty and improving women's body image and self-esteem or simply launching a provocative advertising campaign. Even though the company has not disclosed just how much the advertisements have helped promote its products, it concedes that the campaign has been beneficial for all Dove products, not just the firming creams.

The article notes that the ads were not, however, universally well received. For example, the *Chicago Sun-Times* columnist Richard Roeper characterized the women as "chunky," which earned him angry letters from about a thousand readers. Some skeptics asserted that even though they endorsed the notion of featuring real women who feel good about their bodies in the ads, they believed the ads sent contradictory messages—promoting a product to reduce the curves the models are flaunting. The most impassioned detractors accused the company of appearing hypocritical because the ads aim to profit from "improving" the same curves the campaign exhorts women to celebrate.

The Dove advertising campaign was still under way in early 2010 and had already prompted some attitudinal change. In 2006 the company launched the Dove Self-Esteem Fund (2010, http://campaignforrealbeauty.com/), a program that aims to challenge traditional media definitions of beauty—ultrathin bodies and perfectly symmetrical features—to help girls and women feel better about their looks. The fund aims to educate 5 million young women about self-esteem through workshops and other programs by the end of 2010. The term *Dove beauties* has come to refer to attractive women with healthy bodies as opposed to model-thin frames.

MEDIA EMBRACE HEALTHY MODELS. In September 2009 *Glamour* magazine ran an unretouched nearly nude photo of the plus-sized model Lizzi Miller (1989–), in which her rounded belly was clearly visible. The photo touched a nerve with readers who were generally overjoyed to see the photograph of a clearly happy, self-confident young woman who was not extremely thin. Readers and others in the media pleaded for more images of beautiful women of all sizes, and the magazine complied with its November 2009 issue, which featured photos of seven models who were all several sizes larger than most models. Among the models was Crystal Renn (1986–), the coauthor (with Marjorie Ingall) of *Hungry: A Young Model's Story of Appetite, Ambition, and the Ultimate Embrace of Curves* (2009), a memoir that describes her as having an eating disorder. When she acknowledged her disorder and began to eat healthily, her career as a fashion model took off. Since then, Renn has become a healthy, successful plus-sized model and advocate for media recognition and celebration of women of all sizes.

CHAPTER 4
DIET, NUTRITION, AND WEIGHT ISSUES AMONG CHILDREN AND ADOLESCENTS

So as we've seen, the surge in obesity in this country is nothing short of a public health crisis, and it's threatening our children, it's threatening our families, and more importantly it's threatening the future of this nation. Higher rates of obesity are directly linked ... to higher rates of chronic illnesses like heart disease and cancer and diabetes .... In fact, the health consequences are so severe ... medical experts have warned that our children are on track to be less healthy than we are. And there's never been a generation of young people who are on track to be healthier than their parents—or less healthy than their parents.

—Michelle Obama, "Remarks by the First Lady at Event on Surgeon General's Report" (January 28, 2010)

One of the most disturbing observations about overweight and obesity in the United States is the epidemic of supersized (overweight and obese) kids. Serena Low, Mien Chew Chin, and Mabel Deurenberg-Yap find in "Review on Epidemic of Obesity" (*Annals, Academy of Medicine, Singapore*, vol. 38, no. 1, January 2009) that among developed countries, the United States, Canada, Australia, and England have the highest prevalence of overweight and obese children and adolescents. Among developing countries, the researchers find high rates of overweight and obesity in Bahrain, Chile, and the Russian Federation. The National Center for Health Statistics reports in *Health, United States, 2008* (2008, http://www.cdc.gov/nchs/data/hus/hus08.pdf) that in 2006, the most recent year for which data were available, nearly three times as many American children and adolescents were seriously overweight than were overweight in 1976. In just the last 20 years, from 1988–94 to 2005–06, the prevalence of overweight among children and adolescents increased from 7.2% to 11% for children aged 2 to 5 and from 11.3% to 15.1% for children aged 6 to 11. (See Table 4.1.) Among teenagers aged 12 to 19 the percentage nearly doubled, from 10.5% to 17.8%.

With children and teens as well as adults, the body mass index (BMI; body weight in kilograms divided by

height in meters squared) is used to determine underweight, overweight, and at risk for overweight. Children's body fatness changes over the years as they grow, and girls and boys differ in their body fatness as they mature. In light of these differences, the BMI for children (also referred to as BMI-for-age) is gender and age specific. For example, Figure 4.1 shows BMI percentiles for boys aged two to 20 and demonstrates how different BMI numbers are interpreted for a 10-year-old boy. Figure 4.2 shows that children of different ages (and genders) may have the same BMI number, but that number will fall into a different percentile for each child, classifying a 10-year-old boy as overweight and a 15-year-old as at a healthy weight.

Overweight is defined as at or above the age- and gender-specific 95th percentile on the BMI. (See Table 4.2.) Still, even children at the 85th percentile are considered at risk for overweight- and obesity-induced illnesses and overweight throughout their adult lives.

Overweight children are much more likely to become overweight adults—William H. Dietz of the Centers for Disease Control and Prevention (CDC) indicates in "'Adiposity Rebound': Reality or Epiphenomenon?" (*Lancet*, vol. 356, no. 9247, December 16, 2000) that an estimated 30% of adult obesity begins in childhood—unless they adopt and maintain healthier patterns of eating and exercise. The prevalence of overweight among adolescents is of particular concern because overweight adolescents are at even greater risk than overweight children of becoming overweight adults. Kathleen Rowland and John Coffey confirm in "Are Overweight Children More Likely to Be Overweight Adults?" (*Journal of Family Practice*, vol. 58, no. 8, August 2009) that being overweight at any age in childhood increases the risk of being overweight in adulthood. The researchers also find that the risk increases with age and that boys are at greater risk than girls.

TABLE 4.1

Overweight among children and teens, selected years 1988–2006

[Data are based on interviews and physical examinations of a sample of the civilian noninstitutionalized population]

Health conditions	1988–1994	1999–2000	2001–2002	2003–2004	2005–2006
			Percent of persons under 20 years of age		
Overweight*					
2–5 years	7.2	10.3	10.6	13.9	11.0
6–11 years	11.3	15.1	16.3	18.8	15.1
12–19 years	10.5	14.8	16.7	17.4	17.8

*Overweight is defined as body mass index (BMI) at or above the sex- and age-specific 95th percentile BMI cutoff points from the 2000 CDC Growth Charts: United States. Advance data from vital and health statistics; no 314. Hyattsville, MD: National Center for Health Statistics. 2000. Excludes pregnant girls.

SOURCE: Adapted from "Table 70. Selected Health Conditions and Risk Factors: United States, 1988–1994 through 2005–2006," in *Health, United States, 2008*, Centers for Disease Control and Prevention, National Center for Health Statistics, 2008, http://www.cdc.gov/nchs/data/hus/hus08.pdf (accessed October 18, 2009)

According to Victoria Porter, in "Even Children Have Heart Disease—Especially Those Who Are Overweight" (*Medscape Cardiology*, vol. 8, no. 1, 2004), 50% to 80% of obese teens become obese adults. Type 2 diabetes, high blood lipid levels, and hypertension (high blood pressure) occur with increased frequency among overweight youth. Overweight children and teens are also at risk for psychosocial problems ranging from teasing and ostracism to social isolation and discrimination. The CDC reports in *Obesity—At a Glance 2009* (February 2009, http://www.cdc.gov/nccdphp/publications/AAG/pdf/obesity.pdf) that among 5- to 17-year-olds, "70% of obese children had at least one risk factor for cardiovascular disease and 39% of obese children had at least two risk factors."

PREVALENCE OF OVERWEIGHT AND OBESE TEENS BY SEX, GRADE, RACE, AND ETHNICITY

The Youth Risk Behavior Surveillance System (YRBSS) is a national school-based survey conducted by the CDC. It examines health-risk behaviors among youth and young adults, including unhealthy dietary behaviors, physical inactivity, and overweight.

The 2007 YRBSS found that throughout the United States, 15.8% of students were overweight. (See Table 4.3.) The prevalence of overweight was higher among Hispanic males (18.3%) and non-Hispanic African-American males (16.6%) than among non-Hispanic white males (15.7%). For females, the prevalence of overweight was higher among non-Hispanic African-Americans (21.4%) and Hispanics (17.9%) than among non-Hispanic whites (12.8%). Overall, the prevalence of overweight was higher among non-Hispanic African-Americans (19%) and Hispanics (18.1%) than among non-Hispanic whites (14.3%).

The prevalence of overweight was higher among 9th-grade students (17.6%) than among 12th-grade students (14%) and higher among 9th-grade females (18.3%) than among 10th-grade (14.2%), 11th-grade (14.2%), and 12th-grade (13.1%) females. (See Table 4.3.) The prevalence of overweight ranged from 11.4% to 18.2% across state surveys and from 12.5% to 22.2% across local surveys. (See Table 4.4.)

The 2007 YRBSS found that 13% of high school students were obese. (See Table 4.3.) The prevalence of obesity was higher among male (16.3%) than among female (9.6%) students. It was also higher among non-Hispanic African-American females (17.8%) and Hispanic females (12.7%) than among non-Hispanic white females (6.8%) and higher among non-Hispanic African-American males (18.9%) and Hispanic males (20.3%) than non-Hispanic white males (14.6%). Overall, there were higher rates of obesity among non-Hispanic African-American (18.3%) and Hispanic (16.6%) students than among non-Hispanic white (10.8%) students.

The prevalence of obesity was higher among 9th-grade males (16.6%), 10th-grade males (16.4%), 11th-grade males (17.3%), and 12th-grade males (14.7%) than among 9th-grade females (10.7%), 10th-grade females (9.8%), 11th-grade females (8.1%), and 12th-grade females (9.3%). (See Table 4.3.) The prevalence of obesity was higher among 9th-grade females (10.7%) than among 11th-grade female (8.1%) students. The prevalence of obesity ranged from 8.7% to 17.9% across state surveys and from 8.4% to 19.3% across local surveys. (See Table 4.4.)

The 2007 YRBSS finding of increasing percentages of overweight and obese teens in lower grades suggests the likelihood of yet another generation of overweight adults who may be at risk for subsequent overweight- and obesity-related health problems. According to Youfa Wang et al., in "Will All Americans Become Overweight or Obese? Estimating the Progression and Cost of the US Obesity Epidemic" (*Obesity*, vol. 16, no. 10, October 2008), forecasts based on the National Health and Nutrition Examination Surveys predict that if the current trends continue, 51.1% of adults will be obese and 86.3% will be overweight or obese by 2030. In children,

FIGURE 4.1

Body mass index (BMI) percentiles for boys, ages 2–20

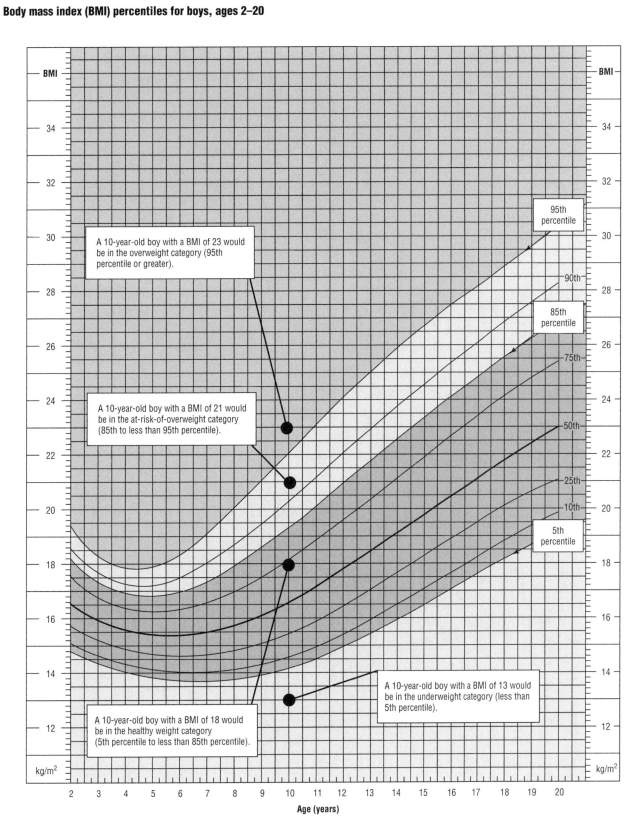

SOURCE: "Body Mass Index-for-Age Percentiles: Boys, 2 to 20 Years," in *About BMI for Children and Teens*, Centers for Disease Control and Prevention, National Center for Chronic Disease Prevention and Health Promotion, Division of Nutrition, Physical Activity, and Obesity, January 27, 2009, http://cdc.gov/nccdphp/dnpa/bmi/childrens_BMI/about_childrens_BMI.htm (accessed October 30, 2009)

FIGURE 4.2

The interpretation of body mass index (BMI) varies by age

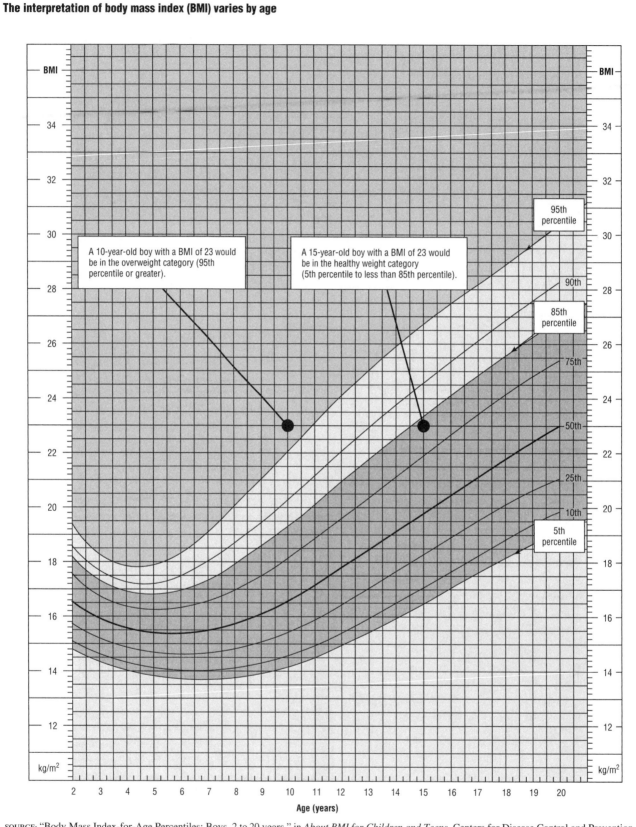

SOURCE: "Body Mass Index-for-Age Percentiles: Boys, 2 to 20 years," in *About BMI for Children and Teens*, Centers for Disease Control and Prevention, National Center for Chronic Disease Prevention and Health Promotion, Division of Nutrition, Physical Activity, and Obesity, January 27, 2009, http://cdc.gov/nccdphp/dnpa/bmi/childrens_BMI/about_childrens_BMI.htm (accessed October 30, 2009)

TABLE 4.2

Weight status categories by BMI-for-age percentiles

Weight status category	Percentile range
Underweight	Less than the 5th percentile
Healthy weight	5th percentile to less than the 85th percentile
At risk of overweight	85th to less than the 95th percentile
Overweight	Equal to or greater than the 95th percentile

SOURCE: "Weight Status Category," in *About BMI for Children and Teens*, Centers for Disease Control and Prevention, National Center for Chronic Disease Prevention and Health Promotion, Division of Nutrition, Physical Activity, and Obesity, January 27, 2009, http://www.cdc.gov/nccdphp/dnpa/bmi/childrens_BMI/about_childrens_BMI .htm (accessed October 30, 2009)

at the current rate, the prevalence of overweight is likely to nearly double by 2030.

WHY ARE SO MANY CHILDREN AND TEENS OVERWEIGHT?

Most children are overweight for the same reason as their adult counterparts: they consume more calories than they expend. Infants and toddlers appear to be effective regulators of caloric consumption, taking in only the calories needed for growth and development. By the time children are school age, this self-regulatory mechanism has weakened and when offered larger portions, they will eat them.

Heredity and environment play key roles in determining a child's risk of becoming overweight or obese. The American Academy of Child and Adolescent Psychiatry notes in "Obesity in Children and Teens" (May 2008, http://www.aacap.org/cs/root/facts_for_families/ obesity_in_children_and_teens) that if one parent is obese, then there is a 50% chance that a child will be obese, and when both parents are obese, a child has an 80% chance of being obese. Even though there is mounting evidence of genetic predisposition and susceptibility to overweight and obesity, childhood obesity is still considered largely an environmental problem—the result of behaviors, attitudes, and preferences learned early in life. Children's relationships with food develop in response to family and cultural values and practices as well as to the influences of school, peers, and the media.

The question remains: Which environmental factors have given rise to the increasing prevalence of overweight children and teens during the past three decades? Many observers point to a reliance on fat-laden convenience and fast foods, along with time spent watching television, playing video games, and surfing the Internet, instead of being outdoors and getting physical activity. The Federal Interagency Forum on Child and Family Statistics reports in *America's Children: Key National Indicators of Well-Being, 2009* (2009, http://www.childstats .gov/americaschildren/) that only 35% of adolescents get the recommended levels of physical activity. Television viewing, media advertising, dwindling school physical education programs, neighborhoods where it is unsafe for children to play outdoors, and even working parents have been implicated.

Working parents have been accused of a variety of nutritional and parenting infractions that have contributed to children's overindulgence in unhealthful foods. First, they leave children unsupervised and unable to satisfy their hunger with anything except cookies, chips, and

TABLE 4.3

Percentages of overweight and obese high school students by sex, race, ethnicity, and grade, 2007

	Obese			Overweight		
	Female	Male	Total	Female	Male	Total
Category	%	%	%	%	%	%
Race/ethnicity						
White*	6.8	14.6	10.8	12.8	15.7	14.3
Black*	17.8	18.9	18.3	21.4	16.6	19.0
Hispanic	12.7	20.3	16.6	17.9	18.3	18.1
Grade						
9	10.7	16.6	13.8	18.3	17.0	17.6
10	9.8	16.4	13.2	14.2	17.7	16.0
11	8.1	17.3	12.7	14.2	15.9	15.1
12	9.3	14.7	12.0	13.1	14.9	14.0
Total	**9.6**	**16.3**	**13.0**	**15.1**	**16.4**	**15.8**

Notes: Students who were ≥95th percentile for body mass index, by age and sex, based on reference data. Previous Youth Risk Behavior Survey reports used the term "overweight" to describe youth with a BMI ≥95th percentile for age and sex and "at risk for overweight" for those with a BMI ≥85th percentile and <95th percentile. However, this report uses the terms "obese" and "overweight" in accordance with the 2007 recommendations from the Expert Committee on the Assessment, Prevention, and Treatment of Child and Adolescent Overweight and Obesity convened by the American Medical Association (AMA) and cofunded by AMA in collaboration with the Health Resources and Services Administration and CDC. Students who were ≥85th percentile but <95th percentile for body mass index, by age and sex, based on reference data.
*Non-Hispanic.

SOURCE: Adapted from Danice K. Eaton et al., "Table 82. Percentage of High School Students Who Were Obese and Who Were Overweight, by Sex, Race/Ethnicity, and Grade—United States, Youth Risk Behavior Survey, 2007," in "Youth Risk Behavior Surveillance—United States, 2007," *Morbidity and Mortality Weekly Report*, vol. 57, no. SS-4, June 6, 2008, http://www.cdc.gov/mmwr/preview/mmwrhtml/ss5704a1.htm (accessed October 30, 2009)

TABLE 4.4

Percentages of overweight and obese high school students by sex, and selected U.S. sites, 2007

Site	Obese			Overweight		
	Female	Male	Total	Female	Male	Total
	%	%	%	%	%	%
State surveys						
Alaska	9.7	12.5	11.1	14.7	17.6	16.2
Arizona	8.5	14.7	11.7	12.2	16.0	14.2
Arkansas	9.1	18.4	13.9	16.8	14.8	15.8
Connecticut	8.2	16.2	12.3	11.5	14.9	13.3
Delaware	10.9	15.6	13.3	19.2	16.0	17.5
Florida	6.8	15.4	11.2	15.1	15.3	15.2
Georgia	11.1	16.6	13.8	18.9	17.5	18.2
Hawaii	11.3	19.4	15.6	15.5	13.3	14.3
Idaho	6.4	15.5	11.1	13.2	10.4	11.7
Illinois	9.9	15.9	12.9	15.8	15.5	15.7
Indiana	9.9	17.8	13.8	14.8	15.9	15.3
Iowa	8.8	13.7	11.3	10.6	16.2	13.5
Kansas	6.8	15.2	11.1	14.1	14.6	14.4
Kentucky	11.0	19.7	15.6	15.5	17.3	16.4
Maine	7.6	17.5	12.8	12.3	13.8	13.1
Maryland	9.2	16.7	13.1	15.4	15.1	15.2
Massachusetts	7.1	14.8	11.1	15.2	14.1	14.6
Michigan	9.8	15.0	12.4	15.6	17.3	16.5
Mississippi	14.7	21.2	17.9	18.8	16.9	17.9
Missouri	8.6	15.3	12.0	13.6	14.9	14.3
Montana	6.3	13.7	10.1	12.9	13.8	13.3
Nevada	7.6	14.2	11.0	13.9	15.1	14.5
New Hampshire	7.2	15.9	11.7	13.1	15.7	14.4
New Mexico	6.0	15.5	10.9	13.8	13.2	13.5
New York	7.6	14.1	10.9	16.3	16.3	16.3
North Carolina	9.5	15.9	12.8	17.2	17.0	17.1
North Dakota	8.0	11.8	10.0	11.2	16.0	13.7
Ohio	8.5	16.0	12.4	14.6	15.4	15.0
Oklahoma	9.8	19.2	14.7	16.8	13.7	15.2
Rhode Island	7.5	13.8	10.7	16.2	16.3	16.2
South Carolina	12.2	16.6	14.4	18.9	15.3	17.1
South Dakota	7.6	10.6	9.1	12.4	16.5	14.5
Tennessee	12.0	21.6	16.9	19.9	16.4	18.1
Texas	11.6	19.9	15.9	15.8	15.5	15.6
Utah	5.1	12.1	8.7	9.9	13.4	11.7
Vermont	8.0	15.1	11.8	13.8	15.0	14.5
West Virginia	11.7	17.6	14.7	19.0	15.0	17.0
Wisconsin	7.2	14.7	11.1	12.6	15.3	14.0
Wyoming	6.6	11.8	9.3	10.0	12.7	11.4
Median	*8.5*	*15.5*	*12.0*	*14.8*	*15.3*	*15.0*
Range	*5.1–14.7*	*10.6–21.6*	*8.7–17.9*	*9.9–19.9*	*10.4–17.6*	*11.4–18.2*
Local surveys						
Baltimore, MD	19.0	17.9	18.5	21.0	18.6	19.9
Boston, MA	11.7	17.2	14.5	22.0	15.2	18.5
Broward County, FL	6.5	10.2	8.4	17.2	13.7	15.4
Charlotte-Mecklenburg, NC	8.9	10.7	9.8	14.8	18.2	16.5
Chicago, IL	13.6	18.0	15.8	20.7	16.6	18.7
Dallas, TX	15.7	22.9	19.3	21.2	16.7	19.0
DeKalb County, GA	13.4	12.8	13.1	16.9	15.8	16.3
Detroit, MI	17.1	19.9	18.4	24.6	17.8	21.3
District of Columbia	15.8	19.6	17.7	19.9	15.8	17.8
Hillsborough County, FL	8.4	14.6	11.5	13.0	14.1	13.6
Houston, TX	11.5	21.7	16.7	19.7	15.9	17.7
Los Angeles, CA	11.7	20.9	16.5	24.1	20.4	22.2
Memphis, TN	13.7	19.0	16.2	23.3	15.7	19.7
Miami-Dade County, FL	8.9	16.8	13.0	14.5	15.5	15.0
Milwaukee, WI	15.4	20.0	17.7	24.2	13.8	19.0
New York City, NY	9.4	13.6	11.5	17.7	14.9	16.3
Orange County, FL	8.6	16.5	12.6	14.7	14.1	14.4
Palm Beach County, FL	6.1	10.9	8.5	11.0	14.0	12.5

soda. Some observers speculate that these children are starved emotionally—for time and attention—as well as nutritionally. They may also be hungry for information, because even though many adolescents are responsible for choosing and preparing their own food, they are often unprepared to make healthy choices.

Eating alone, in front of a television or computer, kids are more likely to overeat because they are lonely, bored, or susceptible to advertising cues. Overcome with guilt because they are not home to prepare meals, some working parents may intensify the problem by indulging their children with too many food treats.

TABLE 4.4

Percentages of overweight and obese high school students by sex, and selected U.S. sites, 2007 [CONTINUED]

	Obese			Overweight		
	Female	Male	Total	Female	Male	Total
Site	%	%	%	%	%	%
Philadelphia, PA	14.1	16.6	15.2	18.8	18.0	18.4
San Bernardino, CA	12.6	17.3	15.0	19.8	16.8	18.3
San Diego, CA	6.7	17.5	12.3	16.2	14.1	15.1
San Francisco, CA	3.7	13.0	8.5	12.1	12.9	12.5
Median	*11.7*	*17.2*	*14.8*	*19.2*	*15.7*	*17.7*
Range	*3.7–19.0*	*10.2–22.9*	*8.4–19.3*	*11.0–24.6*	*12.9–20.4*	*12.5–22.2*

Notes: Students who were ≥95th percentile for body mass index, by age and sex, based on reference data. Previous Youth Risk Behavior Survey reports used the term "overweight" to describe youth with a BMI ≥95th percentile for age and sex and "at risk for overweight" for those with a BMI ≥85th percentile and <95th percentile. However, this report uses the terms "obese" and "overweight" in accordance with the 2007 recommendations from the Expert Committee on the Assessment, Prevention, and Treatment of Child and Adolescent Overweight and Obesity convened by the American Medical Association (AMA) and cofunded by AMA in collaboration with the Health Resources and Services Administration and CDC. Students who were ≥85th percentile but <95th percentile for body mass index, by age and sex, based on reference data.

SOURCE: Danice K. Eaton et al., "Table 83. Percentage of High School Students Who Were Obese and Who Were Overweight, by Sex—Selected U.S. Sites, Youth Risk Behavior Survey, 2007," in "Youth Risk Behavior Surveillance—United States, 2007," *Morbidity and Mortality Weekly Report*, vol. 57, no. SS-4, June 6, 2008, http://www.cdc.gov/mmwr/preview/mmwrhtml/ss5704a1.htm (accessed October 30, 2009)

Stay-at-home parents do not necessarily convey healthier attitudes about food, eating, and nutrition than parents who work outside the home. Both groups may use food, especially sweets, to reward good behavior or may pressure children to clean their plates. Though these suppositions remain unproven, it is known that parents with eating disorders, obsessive dieters, and those with unhealthy eating habits are powerful, negative role models for children.

HOW HIGH SCHOOL STUDENTS EAT AND DIET

The 2007 YRBSS found that only about one-fifth (21.4%) of students had eaten fruits and vegetables at least five times per day during the seven days preceding the survey. (See Table 4.5.) More male (22.9%) than female (19.9%) students reported eating fruits and vegetables five or more times per day.

Even fewer students (14.1%) had drunk at least three glasses of milk per day than had eaten the recommended servings of fruits and vegetables during the seven days preceding the survey. (See Table 4.5.) The prevalence of having consumed at least three glasses of milk per day was higher among male (19.4%) than among female (8.8%) students.

Table 4.6 reveals that less than one-third (29.3%) of high school students described themselves as "slightly" or "very" overweight. More teenaged girls (34.5%) than teenaged boys (24.2%) considered themselves overweight. Almost half (45.2%) of the students said they

TABLE 4.5

Percentage of students who ate five or more servings per day of fruits and vegetables during the past seven days, 2007

	Ate fruits and vegetables five or more times/day			Drank three or more glasses/day of milk		
	Female	Male	Total	Female	Male	Total
Category	%	%	%	%	%	%
Race/ethnicity						
White*	17.6	20.1	18.8	9.9	22.2	16.1
Black*	23.4	26.6	24.9	5.7	13.6	9.7
Hispanic	22.1	25.9	24.0	8.1	17.3	12.7
Grade						
9	22.0	25.4	23.7	10.2	19.0	14.7
10	21.6	23.1	22.4	9.3	20.7	15.0
11	17.2	22.6	19.9	7.6	19.4	13.5
12	18.3	19.0	18.6	7.9	18.4	13.1
Total	**19.9**	**22.9**	**21.4**	**8.8**	**19.4**	**14.1**

Notes: 100% fruit juice, fruit, green salad, potatoes (excluding French fries, fried potatoes, or potato chips), carrots, or other vegetables. During the 7 days before the survey.
*Non-Hispanic.

SOURCE: Adapted from Danice K. Eaton et al., "Table 70. Percentage of High School Students Who Ate Fruits and Vegetables Five or More Times/Day and Who Drank Three or More Glasses/Day of Milk, by Sex, Race/Ethnicity, and Grade—United States, Youth Risk Behavior Survey, 2007," in "Youth Risk Behavior Surveillance—United States, 2007," *Morbidity and Mortality Weekly Report*, vol. 57, no. SS-4, June 6, 2008, http://www.cdc.gov/mmwr/preview/mmwrhtml/ss5704a1.htm (accessed October 30, 2009)

TABLE 4.6

Percentage of students who described themselves as overweight and percentage trying to lose weight, by sex, race, ethnicity, and grade, 2007

	Described themselves as overweight			Were trying to lose weight		
	Female	Male	Total	Female	Male	Total
Category	%	%	%	%	%	%
Race/ethnicity						
White*	34.0	23.6	28.8	62.3	29.0	45.6
Black*	30.1	19.1	24.6	49.5	24.9	37.1
Hispanic	39.3	28.3	33.8	62.1	38.5	50.2
Grade						
9	33.6	24.3	28.8	58.6	31.0	44.4
10	33.8	24.8	29.2	60.2	31.6	45.8
11	36.2	25.8	31.0	61.3	30.1	45.8
12	34.9	21.6	28.3	61.6	28.7	45.3
Total	**34.5**	**24.2**	**29.3**	**60.3**	**30.4**	**45.2**

*Non-Hispanic.

SOURCE: Adapted from Danice K. Eaton et al., "Table 84. Percentage of High School Students Who Described Themselves as Slightly or Very Overweight and Who Were Trying to Lose Weight, by Sex, Race/Ethnicity, and Grade—United States, Youth Risk Behavior Survey, 2007," in "Youth Risk Behavior Surveillance—United States, 2007," *Morbidity and Mortality Weekly Report*, vol. 57, no. SS-4, June 6, 2008, http://www.cdc.gov/mmwr/preview/mmwrhtml/ss5704a1.htm (accessed October 30, 2009)

were trying to lose weight, but about twice as many female teens (60.3%) as male teens (30.4%) reported making an effort to lose weight.

Strategies for losing weight varied. Table 4.7 shows that more than two-thirds (67%) of teenaged girls and more than half (55%) of teenaged boys exercised to lose or maintain their weight. More than half (53.2%) of female teens and over a quarter (28.3%) of male teens said they had tried to lose or control their weight by eating less, counting calories, or choosing foods low in fat during the month preceding the survey. However,

16.3% of teen girls and 7.3% of teen boys said they had gone without eating for 24 hours or more, and 7.5% of teen girls and 4.2% of teen boys had taken diet pills, powders, or liquids without a doctor's advice in an effort to lose weight. (See Table 4.8.)

Is Fast Food to Blame?

In "Effects of Fast-Food Consumption on Energy Intake and Diet Quality among Children in a National Household Survey" (*Pediatrics*, vol. 113, no. 1, January 2004), Shanthy A. Bowman et al. state that one-third of

TABLE 4.7

Percentage of students who exercised and ate less, counted calories, or chose foods low in fat to lose or keep from gaining weight, 2007

	Ate less food, fewer calories, or low-fat foods to lose weight or to keep from gaining weight			Exercised to lose weight or to keep from gaining weight		
	Female	Male	Total	Female	Male	Total
Category	%	%	%	%	%	%
Race/ethnicity						
White*	58.4	28.3	43.3	71.5	53.3	62.4
Black*	34.6	21.0	27.8	50.7	53.7	52.2
Hispanic	52.0	32.3	42.1	66.4	60.1	63.2
Grade						
9	50.5	27.3	38.6	70.6	58.7	64.5
10	53.0	29.1	40.9	67.7	54.2	60.9
11	54.0	29.8	42.0	65.0	54.9	59.9
12	56.4	27.4	42.0	63.7	51.1	57.5
Total	**53.2**	**28.3**	**40.6**	**67.0**	**55.0**	**60.9**

Notes: To lose weight or to keep from gaining weight during the 30 days before the survey.
*Non-Hispanic.

SOURCE: Adapted from Danice K. Eaton et al., "Table 86. Percentage of High School Students Who Ate Less Food, Fewer Calories, or Low-fat Foods and Who Exercised, by Sex, Race/Ethnicity, and Grade—United States, Youth Risk Behavior Survey, 2007," in "Youth Risk Behavior Surveillance—United States, 2007," *Morbidity and Mortality Weekly Report*, vol. 57, no. SS-4, June 6, 2008, http://www.cdc.gov/mmwr/preview/mmwrhtml/ss5704a1.htm (accessed October 30, 2009)

TABLE 4.8

Percentage of students who went without eating for 24 hours and took diet pills, powders or liquids to lose or keep from gaining weight, 2007

Category	Did not eat for 24 or more hours to lose weight or to keep from gaining weight			Took diet pills, powders, or liquids to lose weight or to keep from gaining weight[a]		
	Female	Male	Total	Female	Male	Total
	%	%	%	%	%	%
Race/ethnicity						
White[b]	16.7	5.7	11.2	8.3	3.7	6.0
Black[b]	13.2	7.4	10.3	3.9	3.6	3.7
Hispanic	17.4	10.7	14.1	7.8	5.1	6.4
Grade						
9	16.8	6.5	11.6	6.1	2.9	4.4
10	19.1	6.5	12.7	6.9	3.8	5.3
11	14.8	8.1	11.5	7.4	5.0	6.2
12	13.6	8.0	10.9	10.2	5.7	8.0
Total	**16.3**	**7.3**	**11.8**	**7.5**	**4.2**	**5.9**

Note: To lose weight or to keep from gaining weight during the 30 days before the survey.
[a]Without a doctor's advice.
[b]Non-Hispanic.

SOURCE: Adapted from Danice K. Eaton et al., "Table 88. Percentage of High School Students Who Did Not Eat for 24 or More Hours and Who Took Diet Pills, Powders, or Liquids, by Sex, Race/Ethnicity, and Grade—United States, Youth Risk Behavior Survey, 2007," in "Youth Risk Behavior Surveillance—United States, 2007," *Morbidity and Mortality Weekly Report*, vol. 57, no. SS-4, June 6, 2008, http://www.cdc.gov/mmwr/preview/mmwrhtml/ss5704a1.htm (accessed October 30, 2009)

U.S. children eat fast food on any given day, consuming extra calories, sugar, and fat in the process. When the researchers looked at the diets of 6,212 children and teens, they found that children of all races, incomes, and regions commonly consumed fast-food meals. Bowman et al. indicate that on a typical day more than 30% of U.S. children aged four to 19 ate burgers, fries, and other fast-food fare. The researchers report that children who ate fast food consumed an average of 187 more calories than did those who did not eat fast food, and, on average, children ate 126 extra calories on the days they ate fast food, compared with fast food–free days. Bowman et al. calculate that the extra fast-food calories could result in an additional 6 pounds (2.7 kg) of weight gain in a year.

To determine how much soda and fast food California teenagers consume, Theresa A. Hastert et al. of the University of California, Los Angeles, Center for Health Policy Research analyzed data from 4,010 12- to 17-year-old participants in the 2003 California Health Interview Survey and reported their findings in *More California Teens Consume Soda and Fast Food Each Day than Five Servings of Fruits and Vegetables* (September 2005, http://www.healthpolicy.ucla.edu/pubs/files/teen_fastfood _PB.pdf). The researchers find that over 2 million California teens (66.3% of the total teen population in the state) drink soda every day and about 1.5 million (48%) eat fast food daily. The average California teen drinks 1.4 sodas per day, and the consumption of soda and other sugary beverages increases with age. Seventeen-year-olds reported drinking 40% more soda (1.7 per day) than 12-year-olds (1.2 per day). Teenaged boys drink about 25%

more soda and sweet drinks than do teenaged girls, and African-American teens drink the most—averaging two sodas per day. Soda consumption declines with increasing household income. Teens with household income below 300% of the federal poverty limit drink more soda (1.5 to 1.6 per day) than teens from more affluent homes. Soda consumption was 25% higher among teens who said that sodas were available in school vending machines.

Nearly half (48%) of California teens eat fast food every day, and many eat fast food more than once a day. Almost 10% (over 300,000 California teens) have fast food twice a day, and 2.7% (90,000) eat fast food three or four times a day. As with soda consumption, more teens from low- and moderate-income homes eat fast food every day, and daily fast-food consumption increases with age, from 43.7% of 12-year-olds to 51.9% of 17-year-olds. Hastert et al. find that 20.9% of California teens eat the recommended five servings of fruits and vegetables per day. Not surprisingly, they also note a relationship between fast-food consumption and eating the recommended servings of fruits and vegetables. The more often teens eat fast food the less likely they are to eat fruits and vegetables. Significantly more teens who do not eat fast food eat five or more servings of fruits and vegetables per day.

The 2007 YRBSS confirmed that soda remains popular with high school students. About one-third (33.8%) of students reported drinking at least one soda per day. (See Table 4.9.) More males (38.6%) than females (29%) drank one or more sodas per day.

TABLE 4.9

Percentage of students who drank soda at least once a day, 2007

Category	Female %	Male %	Total %
Race/ethnicity			
White*	27.3	40.6	34.0
Black*	37.2	38.0	37.6
Hispanic	29.5	37.3	33.4
Grade			
9	31.5	39.5	35.6
10	29.8	36.6	33.2
11	26.5	39.0	32.8
12	27.2	39.2	33.1
Total	**29.0**	**38.6**	**33.8**

Notes: Not including diet soda or diet pop.
During the 7 days before the survey.
*Non-Hispanic.

SOURCE: Adapted from Danice K. Eaton et al., "Table 72. Percentage of High School Students Who Drank a Can, Bottle, or Glass of Soda or Pop, at Least One Time/Day, United States, Youth Risk Behavior Survey, 2007," in "Youth Risk Behavior Surveillance—United States, 2007," *Morbidity and Mortality Weekly Report*, vol. 57, no. SS-4, June 6, 2008, http://www.cdc.gov/mmwr/preview/mmwrhtml/ss5704a1.htm (accessed October 30, 2009)

The Role of the Media

Despite recent television and print media antiobesity campaigns, many industry observers condemn corporate marketing efforts and media for continuing to assault children with unhealthy messages that encourage them to eat junk foods. The CDC defines junk foods as those that provide calories primarily through fats or added sugars and have minimal amounts of vitamins and minerals. According to Daniel Redwood, in "Battling Junk Food, Scientific Conflicts of Interest, and Misleading Ads: Interview with Michael Jacobson, PhD" (*Health Insights Today*, vol. 3, no. 1, January–February 2010), Michael F. Jacobson, the executive director of the Center for Science in the Public Interest (CSPI), a nonprofit nutrition advocacy group based in Washington, D.C., believes the United States has permitted junk-food marketers—not only fast-food companies but also makers of sugary cereals and high-fat, high-calorie chips—to target children. He charges that the marketing of fatty, sugary, and low-nutrient foods has reached an all-time high and is fueling childhood obesity, and he calls for restricting promotions targeted at the young.

Jacobson suggests that CSPI has made some important strides in terms of limiting junk-food marketing to children. He asserts, "We threatened to sue Kellogg for junk food advertising on television and they agreed to negotiate. Over more than a year, we worked out a legal agreement by which they set limits on the nutritional quality of the products that they advertise to kids. They agreed to limits of no more than a certain amount of fat and sodium and sugar per serving of food. That set the stage for many other companies to agree to limits."

In the press release "Proposed Federal Standards for Foods Marketed to Kids Praised" (December 15, 2009, http://www.cspinet.org/new/200912151.html), Margo G. Wooten, the CSPI nutrition policy director, observes, "The federal government is headed in exactly the right direction with the draft nutrition standards proposed for foods that are marketed to children.... If these standards are adopted, it would be one of the most significant developments in this area in 30 years." Wooten hopes that adherence to these guidelines is the first step in eliminating "the discredited practice of marketing junk food to kids altogether."

According to Kevin McCarthy, in "Will the U.S. Curb the Marketing of Junk Food to Kids and Teens?" (March 13, 2009, http://blogs.consumerreports.org/health/2009/03/will-the-us-curb-the-marketing-of-junk-food-to-kids-and-teens.html), efforts to restrict food marketing that targets children have been under way since 2005. Based on these efforts, many food companies have promised to improve the nutritional content of their products and/or to stop marketing specific products to children younger than age 12. Even though these measures have had some impact on junk-food marketing to children, many industry observers believe stringent standards are needed.

The congressional omnibus appropriations bill that was signed into law by President Barack Obama (1961–) in March 2009 aimed to set such standards for marketing foods to children aged 17 and younger. The bill established the Interagency Working Group on Food Marketed to Children with representation from the Federal Trade Commission, the CDC, the U.S. Food and Drug Administration, and the U.S. Department of Agriculture (USDA) to recommend standards for the marketing of food to children and to determine which media should adhere to these new standards. The bill stipulated that the standards should consider "calories, portion size, saturated fat, trans fat, sodium, added sugars, and the presence of nutrients, fruits, vegetables, and whole grains to the diets of such children," as well as "evidence concerning the role of consumption of nutrients, ingredients, and foods in preventing or promoting the development of obesity among such children."

The group reports in *Interagency Working Group on Food Marketed to Children Tentative Proposed Nutrition Standards* (December 15, 2009, http://cspinet.org/new/pdf/ftcnewstandards.pdf) that it met in December 2009 and developed voluntary measures and standards aimed at ensuring more responsible marketing to children. As of January 2010, unresolved issues included whether the new standards should include children younger than the age of 2; be different for children and teens; limit marketing of additional ingredients such as caffeine, artificial sweeteners, and cholesterol; and apply to generic brands and restaurant advertising. The public was invited to comment on the recommendations prior to the group's submission of them in a report to Congress in July 2010.

Educators and marketers observe that even though some corporations may have agreed not to advertise to children on television or in schools, they remain eager to maintain a high-profile presence in schools, which enables them to remain highly visible to students. In 2005 McDonald's launched its "Passport to Play" program, which provides free lesson plans and materials to third- through fifth-grade physical education teachers. In the fact sheet "McDonald's Commitment to Balanced, Active Lifestyles" (June 7, 2006, http://www.mcdepk.com/2006worldcupresourcecenter/mediadocs/global_bal_fact_sheet.pdf), McDonald's describes the program, which has been distributed to elementary schools nationwide, as reflecting the company's "commitment to balanced, active lifestyles today." Some critics object to commercialism of any kind in the schools, even if the message encourages healthful choices. Others believe that it is hypocritical for purveyors of low-nutrient foods to link these foods to physical fitness or athletic prowess.

The CSPI asserts in the press release "Food Industry Seeks to Maintain Junk-Food Marketing in Schools" (September 22, 2009, http://www.cspinet.org/new/200909221.html) that the food industry's self-regulation is sorely lacking. In "Fact Sheet on the Elementary School Advertising Principles" (April 2009, http://www.bbb.org/us/storage/0/Shared%20Documents/ESFactSheetFinalWord.pdf), the Children's Food and Beverage Advertising Initiative states that member companies, which include Burger King, Coca-Cola, General Mills, Hershey Company, McDonald's, and the Campbell Soup Company, will not advertise food or beverages in elementary schools. However, the companies are permitted to place promotional messages on vending machines, sponsor label-collection programs, and supply display racks and tray liners that promote food to schools. The companies may also sponsor curricula and other educational materials. Corporate icons such as Ronald McDonald and Tony the Tiger are permitted in the schools, and the sale of low-nutrition foods is permitted at school fund-raisers. Margo G. Wootan, the CSPI nutrition policy director, decries the guidelines as a "sham, written more to protect the commercial needs of food marketers than the health of children" and observes that they only cover elementary school and do not apply to after-school activities. She asks rhetorically, "Who wants their son or daughter to be enlisted in an unpaid, drone army actually selling junk food?"

However, students are beginning to have some healthier beverage and food options in school. In *School Health Profiles 2008: Characteristics of Health Programs among Secondary Schools* (2009, http://www.cdc.gov/healthyyouth/

profiles/2008/profiles_report.pdf), Nancy D. Brener et al. of the CDC find that fewer secondary schools in the United States sold less nutritious foods and beverages in vending machines, school stores, and snack bars in 2008 than in 2006. In 17 states the majority of secondary schools no longer sell less nutritious foods and beverages. For example, in 2008 more than two-thirds of secondary schools in California, Connecticut, Hawaii, and Maine did not sell baked goods, salty snacks that were high in fat, candy, soda, and fruit drinks that were not 100% juice.

Even though there is widespread agreement that removing soda from schools is a healthy move, some nutritionists feel the proposed beverage choices, which include sports drinks and vitamin-enhanced water that also contains sugar, still favor beverage company interests rather than students' health. Brener et al. confirm that in 2008 many schools still offered less nutritious food and beverages that students could purchase. (See Figure 4.3.)

Many Schools Offer and Promote Unhealthy Food Choices

Food manufacturers and marketers know that schools are ideal sites to promote their products to children and teens. Nearly all youth attend school and spend many of their waking hours at school. Furthermore, the presence of foods in schools allows food companies to benefit from the implied endorsement of the schools and teachers. According to Brener et al., in 2008 many schools had vending machines, stores, or snack bars on campus that sold "competitive foods [which] are any foods and beverages sold at school separately from the USDA school meal programs. Although foods and beverages sold through the school meal programs must meet federal nutrition requirements, competitive foods are not subject to any federal nutrition standards unless they are sold inside the food service area during mealtimes." Figure 4.4 shows the types and sources of competitive foods in schools. The nutritional value of competitive foods is essentially unregulated, and students often purchase these foods instead of, or in addition to, school meals.

Besides selling food in schools, food manufacturers advertise on vending machines, posters, book covers, scoreboards, and banners and offer schools educational materials, contests in which children receive prizes or food rewards for achievement, and fund-raising opportunities. Some critics, including the CSPI, assert that the manufacturers are taking unfair advantage of cash-strapped school districts.

Food for Thought Has New Meaning at Many Schools

The 2004 reauthorization of the federal Child Nutrition Act required every school district that received federal funds to establish a local wellness policy by June 30, 2006, and USDA dietary guidelines released in January 2005 prompted many schools' food services to offer more

FIGURE 4.3

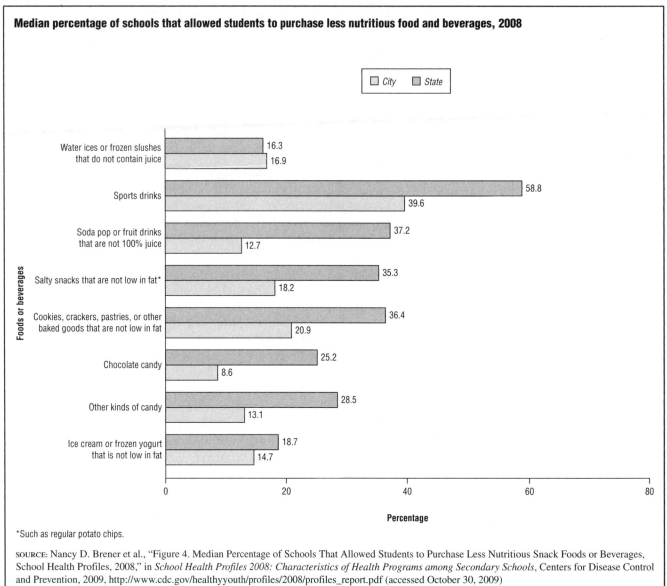

Median percentage of schools that allowed students to purchase less nutritious food and beverages, 2008

☐ City   ■ State

*Such as regular potato chips.

SOURCE: Nancy D. Brener et al., "Figure 4. Median Percentage of Schools That Allowed Students to Purchase Less Nutritious Snack Foods or Beverages, School Health Profiles, 2008," in *School Health Profiles 2008: Characteristics of Health Programs among Secondary Schools*, Centers for Disease Control and Prevention, 2009, http://www.cdc.gov/healthyyouth/profiles/2008/profiles_report.pdf (accessed October 30, 2009)

whole grains and fresh fruits and vegetables. Even before legislation mandated changes, and certainly afterward, many school districts replaced some of the food and beverages available in their schools.

In 2004 schools in Philadelphia, Pennsylvania, instituted a no-soda policy, and in 2005 California banned the sale of soda in public high schools. Connecticut passed a ban on selling sugar-sweetened drinks, including soda and sports drinks, in schools in 2006. According to the CDC, in "Availability of Less Nutritious Snack Foods and Beverages in Secondary Schools—Selected States, 2002–2008" (*Morbidity and Mortality Weekly Report*, vol. 58, October 5, 2009), from 2006 to 2008 the percentage of schools in which students could not purchase soda or fruit drinks that were not 100% juice rose in all 34 participating states. The percentage in which students could not purchase soda ranged from 25.6% to 92.8%.

New Jersey schools have adopted what may be the most ambitious statewide school nutrition policy in the nation. Since 2007 all the state's public schools adhere to a policy stipulating that soda, any food item listing sugar as its first ingredient, all forms of candy, and foods of minimal nutritional value (per the USDA definition) cannot be served, sold, or given for free anytime during the school day. Snacks and drinks sold anywhere on a school campus must have no more than 8 grams of fat and 2 grams of saturated fat per serving, and drinks cannot exceed more than 12 ounces (355 mL), except bottled water. This policy applies to vending machines, cafeterias, à la carte items, school stores, school fund-raisers, and the after-school snack program. The policy also makes nutrition education a requirement in school curricula.

However, Brener et al. indicate that schools in many other states continue to sell less nutritious foods. For

FIGURE 4.4

Categories and sources of competitive foods in schools

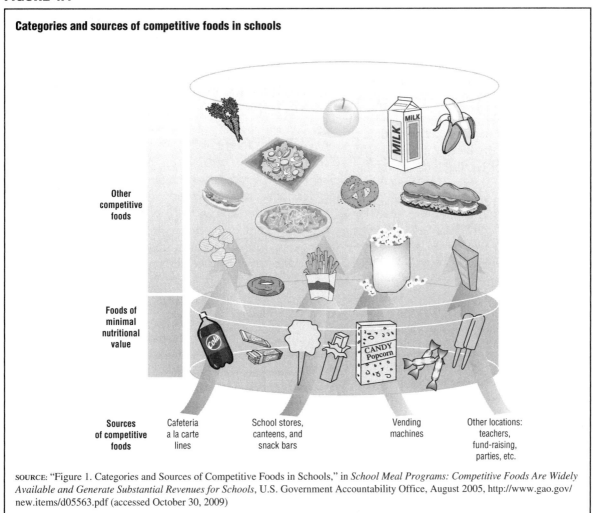

Other competitive foods

Foods of minimal nutritional value

| Sources of competitive foods | Cafeteria a la carte lines | School stores, canteens, and snack bars | Vending machines | Other locations: teachers, fund-raising, parties, etc. |

SOURCE: "Figure 1. Categories and Sources of Competitive Foods in Schools," in *School Meal Programs: Competitive Foods Are Widely Available and Generate Substantial Revenues for Schools*, U.S. Government Accountability Office, August 2005, http://www.gao.gov/new.items/d05563.pdf (accessed October 30, 2009)

example, in 2008 more than two-thirds of secondary schools in Idaho, Kansas, Nebraska, and Utah sold baked goods, salty snacks that were high in fat, candy, soda, and fruit drinks that were not 100% juice. Furthermore, research reveals that banning soft drink sales in schools may not significantly reduce children's soda consumption. In "The Effect of Soft Drink Availability in Elementary Schools on Consumption" (*Journal of the American Dietetic Association*, vol. 108, no. 9, September 2008), Meenakshi M. Fernandes of the RAND Corporation reports the results of a study that looked at soft drink consumption of 10,215 fifth-graders in 40 states. Fernandes notes that 26% of children who had access to soda at school drank it, and those who consumed more soft drinks at school had higher total soft drink consumption. Limiting the availability of soft drinks at school was associated with a scant 4% decrease in overall consumption.

The Media Can Deliver Powerful Nutrition and Health Education

Greater emphasis on children's diets has inspired the media to offer nutrition education. In 2008 *Sesame Street* launched the "Healthy Habits for Life" program. Rather than subsisting on a diet of cookies alone, *Sesame Street*'s Cookie Monster now champions healthful food choices. The beloved character also sings a new tune, "A Cookie Is a Sometimes Food." SpongeBob SquarePants, who in the past appeared on Breyer's ice cream cartons and Kellogg's sweetened cereals, has been relocated to the produce section and is advocating fresh produce consumption. Along with SpongeBob SquarePants, Dora the Explorer and other Nickelodeon characters appear on packages of fruits and vegetables, under licensing agreements with produce companies. Clifford the Big Red Dog promotes an organic cereal with his name and likeness, and Arthur the aardvark has lent his name and likeness to Arthur's Loops, another organic cereal.

Children's television programming such as Disney's *The Wiggles* and Nickelodeon's *Dora the Explorer* aim to inspire young viewers to be physically active. Blending fitness and entertainment, video game makers have developed a genre of active rhythm games including *Dance Dance Revolution*, which features a workout mode that can track how many calories the user burns while playing. *In the Groove* and *Pump It Up: Exceed* are video games in which players try to match the onscreen action by stepping on different sections of a floor pad, and *Yourself!Fitness* and *Kinetic* offer teens exercise routines in video game formats. *Escape from Obeez City* is an interactive DVD game that teaches children about the dangers of poor nutrition and inactivity, motivating them to change their behavior. Nintendo's *Wii Fit* instructs and coaches users in yoga, balance games, strength training, aerobics, and simulated sports. As part of its antiobesity efforts, the National Institutes of Health (NIH) is funding video game research projects in the United States.

The article "US to Unleash 'Wild Things' to Fight Childhood Obesity" (AFP, September 10, 2009) reports that in September 2009 the HHS announced its plan to use the characters from Maurice Sendak's (1928–) children's story *Where the Wild Things Are* to combat childhood overweight and obesity. The campaign promotes physical activity and encourages children to make time for active play everyday. The campaign builds on an ongoing collaboration between the Ad Council and the HHS that debuted in 2005 and has already featured characters from *Shrek* and professional football players exhorting children to be physically active for an hour per day.

School Physical Education Programs

School physical education (PE) programs, especially at the high school level, have been found lacking school nutrition programs. According to Brener et al., the percentage of schools that required PE for students in grades six through 12 ranged from 52.4% to 100% in 2008. Figure 4.5 shows the median (average) percentage of schools that had a required PE course in each grade in 2008. The percentage ranged from 95.3% in grade six to just 40.1% in grade 12. Danice K. Eaton et al. of the CDC note in "Youth Risk Behavior Surveillance—United States, 2007" (*Morbidity and Mortality Weekly Report*, vol. 57, no. SS-04, June 6, 2008) that in 2007 nearly 65% of students did not meet the recommended levels of physical activity (they were not physically active enough to increase their heart rate and cause them to breathe hard some of the time for a total of at least 60 minutes per day on five or more days during the seven days before the survey).

The importance of school PE programs cannot be underestimated, especially in view of the 2007 YRBSS finding that only a little more than one-third (34.7%) of high school students had participated in sufficient physical activity during the week preceding the survey. (See Table 4.10.) Many more male teens (43.7%) than female teens (25.6%) said they had been active for 60 minutes or more on at least five of the past seven days.

Further reinforcing the notion that American teens lead relatively sedentary lives, 37.5% of male high school students and 33.2% of female students reported watching three or more hours of television on an average school day. (See Table 4.11.) Nearly a quarter (24.9%) of teens played video or computer games or used computers (for nonschool related activities) for three or more hours per day.

HEALTH RISKS AND CONSEQUENCES

The harmful health consequences of overweight and obesity can begin during childhood and adolescence. According to John J. Reilly et al., in "Health Consequences of Obesity" (*Archives of Disease in Childhood*, vol. 88, no. 9, 2003), nearly 60% of overweight children have at least one cardiovascular risk factor, compared with 10% of those with a BMI-for-age less than the 85th percentile, and 25% of overweight children have two or more risk factors. The most frequently occurring medical consequences of overweight among children and adolescents are:

- Elevated blood lipids—overweight children and adolescents display the same elevated levels of cholesterol, triglycerides (a fatty substance found in the blood), and/or low-density lipoproteins as overweight adults. These hyperlipidemias are linked to an increased risk for cardiovascular disease and premature mortality (death) in adulthood.

- Glucose intolerance and Type 2 diabetes—glucose intolerance, a carbohydrate intolerance that varies in severity, is a forerunner of diabetes. The incidence of Type 2 diabetes (also called noninsulin-dependent diabetes mellitus) among adolescents is increasing in response to the national rise of overweight teens. A skin condition known as acanthosis nigricans (velvety thickening and darkening of skinfold areas at the neck, elbow, and behind the knee) often coexists with glucose intolerance in youth.

- Fatty liver disease—high concentrations of liver enzymes are associated with fatty degeneration of the liver (also called hepatic steatosis) and have been found in overweight children and adolescents. Excessively high blood insulin levels (hyperinsulinemia) may contribute to the genesis of this disease.

- Gallstones—even though gallstones occur less frequently among children and adolescents who are overweight than in obese adults, nearly half of the cases of inflammation of the gallbladder (also called cholecystitis) in adolescents may be associated with overweight. Like adults, the risk for cholecystitis and gallstones in adolescents may decrease with weight reduction.

Another common health consequence of overweight is early maturation, a condition in which the skeletal age is more than three months greater than the chronological age. Early maturation is linked to overweight in adulthood and is also associated with the distribution of fat—it

FIGURE 4.5

Median percentage of schools that had a required physical education course in each grade, 2008

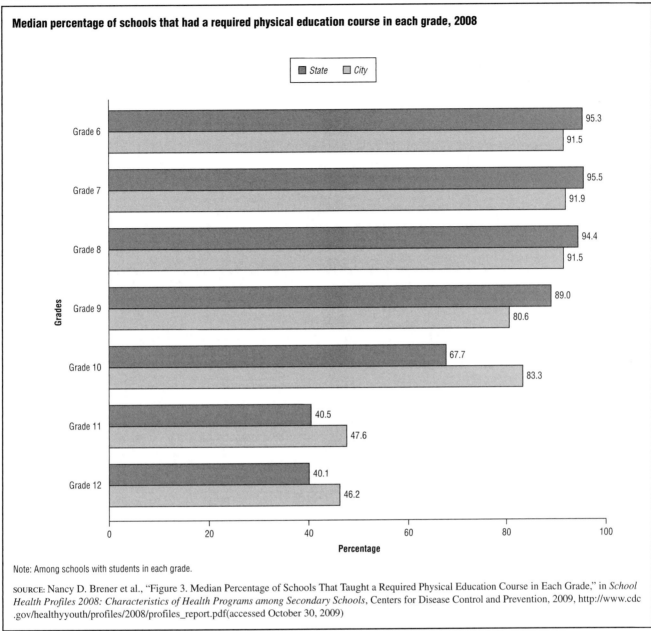

Note: Among schools with students in each grade.

SOURCE: Nancy D. Brener et al., "Figure 3. Median Percentage of Schools That Taught a Required Physical Education Course in Each Grade," in *School Health Profiles 2008: Characteristics of Health Programs among Secondary Schools*, Centers for Disease Control and Prevention, 2009, http://www.cdc.gov/healthyyouth/profiles/2008/profiles_report.pdf(accessed October 30, 2009)

predicts the fat predominantly located on the abdomen and trunk that is in turn predictive of increased disease risk.

Less frequently occurring health consequences include hypertension, a condition that is nine times more frequent among children who are overweight, compared with children who have a healthy weight; obstructive sleep apnea (breathing becomes shallow or stops completely for short periods during sleep), a condition that afflicts an estimated 7% of overweight children; and orthopedic problems resulting from excessive stress on the feet, legs, and hips. Hypertension for children and adolescents aged one to 17 years is defined as average blood pressure readings at or above the 95th percentile (based on age, sex, and height) on at least three separate occasions. (See Table 4.12 and Table 4.13 for blood pressures by age and gender that are

considered indicative of hypertension or at risk for hypertension; children and adolescents between the 90th and 95th percentiles for their age, sex, and height are at risk for developing hypertension.)

Several studies confirm that blood pressure and change in BMI during childhood are the two most powerful predictors of adult blood pressure across all ages and both genders. In "Childhood Obesity Predicts Adult Metabolic Syndrome: The Fels Longitudinal Study" (*Journal of Pediatrics*, vol. 152, no. 2, February 2008), Shumei S. Sun et al. confirm that children with high BMI and waist circumference are at increased risk of developing metabolic syndrome, which includes elevated blood pressure as well as elevated blood glucose and lipids. Sudhir K. Mehta et al. opine in "Abdominal Obesity, Waist Circumference,

TABLE 4.10

Percentages of high school students who met recommended levels of physical activity by sex, race, ethnicity, and grade, 2007

	Met recommended levels of physical activity			Did not participate in 60 or more minutes of physical activity on any day		
	Female	Male	Total	Female	Male	Total
Category	%	%	%	%	%	%
Race/ethnicity						
White*	27.9	46.1	37.0	28.2	16.7	22.4
Black*	21.0	41.3	31.1	42.1	21.8	32.0
Hispanic	21.9	38.6	30.2	35.2	18.8	27.1
Grade						
9	31.5	44.4	38.1	26.1	17.1	21.5
10	24.4	45.1	34.8	31.7	16.3	24.0
11	24.6	45.2	34.8	34.3	18.0	26.2
12	20.6	38.7	29.5	36.2	21.5	28.9
Total	**25.6**	**43.7**	**34.7**	**31.8**	**18.0**	**24.9**

Notes: Were physically active doing any kind of physical activity that increased their heart rate and made them breathe hard some of the time for a total of at least 60 minutes/day on 5 or more days during the 7 days before the survey.
Did not participate in 60 or more minutes of any kind of physical activity that increased their heart rate and made them breathe hard some of the time on at least 1 day during the 7 days before the survey.
*Non-Hispanic.

SOURCE: Adapted from Danice K. Eaton et al., "Table 74. Percentage of High School Students Who Met Recommended Levels of Physical Activity and Who Did Not Participate in 60 or More Minutes of Physical Activity on Any Day, by Sex, Race/Ethnicity, and Grade—United States, Youth Risk Behavior Survey, 2007," in "Youth Risk Behavior Surveillance—United States, 2007," *Morbidity and Mortality Weekly Report*, vol. 57, no. SS-4, June 6, 2008, http://www.cdc.gov/mmwr/preview/mmwrhtml/ss5704a1.htm (accessed October 30, 2009)

TABLE 4.11

Percentages of high school students who played video or computer games or used a computer for 3 or more hours/day and who watched 3 or more hours/day of television, by sex, race/ethnicity, and grade, 2007

	Used computers 3 or more hours/day			Watched television 3 or more hours/day		
	Female	Male	Total	Female	Male	Total
Category	%	%	%	%	%	%
Race/ethnicity						
White*	18.2	26.9	22.6	24.0	30.4	27.2
Black*	26.7	34.0	30.5	60.6	64.6	62.7
Hispanic	21.8	30.7	26.3	43.6	42.4	43.0
Grade						
9	24.9	30.5	27.8	37.2	42.0	39.7
10	22.6	30.0	26.3	35.9	38.1	37.0
11	17.9	29.5	23.7	29.6	35.4	32.5
12	14.8	25.6	20.1	28.9	32.8	30.8
Total	**20.6**	**29.1**	**24.9**	**33.2**	**37.5**	**35.4**

Notes: For something that was not school work.
On an average school day.
*Non-Hispanic.

SOURCE: Adapted from Danice K. Eaton et al., "Table 76. Percentage of High School Students Who Played Video or Computer Games or Used a Computer for 3 or More Hours/Day and Who Watched 3 or More Hours/Day of Television, by Sex, Race/Ethnicity, and Grade—United States, Youth Risk Behavior Survey, 2007," in "Youth Risk Behavior Surveillance—United States, 2007," *Morbidity and Mortality Weekly Report*, vol. 57, no. SS-4, June 6, 2008, http://www.cdc.gov/mmwr/preview/mmwrhtml/ss5704a1.htm (accessed October 30, 2009)

Body Mass Index, and Echocardiographic Measures in Children and Adolescents" (*Congenital Heart Diseases*, vol. 4, no. 5, September 2009) that waist circumference in children and teens may better predict future risk of cardiovascular disease than BMI alone because waist circumference assesses abdominal obesity, which is associated with increased risk of heart disease in youth as well as in adults.

Metabolic Syndrome

The metabolic syndrome is a group of risk factors for atherosclerotic cardiovascular disease and Type 2 diabetes mellitus in adults that include insulin resistance, obesity, hypertension, and hyperlipidemia. (Atherosclerosis is a hardening of the walls of the arteries caused by the buildup of fatty deposits on the inner walls of the arteries that interferes with blood flow.) Atherosclerotic cardiovascular

TABLE 4.12

Blood pressure levels for the 90th and 95th percentiles of blood pressure for boys ages 1 to 17 years

Age	BP percentile*	Systolic BP (mm Hg), by height percentile from standard growth curves							Diastolic BP (mm Hg), by height percentile from standard growth curves						
		5%	10%	25%	50%	75%	90%	95%	5%	10%	25%	50%	75%	90%	95%
1	90th	94	95	97	98	100	102	102	50	51	52	53	54	54	55
	95th	98	99	101	102	104	106	106	55	55	56	57	58	59	59
2	90th	98	99	100	102	104	105	106	55	55	56	57	58	59	59
	95th	101	102	104	106	108	109	110	59	59	60	61	62	63	63
3	90th	100	101	103	105	107	108	109	59	59	60	61	62	63	63
	95th	104	105	107	109	111	112	113	63	63	64	65	66	67	67
4	90th	102	103	105	107	109	110	111	62	62	63	64	65	66	66
	95th	106	107	109	111	113	114	115	66	67	67	68	69	70	71
5	90th	104	105	106	108	110	112	112	65	65	66	67	68	69	69
	95th	108	109	110	112	114	115	116	69	70	70	71	72	73	74
6	90th	105	106	108	110	111	113	114	67	68	69	70	70	71	72
	95th	109	110	112	114	115	117	117	72	72	73	74	75	76	76
7	90th	106	107	109	111	113	114	115	69	70	71	72	72	73	74
	95th	110	111	113	115	116	118	119	74	74	75	76	77	78	78
8	90th	107	108	110	112	114	115	116	71	71	72	73	74	75	75
	95th	111	112	114	116	118	119	120	75	76	76	77	78	79	80
9	90th	109	110	112	113	115	117	117	72	73	73	74	75	76	77
	95th	113	114	116	117	119	121	121	76	77	78	79	80	80	81
10	90th	110	112	113	115	117	118	119	73	74	74	75	76	77	78
	95th	114	115	117	119	121	122	123	77	78	79	80	80	81	82
11	90th	112	113	115	117	119	120	121	74	74	75	76	77	78	78
	95th	116	117	119	121	123	124	125	78	79	79	80	81	82	83
12	90th	115	116	117	119	121	123	123	75	75	76	77	78	78	79
	95th	119	120	121	123	125	126	127	79	79	80	81	82	83	83
13	90th	117	118	120	122	124	125	126	75	76	76	77	78	79	80
	95th	121	122	124	126	128	129	130	79	80	81	82	83	83	84
14	90th	120	121	123	125	126	128	128	76	76	77	78	79	80	80
	95th	124	125	127	128	130	132	132	80	81	81	82	83	84	85
15	90th	123	124	125	127	129	131	131	77	77	78	79	80	81	81
	95th	127	128	129	131	133	134	135	81	82	83	83	84	85	86
16	90th	125	126	128	130	132	133	134	79	79	80	81	82	82	83
	95th	129	130	132	134	136	137	138	83	83	84	85	86	87	87
17	90th	128	129	131	133	134	136	136	81	81	82	83	84	85	85
	95th	132	133	135	136	138	140	140	85	85	86	87	88	89	89

*Blood pressure percentile determined by a single measurement.

SOURCE: "Table 16. Blood Pressure Levels for the 90th and 95th Percentiles of Blood Pressure for Boys Ages 1 to 17 Years," in *Overweight Children and Adolescents: Screen, Access, and Manage,* Centers for Disease Control and Prevention, National Center for Chronic Disease Prevention and Promotion, Division of Nutrition, Physical Activity and Obesity, May 2000, http://www.cdc.gov/nccdphp/dnpa/growthcharts/training/modules/module3/text/hypertension_tables.htm (accessed October 30, 2009)

Diet, Nutrition, and Weight Issues among Children and Adolescents

TABLE 4.13

Blood pressure levels for the 90th and 95th percentiles of blood pressure for girls ages 1 to 17 years

Age	BP percentile*	Systolic BP (mm Hg), by height percentile from standard growth curves							Diastolic BP (mm Hg), by height percentile from standard growth curves						
		5%	10%	25%	50%	75%	90%	95%	5%	10%	25%	50%	75%	90%	95%
1	90th	97	98	99	100	102	103	104	53	53	53	54	55	56	56
	95th	101	102	103	104	105	107	107	57	57	57	58	59	60	60
2	90th	99	99	100	102	103	104	105	57	57	58	58	59	60	61
	95th	102	103	104	105	107	108	109	61	61	62	62	63	64	65
3	90th	100	100	102	103	104	105	106	61	61	61	62	63	63	64
	95th	104	104	105	107	108	109	110	65	65	65	66	67	67	68
4	90th	101	102	103	104	106	107	108	63	63	64	65	65	66	67
	95th	105	106	107	108	109	111	111	67	67	68	69	69	70	71
5	90th	103	103	104	106	107	108	109	65	66	66	67	68	68	69
	95th	107	107	108	110	111	112	113	69	70	70	71	72	72	73
6	90th	104	105	106	107	109	110	111	67	67	68	69	69	70	71
	95th	108	109	110	111	112	114	114	71	71	72	73	73	74	75
7	90th	106	107	108	109	110	112	112	69	69	69	70	71	72	72
	95th	110	110	112	113	114	115	116	73	73	73	74	75	76	76
8	90th	108	109	110	111	112	113	114	70	70	71	71	72	73	74
	95th	112	112	113	115	116	117	118	74	74	75	75	76	77	78
9	90th	110	110	112	113	114	115	116	71	72	72	73	74	74	75
	95th	114	114	115	117	118	119	120	75	76	76	77	78	78	79
10	90th	112	112	114	115	116	117	118	73	73	73	74	75	76	76
	95th	116	116	117	119	120	121	122	77	77	77	78	79	80	80
11	90th	114	114	116	117	118	119	120	74	74	75	75	76	77	77
	95th	118	118	119	121	122	123	124	78	78	79	79	80	81	81
12	90th	116	116	118	119	120	121	122	75	75	76	76	77	78	78
	95th	120	120	121	123	124	125	126	79	79	80	80	81	82	82
13	90th	118	118	119	121	122	123	124	76	76	77	78	78	79	80
	95th	121	122	123	125	126	127	128	80	80	81	82	82	83	84
14	90th	119	120	121	122	124	125	126	77	77	78	79	79	80	81
	95th	123	124	125	126	128	129	130	81	81	82	83	83	84	85
15	90th	121	121	122	124	125	126	127	78	78	79	79	80	81	82
	95th	124	125	126	128	129	130	131	82	82	83	83	84	85	86
16	90th	122	122	123	125	126	127	128	79	79	79	80	81	82	82
	95th	125	126	127	128	130	131	132	83	83	83	84	81	86	86
17	90th	122	123	124	125	126	128	128	79	79	79	80	81	82	82
	95th	126	126	127	129	130	131	132	83	83	83	84	85	86	86

*Blood pressure percentile determined by a single measurement.

SOURCE: "Table 17. Blood Pressure Levels for the 90th and 95th Percentiles of Blood Pressure for Girls Ages 1 to 17 Years," in *Overweight Children and Adolescents: Screen, Access, and Manage,* Centers for Disease Control and Prevention, National Center for Chronic Disease Prevention and Promotion, Division of Nutrition, Physical Activity and Obesity, May 2000, http://www.cdc.gov/nccdphp/dnpa/growthcharts/training/modules/module3/text/hypertension_tables.htm (accessed October 30, 2009)

disease is the leading cause of death among adults, but it rarely occurs in young people. Recently, however, the risk factors—high blood pressure, elevated triglycerides, obesity, and low levels of the "good" high-density lipoprotein (HDL) cholesterol—that are associated with the development of metabolic syndrome have been appearing during childhood.

Joanne S. Harrell, Ann Jessup, and Natasha Greene of the University of North Carolina, Chapel Hill, find in "Changing Our Future: Obesity and the Metabolic Syndrome in Children and Adolescents" (*Journal of Cardiovascular Nursing*, vol. 21, no. 4, July–August 2006), a study of 3,200 boys and girls aged eight to 17 years, that there was a much higher prevalence of risk factors for metabolic syndrome than in previous studies. More than half of the subjects had at least one of six risk factors—obesity, high blood pressure, high triglycerides, low levels of HDL cholesterol, glucose intolerance, and elevated insulin levels—for metabolic syndrome. The most common risk factor, found in more than 43% of the subjects, was a low HDL cholesterol level. More than 27% had two or more risk factors, and 13.5% had at least three risk factors. More girls (16.3%) than boys (10.7%) had at least three risk factors for metabolic syndrome. More than 8% of the children who had three or more factors were between eight and nine years old. Harrell, Jessup, and Greene hope that the results of their study will serve as a warning that without effective intervention many children and teenagers with these risk factors will develop Type 2 diabetes and heart disease.

In "Diagnosis of the Metabolic Syndrome in Children" (*Current Opinion in Lipidology*, vol. 14, no. 6, December 2003), Julia Steinberger of the University of Minnesota Medical School finds that the process of atherosclerosis starts at an early age and is linked to obesity in childhood. Obesity beginning in childhood often precedes hyperinsulinemia, and other components of the metabolic syndrome are also present in children and adolescents. Being overweight during childhood and adolescence is significantly associated with insulin resistance, dyslipidemia (high low-density lipoprotein and triglycerides, and low HDL), and high blood pressure in young adulthood. In view of the increasing prevalence of metabolic syndrome in children and adolescents, Steinberger recommends that "the first approach should focus on prevention of obesity in childhood. More attention should be paid to increasing physical activity and decreasing calorie consumption in this age group. Once obesity is established in a child or adolescent, vigorous clinical efforts should be directed at treating it."

Sarah P. Garnett et al. of the Institute of Endocrinology and Diabetes in Westmead, Australia, observe in "Body Mass Index and Waist Circumference in Midchildhood and Adverse Cardiovascular Disease Risk Clustering in Adolescence" (*American Journal of Clinical Nutrition*, vol. 86, no. 3, September 2007) that overweight and obese eight-year-olds were seven times more likely than their healthy-weight peers to have heart disease risk factors such as high blood pressure, unhealthy cholesterol levels, and elevations in blood sugar and insulin by the age of 15. The researchers opine that their findings—that these risk factors persist and increase over time—underscore the importance of preventing childhood obesity.

Mental Health Consequences

One of the most immediate, distressing, and widespread consequences of being overweight as described by children themselves is social discrimination and low self-esteem. Overweight and obese children and adolescents are at risk for psychological and social adjustment problems such as considering themselves less competent than normal-weight youth in social, athletic, and appearance arenas, and for suffering from overall diminished self-worth. In "Health-Related Quality of Life and Depressive Symptoms in Adolescents with Extreme Obesity Presenting for Bariatric Surgery" (*Pediatrics*, vol. 117, no. 4, April 2006), Meg H. Zeller et al. of the Cincinnati Children's Hospital Medical Center find that obese adolescents seeking bariatric surgery have a severely impaired quality of life compared with healthy-weight adolescents. The researchers analyze measurements of health-related quality of life (HRQoL; this considers physical functioning, emotional well-being, social relations, and school functioning) for 33 extremely obese adolescents and find that the mean score for total self-reported HRQoL was 54.9 for extremely obese adolescents, compared with 83.0 for healthy-weight adolescents.

Lucy Jane Griffiths et al. report in "Obesity and Bullying: Different Effects for Boys and Girls" (*Archives of Disease in Childhood*, vol. 91, no. 2, February 2006) that obese children engage in more bullying behavior, at least in part because they deviate from appearance ideals. Obese boys were more than one and a half times more likely to use their physical dominance to bully other children or to be the victims of bullying than their normal-weight or overweight peers. Obese girls were more likely to be the victims of bullying than their normal-weight or overweight peers.

In "Obesity, Shame, and Depression in School-Aged Children: A Population Study" (*Pediatrics*, vol. 116, no. 3, September 2005), Rickard L. Sjöberg, Kent W. Nilsson, and Jerzy Leppert indicate that depression is common among obese teenagers and largely results from teens' experiences of being shamed. The researchers analyzed data from 4,703 teens aged 15 and 17 years and found that obese teens reported experiencing more symptoms of depression than their normal-weight or overweight peers and had a higher risk of depression. Obese teens were more likely than their normal-weight or overweight peers to say they had been treated in a degrading manner, had been ignored, or had shaming experiences within the past three months. Furthermore, adolescents who reported the highest number of shaming experiences were 11 times more likely to be depressed than those who reported the lowest number of shaming experiences. Sjöberg, Nilsson, and Leppert conclude, "These results suggest that clinical treatment of obesity may sometimes not just be a matter of diet and exercise but also of dealing with issues of shame and social isolation."

Obese children are also absent from school more frequently than their healthy-weight peers. Andrew B. Geier et al. find in "The Relationship between Relative Weight and School Attendance among Elementary Schoolchildren" (*Obesity*, vol. 15, no. 8, August 2007) that on average the healthy-weight students were absent 10.1 days, overweight children missed 10.9 days, and obese children missed 12.2 days. The researchers note that being overweight or obese is a better predictor of absenteeism than the factors (race, socioeconomic status, age, and gender) previously thought to have the best predictive value for school attendance. Even though some of the increased absenteeism may be due to health problems, Geier et al. think that social problems such as fear of being bullied, embarrassed, or excluded account for a considerable amount of the observed absences.

SCREENING AND ASSESSMENT OF OVERWEIGHT CHILDREN AND ADOLESCENTS

In view of the rising prevalence of overweight youth, screening children and adolescents for overweight and risk for overweight has assumed a prominent place in pediatric practice (the medical specialty devoted to the diagnosis and treatment of children) and public health programs. The Recommendations for Preventive Pediatric Health Care by the American Academy of Pediatrics advise a frequent schedule of accurate weight and height measurements to determine whether children require further assessment or treatment for overweight. Screening distinguishes between youths who are not at risk of overweight, at risk of overweight, and overweight. Those deemed to be overweight receive an in-depth medical assessment; those considered at risk are assessed for changes in BMI, blood pressure, and cholesterol levels; and annual screening is advised for those who are not at risk of being overweight.

The comprehensive assessment performed on overweight children and adolescents generally includes obtaining a detailed medical history to identify any underlying medical conditions that may contribute to overweight and analyzing family history for the presence of familial risks for overweight or obesity. Relevant familial factors include the occurrence of obesity, eating

disorders, Type 2 diabetes, heart disease, high blood pressure, and abnormal lipid profiles such as high cholesterol among immediate family members. The assessment may also involve:

- A dietary evaluation to consider the quantity, quality, and timing of food consumed to identify foods and patterns of eating that may lead to excessive calorie intake. A food record or food diary may be used to assess eating habits.

- An evaluation of daily activities. This assessment involves an estimate of time devoted to exercise and activity as well as time spent on sedentary behaviors such as television, video games, and computer use.

- A physical examination to provide information about the extent of overweight and any complications of overweight, including high blood pressure. Children and adolescents with a BMI-for-age at or above the 95th percentile and who are athletic and muscular may be further assessed using the triceps skinfold measurement to assess body fat. A measurement of greater than the 95th percentile indicates that the child has excess fat rather than increased lean body mass or a large frame.

- Laboratory tests, such as cholesterol screening, that are dictated by the degree of overweight, family history, and the results of the physical examination. Table 4.14 shows the range of values for total blood cholesterol and low-density lipoprotein cholesterol that are considered acceptable, borderline, and high.

- A mental health evaluation to determine the readiness of children and adolescents to change behaviors and to identify a history of eating disorders or depression that may require treatment. An assessment of the family's ability to support a child's weight-loss or weight-management efforts may also be performed.

TABLE 4.14

Classification of cholesterol levels in high-risk children and adolescents

	Total cholesterol, ng/dL	LDL cholesterol, ng/dL
Acceptable	<170	<110
Borderline	170–199	110–129
High	Greater than or equal to 200	Greater than or equal to 130

Note: High-risk children are defined as those from families with hypercholesterolemia or premature cardiovascular disease.

SOURCE: "Table 15. Classification of Cholesterol Levels in High-Risk Children and Adolescents," in *Overweight Children and Adolescents: Screen, Assess, and Manage*, Centers for Disease Control and Prevention, National Center for Chronic Disease Prevention and Promotion, Division of Nutrition, Physical Activity and Obesity, 2001, http://www.cdc.gov/nccdphp/dnpa/growthcharts/training/modules/module3/text/cholesterol.htm (accessed October 30, 2009)

Research suggests that mental health evaluations and timely treatment may play a key role in preventing childhood obesity because children with emotional problems are at greater risk of becoming obese as adults. In "Childhood Emotional Problems and Self-Perceptions Predict Weight Gain in a Longitudinal Regression Model" (*BMC Medicine*, vol. 7, no. 46, September 11, 2009), Andrew Ternouth, David Collier, and Barbara Maughan of the Social, Genetic, and Developmental Psychiatry Centre in London, England, examined the records of 6,526 people born in 1970 to determine if weight gain in adulthood could be predicted by childhood emotional problems and self-perceptions. The subjects' BMI was measured by a nurse at age 10 and then self-reported at age 30. Their self-esteem and emotional problems in childhood were also assessed using reliable measures. Ternouth, Collier, and Maughan conclude that "emotional problems, low self-esteem and an external locus of control in childhood predict weight gain into adulthood. This has important clinical implications as it highlights a direction for early intervention strategies that may contribute to efforts to combat the current obesity epidemic."

INTERVENTION AND TREATMENT OF OVERWEIGHT AND OBESITY

In the absence of acute medical necessity, such as with children who are dangerously obese, most health professionals concur that drastic caloric restriction is an inappropriate weight-loss strategy for children who are still growing. Instead, they advise efforts to stabilize body weight with a healthy, balanced diet, increased physical activity, and education about nutrition, food choices, and preparation. This approach is especially effective for children who are just slightly overweight, because maintaining body weight often allows them to outgrow overweight and become normal-weight adults.

When active weight loss is indicated, it is generally for children with a BMI greater than the 95th percentile or those experiencing complications of overweight or obesity. Among children aged two to seven, gradual weight loss of about 1 pound (0.5 kg) per month is advised. Older children with serious health risks who are severely overweight (BMI greater than 35) may be advised to lose between 1 and 2 pounds (0.5 to 0.9 kg) per week.

Many studies confirm that dietary interventions with children and teens are as ineffective long term as they are with adults. In "Clinical Review: Behavioral Interventions to Prevent Childhood Obesity: A Systematic Review and Metaanalyses of Randomized Trial" (*Journal of Clinical Endocrinology and Metabolism*, vol. 93, no. 12, December 2008), Celia C. Kamath et al. of the Mayo Clinic College of Medicine in Rochester, Minnesota, observe that interventions aimed at preventing pediatric obesity had only a small effect on the behaviors they aimed to change and no

significant effect on BMI compared with control groups that did not receive the intervention. The researchers observe that nearly three-quarters of programs that have nutritional outcomes as measures reported positive changes and 64% of interventions aiming to increase physical activity said they achieve this objective. Interventions intended to reduce unhealthy behaviors such as decreasing sedentary behaviors and consumption of dietary fat appeared to be more effective than those promoting positive behaviors such as increasing physical activity and consumption of fruits and vegetables. As might be anticipated, interventions of longer duration (lasting more than six months) produced slightly better results than shorter ones.

Robert I. Berkowitz et al. compared the efficacy of family-based behavioral treatment alone to a combined regimen of family-based behavioral therapy and weight-loss medication among adolescents. The researchers reported their results in "Behavior Therapy and Sibutramine for the Treatment of Adolescent Obesity" (*Journal of the American Medical Association*, vol. 289, no. 14, April 9, 2003). For the first six months of the study, 82 participants aged 13 to 17 with BMIs ranging from 32 to 44 received behavior therapy and sibutramine (an anorexiant medication) or behavior therapy and a placebo (an inactive compound). During the second six months, all participants received behavioral treatment and sibutramine.

During the first phase, behavioral treatment called for participants to attend 13 weekly group sessions followed up by six biweekly group sessions. In the second phase, the group sessions were conducted biweekly from months seven to nine and monthly from months 10 to 12. Parents met in separate group sessions held on the same schedule as the adolescents' meetings. Dietitians, psychologists, or psychiatrists conducted the groups. Participants in both treatment groups were instructed to consume a 1,200- to 1,500-calorie diet of conventional foods, with approximately 30% of their calories derived from fat, 15% from protein, and the remainder from carbohydrates. They were advised to incrementally increase their physical activity with the goal of walking or participating in aerobic activity for 120 minutes per week or more. Participants kept daily eating and activity logs that they submitted at each session.

At the end of the first six months, participants in the behavioral treatment and sibutramine group lost a mean of 17.2 pounds (7.8 kg) and had an 8.5% reduction in BMI, which was significantly more than the weight loss of 7.1 pounds (3.2 kg) and a reduction in BMI of 4% in the behavioral treatment and placebo group. Participants who received behavioral treatment and sibutramine also reported significantly less hunger. From months seven to 12, participants initially treated with sibutramine maintained their weight loss with continued use of the medication, whereas those who switched from placebo to sibutramine lost an additional 2.9 pounds (1.3 kg). Berkowitz et al. explain the behavioral treatment and sibutramine participants' failure to lose further weight during the second phase of the study as consistent with the observation that weight loss tends to plateau in obese adults after six months of treatment with behavior therapy or pharmacotherapy.

Berkowitz et al. conclude that weight-loss medications may be of benefit to adolescents. However, they caution that their use must be carefully monitored in adolescents, as in adults, to control increases in blood pressure and pulse rate. Absent the many large-scale studies necessary to confirm the safety and effectiveness of pharmacological treatment of obesity in adolescents, Berkowitz et al. advise that "medications for weight loss should be used only on an experimental basis in adolescents and children."

William H. Dietz of the CDC acknowledges in "What Constitutes Successful Weight Management in Adolescents?" (*Annals of Internal Medicine*, vol. 145, no. 2, July 18, 2006) that even though Berkowitz et al. demonstrate the significant benefits of weight-loss drug therapy, it is vitally important to carefully weigh the decision to prescribe drug therapy, because the long-term risks or benefits of drug therapy in children and adolescents are still as yet unknown.

Some adolescents who are obese may be treated with weight-loss surgery. The NIH criteria for adolescents aged 13 to 17 are the same as those applied to adults—a BMI greater than or equal to 40 or a BMI greater than or equal to 35 with one or more comorbidity (a coexisting serious medical condition such as Type 2 diabetes, hypertension, or obstructive sleep apnea). In "Morbidity in Obese Adolescents Who Meet the Adult NIH Criteria for Bariatric Surgery" (*Journal of Pediatric Surgery*, vol. 44, no. 10, October 2009), Evan P. Nadler et al. compare the medical records of 134 adolescents who met the NIH criteria for weight-loss surgery to the records of 4,736 adolescents who did not meet the criteria to determine the differences between these populations and whether stricter criteria should be adopted for teens. The researchers find that "adolescents who meet NIH consensus criteria for weight loss surgery in adults require specialized health services and have functional impairment. Thus, we advocate the use of the standard adult criteria defined by the NIH as the initial screening requirements so that enhanced access to weight loss surgery for morbidly obese adolescents may be achieved."

Because maintenance (keeping pounds lost off over time) is an issue for adults and children, Denise E. Wilfley et al. examine in "Efficacy of Maintenance Treatment Approaches for Childhood Overweight" (*Journal of the American Medical Association*, vol. 298, no. 14, October 10, 2007) how effectively children and parents who completed a five-month weight-loss program and

lost an average of 11% of their bodyweight maintained their weight loss. Children who received the most intensive follow-up, which included socializing with more physically active peers, learning how to cope with teasing, and improving their body image, fared the best in terms of maintaining weight loss. However, at the one- and two-year follow-up, many had regained the weight they had lost.

Educating Parents

Researchers agree that primary prevention is the strategy with the greatest potential for reversing the alarming rise in overweight and obesity among children and teens. Public health educators recommend counseling parents and caregivers about healthy eating habits for children. They advise offering children a variety of healthful foods, in reasonable quantities, to assist children to make wise food choices. Children should be encouraged, but not forced, to sample new foods and should not be pressured to clean their plates. No foods or food groups should be entirely off-limits, or children may become fixated on obtaining the forbidden foods.

Even though it is difficult to impress on children the future health risks associated with excess weight, parents should be informed that obese children are more likely to suffer from diabetes, heart, and joint diseases such as osteoarthritis, as well as breast and colon cancer. Adults should model healthy habits by consuming no more than 30% of calories from fat, exercising regularly, and limiting time spent in front of the television. Health educators are especially eager to reduce children's television viewing, with its destructive blend of junk-food advertising and enforced inactivity. Finally, health professionals caution that food should not be used to punish or reward behavior or as a way to comfort or console children. The undivided attention of a parent or caregiver or an expression of sympathy, reassurance, or encouragement may satisfy a child's need better than an ice cream cone or an order of French fries.

In "Factors Associated with Parental Readiness to Make Changes for Overweight Children" (*Pediatrics*, vol. 116, no. 1, July 2005), Kyung E. Rhee et al. find that parents are not always receptive to making lifestyle changes that could help their overweight children lose weight—particularly if the parents do not see their child's weight as a health issue. The researchers studied 151 parents and found that 44% of parents of children who were overweight or obese did not see their child's weight as a problem and as a result were not planning on instituting lifestyle changes soon. Another 17% of parents did recognize that their child had a problem and were considering making behavioral or lifestyle changes, but not soon. Rhee et al. indicate that parents of children who were eight years old or older were more likely to be ready to address their child's weight issue than parents of younger children. The same was true of parents who believed their child's weight was a health issue; they were nearly 10 times more likely than other parents to say they were ready to take actions such as increasing their children's fruit and vegetable consumption, limiting television time, and encouraging exercise. Parents were also more open to change if they viewed themselves as overweight.

EATING DISORDERS

Overweight and obesity are among the most stigmatizing and least socially acceptable conditions in childhood and adolescence. Society, culture, and the media send children powerful messages about body weight and shape ideals. For girls these messages include the "thin ideal" and encouragement to diet and exercise. Messages to boys emphasize a muscular body and pressure to body build and even use potentially harmful dietary supplements and steroids. Gender has not been identified as a specific risk factor for obesity in children, but the pressure placed on girls to be thin may put them at a greater risk for developing eating-disordered behaviors. Even though society presents boys with a wider range of acceptable body images, they are also at risk for developing disordered eating and body image disturbances.

Adolescence is a developmental period marked by great physical change, and it is a time when many teens subject themselves to painful scrutiny. Uneven growth, puberty, and sexual maturation may make teens feel awkward and self-conscious about their bodies. Teenaged girls are especially susceptible to developing negative body images—ignoring other qualities and focusing exclusively on appearance to measure their self-worth. This single-minded, and often distorted, destructive focus can result in lowered self-esteem and increased risk for mental health problems, including eating disorders. The 2007 YRBSS found that 17.7% of high school students engaged in dangerous dieting behaviors. (See Table 4.8.)

Who Is at Risk?

Even though there are biological, genetic, and familial factors that predispose certain people to eating disorders such as anorexia nervosa (intense fear of becoming fat even when dangerously underweight) and bulimia (recurrent episodes of binge eating followed by purging to prevent weight gain), the emergence of these disorders is triggered by environmental factors. Chief among the environmental triggers is body image. Many researchers and health professionals believe that teenaged girls who identify with the idealized body images projected throughout American culture are at an increased risk for eating disorders.

Other risk factors are peer group pressures and sociocultural forces such as the fashion and entertainment industries and the media. The National Eating Disorders Association (NEDA) identifies media definitions of attractiveness, beauty, and health as among the myriad factors contributing to the rise of eating disorders. In the landmark survey *The Commonwealth Fund Survey of the Health of Adolescent Girls* (November 1997, http://www.commonwealthfund.org/usr_doc/Schoen_adolescentgirls.pdf?section=4039), Cathy Schoen et al. find that the media are girls' primary source of information about women's health issues. In another study, "Body Image, Eating Disorders, and the Media" (*Adolescent Medicine State of the Art Review*, vol. 19, no. 3, December 2008), Marjorie J. Hogan and Victor C. Strasburger suggest that media images and articles contribute to body dissatisfaction and increase perceived pressures to be thin. The researchers also opine that in some vulnerable children and adolescents, such media exposure may promote disordered eating or increase the risk of developing an eating disorder.

Historically, most adolescents with eating disorders have been first- or second-born white females from middle- to upper-class families. Girls who suffer from anorexia are often academically successful, with athletic prowess or training in dance. They tend to be perfectionists, well behaved, emotionally dependent, socially anxious, and intent on receiving approval from others. Adolescent girls with bulimia are generally more extroverted and socially involved. According to the Eating Disorders Coalition for Research, Policy, and Action, in the fact sheet "Facts about Eating Disorders: What the Research Shows" (May 20, 2009, http://www.eating disorderscoalition.org/documents/TalkingpointsEating DisordersFactSheetUpdated5-20-09.pdf), in the early 21st century the occurrence of eating disorders is increasing among younger children and throughout diverse ethnic and sociocultural groups.

NEDA confirms in "Research Results on Eating Disorders in Diverse Populations" (2005, http://www.nationa leatingdisorders.org/nedaDir/files/documents/handouts/RsrchPop.pdf) and "Statistics: Eating Disorders and Their Precursors" (2007, http://www.nationaleating disorders.org/nedaDir/files/documents/handouts/Stats.pdf) that a preoccupation with thinness and dieting cuts across all racial and ethnic lines and begins at an early age. One study reports that 42% of first- to third-grade girls said they wanted to be thinner, and another finds that 81% of 10-year-olds feared becoming fat. A survey of female college students finds that 91% had attempted to control their weight by dieting, and 22% said they were "often" or "always" dieting.

Which Variables Are Associated with Dieting, Overweight, and Eating Disorders?

Dianne Neumark-Sztainer and Peter J. Hannan of the University of Minnesota, Minneapolis, analyzed a representative sample of 6,728 adolescents in grades five through 12 who completed the Commonwealth Fund surveys about the health of adolescent girls and boys. The results of the research were detailed in the landmark study "Weight-Related Behaviors among Adolescent Girls and Boys: Results from a National Survey" (*Archives of Pediatrics and Adolescent Medicine*, vol. 154, no. 6, June 2000). The research aimed to assess the prevalence of dieting and disordered eating among adolescents; the sociodemographic, psychosocial, and behavioral variables that were associated with dieting and disordered eating; and whether adolescents report having discussed weight-related issues with their health care providers. (Neumark-Sztainer and Hannan defined disordered eating as weight-related behaviors such as anorexia and bulimia nervosa, self-induced vomiting, binge eating, inappropriate or extreme dieting, and obesity.)

Subjects were assessed by calculating their BMI and eliciting weight-related attitudes and behaviors. For example, dieting was assessed by asking questions such as "Have you ever been on a diet?" and "Why were you dieting?" Behaviors were assessed by posing a question such as "Have you ever binged and purged (which is when you eat a lot of food and then make yourself throw up, vomit, or take something that makes you have diarrhea) or not?" Subjects were also asked "Right now, how would you describe yourself?" to gain an understanding of their perceptions of their weight. Psychosocial and behavioral variables including self-esteem, stress, depression, substance use (of tobacco, alcohol, or illegal drugs), and level of physical activity were also measured and scored using standardized questionnaires and inventories.

Neumark-Sztainer and Hannan reveal that 24% of the population was overweight, with 45% of the girls and 20% of the boys reporting a history of dieting. Twenty percent (13% of girls and 7% of boys) of the population reported disordered eating, which was associated with a range of behavioral variables, including overweight, low self-esteem, depression, suicidal ideation (thoughts, intent, or plans to take one's own life), and substance use. Nearly half of the adolescents recalled discussions about nutrition with a health care provider, but just 24% of girls and 15% of boys said they had discussed eating disorders with a health care provider.

Younger girls (grades five through eight) were significantly less likely to engage in dieting and disordered eating than older girls (grades nine through 12), and dieting was reported by 31.1% of the fifth-grade girls and increased to 62.1% of the 12th-grade girls. The prevalence of disordered eating was highest among Hispanic girls and lowest among non-Hispanic African-American girls; and the

prevalence of dieting was highest among non-Hispanic white girls and lowest among non-Hispanic African-American girls. Neumark-Sztainer and Hannan observe that the prevalence rates of dieting behaviors were lowest among African-American girls, suggesting that African-American girls may experience lower levels of body dissatisfaction than white girls.

Alcohol and drug use were directly associated with dieting and disordered eating among girls and boys; however, the association between substance use and disordered eating was stronger than the association between substance use and dieting. Tobacco use was associated with dieting and disordered eating among girls, but not among boys.

Neumark-Sztainer and Hannan note that "about half of the youth reported that a health care provider had discussed nutrition and weight issues with them" and observe that even though the content of such discussions was unclear, "at least the youth remembered that these issues had been discussed." They conclude that "the high rates of dieting and disordered eating behaviors, coupled with the high prevalence of obesity found in this and previous studies, indicate a clear need for interventions aimed at the primary and secondary prevention of weight-related disorders. The large scope of the problem and the complexity of the issues at hand indicate that there is a need for multiple interventions at the individual and familial level (e.g., within clinical practices), at the group level (e.g., within school settings), and at the community or larger societal level (e.g., changes in the physical and social environment)."

In "Family, Peer, and Media Predictors of Becoming Eating Disordered" (*Archives of Pediatric and Adolescent Medicine*, vol. 162, no. 6, June 2008), a study to identify the predictors of eating disorders in adolescents, Alison E. Field et al. confirm some of the findings reported by Neumark-Sztainer and Hannan and discover other risk factors. The researchers looked at whether various suspected risk factors for eating disorders were independently associated with starting to binge, purge, or both binge and purge over the course of seven years in 12,534 subjects in the Growing Up Today Study, who were nine to 15 years old at the beginning of the study.

Field et al. find that the rates and risk factors varied by sex and age. Girls younger than 14 years whose mothers had a history of an eating disorder were nearly three times more likely than their peers to start purging at least weekly, but a maternal history of an eating disorder was unrelated to the risk of starting to binge or purge in girls older than the age of 14. Frequent dieting and striving to look like people in the media were independent predictors of binge eating in females of all ages. In males, negative comments about weight by fathers predicted starting to binge at least weekly.

CHAPTER 5
DIETARY TREATMENT FOR OVERWEIGHT AND OBESITY

We rarely repent of having eaten too little.

—Thomas Jefferson

Americans have long been consumed with losing weight, seemingly willing to suffer deprivation and to embrace each new diet that debuts—even if the "new diet" is simply a twist on a previous weight-loss plan. The fixation with weight loss is so long-standing that even the word *diet* has assumed a new meaning. As a verb, diet means to eat and drink a prescribed selection of foods; however, since the latter part of the 20th century dieting became synonymous with an effort to lose weight.

During the 19th century fashionable body shapes and sizes varied from decade to decade, but most periods celebrated plumpness as a sign of health and prosperity and considered being thin a sign of poverty and ill health. At the turn of the 20th century rising interest in dieting seemingly coincided with some of the social and cultural changes that would make it necessary: food became increasingly plentiful, and sedentary work and public transportation reduced Americans' level of physical activity. In *Fat History: Bodies and Beauty in the Modern West* (1997), Peter N. Stearns explains how fat became "a turn-of-the-century target" with anti-fat sentiments intensifying from the 1920s to the 21st century.

Stearns asserts that the contemporary obsession with fat arose in tandem with the dramatic growth in consumer culture, women's increasing equality, and changes in women's sexual and maternal roles. Dieting, with its emphasis on deprivation, self-control, and moral discipline, seemed the perfect antidote to the indulgence of consumer culture, and Stearns contends that "weight morality bore disproportionately on women precisely because of their growing independence, or seeming independence, from other standards."

Fashion trends fueled anti-fat sentiments as women shed the corsets that had created the illusion of narrow waists and aspired to duplicate the wasp-waisted silhouettes by becoming slimmer. The shorter, close-fitting "flapper" dresses of the 1920s revealed women's legs and rekindled their desire to be slender. The emergence of the first actuarial tables (data compiled to assess insurance risk and formulate life insurance premiums), which showed the relationship between overweight and premature mortality (death), reinforced the growing sentiment that thinness was the key to health and longevity. Capitalizing on the increasing interest in monitoring and reducing body weight, the new Detecto and Health-o-Meter bathroom scales enabled people to weigh themselves regularly in the privacy of their own homes, as opposed to relying on periodic visits to physicians' offices or pharmacies to use the balance scales.

SELECTED MILESTONES IN THE HISTORY OF DIETING

Not unlike fashion trends, the history of dieting reveals the emergence and popularity of specific diets, which over time are cast aside in favor of different approaches but then are recycled and resurface as "new and miraculous." The first low-carbohydrate diet to earn popular acclaim was described by William Banting (1797–1878) in the 1860s. In *Letter on Corpulence, Addressed to the Public* (1863), Banting, then 66 years old, claimed that by adhering to his low-carbohydrate regimen he was never hungry and had lost 46 pounds (20.9 kg) of his initial 202 pounds (91.6 kg) in one year.

The early 1900s marked the beginning of diets that restricted calories. *Diet and Health, with Key to the Calories* (1918) by Lulu Hunt Peters (1873–1930) advised readers to think in terms of consuming calories rather than food items and remained in print for 20 years. Peters wrote, "You should know and use the word calorie as frequently, or more frequently, than you use the foot, yard, quart, gallon and so forth ... hereafter you are going to eat calories of food. Instead of saying one slice of bread, or a piece of pie, you will say 100 calories of bread, 350 calories of pie." The 1920s saw the rise of very-low-calorie diets to promote weight loss. For example, the Hollywood 18-day diet advised just 585 calories per day, which required the dieter to eat mostly citrus fruit.

Throughout the 1920s and 1930s the low-calorie diet remained a popular weight-loss strategy. However, other approaches, such as food-limiting plans that restricted dieters to just one or two foods (e.g., lamb chops, pineapples, grapefruits, or cabbage), were introduced, as were diets that prescribed combinations of certain foods and forbid others. For example, some diets prohibited eating protein and carbohydrates together; others were more specific, advising which vegetables could be served together. The 1930s also saw the first condemnations of carbohydrates as causes of overweight. A high-fat, low-fiber diet consisting primarily of milk and meat was thought to be protective against disease. The Italian poet Filippo Tommaso Marinetti (1876–1944) exhorted Italians to forgo their pasta because he claimed it made them sluggish, pessimistic, and fat.

In 1943 the U.S. Department of Agriculture (USDA) released the "Basic Seven" food guide in the *National Wartime Nutrition Guide*. It emphasized a patriotic wartime austerity diet that included between two to four servings of protein-rich meat and milk products, three servings of fruits or vegetables, and the rather vague recommendations of "bread, flour, and cereals every day and butter, fortified margarine—some daily."

In 1948 Esther Manz (1908–1996), a 208-pound (94-kg) homemaker, established Take Off Pounds Sensibly (TOPS; http://www.tops.org/), the first support-group program for weight loss. Manz was inspired to start the program after she attended childbirth preparation classes, where women benefited from mutual support and encouragement. As of January 2010, the annual membership of $26 supported the international nonprofit organization, which is based in Milwaukee, Wisconsin. Along with weekly meetings and private weigh-ins, TOPS participants are encouraged to adhere to a calorie-counting meal plan based on a program developed by the American Dietetics Association. In 2009 TOPS (2010, http://www.tops.org/AboutTOPS.aspx) had about 170,000 members in nearly 10,000 chapters worldwide. Members who achieve their weight goals become KOPS (Keep Off Pounds Sensibly) and often keep attending meetings to maintain their weight and serve as role models for others.

In 1950 the American physician and biophysicist John W. Gofman (1918–2007) hypothesized that blood cholesterol was involved in the rise in coronary heart disease. Gofman found not only that heart attacks correlated with elevated levels of cholesterol but also that the cholesterol was contained in one lipoprotein particle:

low-density lipoprotein (LDL). Early reports of the connection between overweight and elevated blood cholesterol intensified interest in weight loss, which was now promoted as a strategy for preventing heart disease. During the late 1950s injections of human chorionic gonadotropin, which was derived from the urine of pregnant women or animals, enjoyed fleeting popularity as a weight-loss agent; however, it was quickly proven entirely ineffective. Fad diets, such as a diet advocating the consumption of several bananas to satisfy sugar cravings and another that involved ingesting a blend of oils to boost metabolism, continued to lure Americans seeking quick weight loss. In 1959 the American Medical Association called dieting a "national neurosis."

In 1960 Metrecal, the first high-protein beverage, was widely advertised by the Mead Johnson Company as a weight-reducing aid. It was originally sold as a powder, which when mixed with 1 quart (0.9 L) of water yielded four 8-ounce (237-mL) glasses intended to serve as four meals per day, totaling 900 calories. The powder was made from milk, soy flour, starch, corn oil, yeast, vitamins, coconut oil, and vanilla, chocolate, or butterscotch flavoring. The low-calorie regimen enabled a dieter to lose 10 pounds (4.5 kg) in a few weeks, without the trouble of meal preparation or counting calories. Later, Metrecal was sold in a premixed, liquid form that could be consumed right from the can. Mead Johnson made over $10 million selling Metrecal in the first two years. It was the forerunner of liquid diet products such as Slim-Fast.

The 1960s also witnessed the birth of Overeaters Anonymous (OA) and Weight Watchers. OA began as a support group modeled on the 12-step emotional, physical, and spiritual recovery program used by Alcoholics Anonymous. In "About OA" (2010, http://www.oa.org/new-to-oa/about-oa.php), the OA notes that about 6,500 OA groups meet each week in more than 75 countries. In 1961 Jean Nidetch (1923–), an overweight housewife in New York City, invited a few friends to her home to gain support for her efforts to diet and overcome an "obsession for cookies." From this first meeting, the friends gathered weekly, offering one another encouragement and sharing advice and ideas. The weekly support meetings proved successful, providing motivation and encouragement for long-term weight loss. In 1963 Nidetch incorporated Weight Watchers, and hundreds of people turned out for its first meeting. Weight Watchers grew in both size and popularity by developing nutritious and convenient eating plans and promoting exercise, cookbooks, healthful prepared food, and a magazine. The company became so successful that in 1978 it was acquired by the H. J. Heinz Company. Weight Watchers states in "About Us: History and Philosophy" (2010, http://www.weightwatchers.com/about/his/hello.aspx) that 50,000 Weight Watcher groups meet weekly.

Two best-selling diet books also debuted during the 1960s. The first was Herman Taller's *Calories Don't Count* (1961), which told dieters to avoid carbohydrates and refined sugars and to eat a high-protein diet that included large quantities of unsaturated fat. The second was Irwin Maxwell Stillman and Samm Sinclair Baker's *The Doctor's Quick Weight Loss Diet* (1967), which instructed dieters to avoid carbohydrates altogether and to consume just meat, poultry, fish, cheese, eggs, and water. Even though Taller and Stillman and Baker were not the first to tout low-carbohydrate diets, they introduced the first modern high-protein weight-loss diets. Taller's career as a diet guru ended abruptly in 1967, when he was convicted of mail fraud for the sale of safflower capsules as weight-loss aids. Stillman and Baker, however, followed up their wildly successful first book with several other additional weight-loss titles, including *The Doctor's Quick Teenage Diet* (1971), one of the first diet books to address the needs of overweight adolescents. High-protein, low-carbohydrate diets washed down by liberal amounts of alcohol were also advocated by other books from the 1960s, including Gardener Jameson's *The Drinking Man's Diet* (1965) and Sidney Petrie's *Martinis and Whipped Cream: The New Carbo-Cal Way to Lose Weight and Stay Slim* (1966) and *The Lazy Lady's Easy Diet: A Fast-Action Plan to Lose Weight Quickly for Sustained Slenderness and Youthful Attractiveness* (1969).

During this same decade, chemically processed, non-nutritive sweeteners were marketed as calorie- and guilt-free substitutes that enabled dieters to enjoy many of their favorite sweet treats. Saccharin, which is 300 times sweeter than sugar, was the first artificial sweetener to be widely used in diet foods and beverages. Other chemically processed, artificial, and nonnutritive sweeteners followed, including cyclamate, which was withdrawn from the U.S. market in 1969 because research findings in animals suggested that it might increase the risk of bladder cancer in humans. According to the National Cancer Institute, in "Artificial Sweeteners and Cancer" (August 5, 2009, http://www.cancer.gov/cancertopics/factsheet/Risk/artificial-sweeteners), recent animal studies have failed to demonstrate that cyclamate is a carcinogen (a substance known to cause cancer) or a cocarcinogen (a substance that enhances the effect of a cancer-causing substance); regardless, cyclamate is not approved for commercial use as a food additive in the United States.

In 1972 the American cardiologist Robert Atkins (1930–2003) published *Dr. Atkins' Diet Revolution: The High Calorie Way to Stay Thin Forever*, which provided a new explanation about how an extremely low-carbohydrate diet targets insulin to promote weight loss. Atkins called insulin, the hormone that regulates blood sugar levels, a "fat-producing hormone." He asserted that most overeaters are continually in a state of hyperinsulinism primed and ever-ready to convert excess carbohydrates to fat. As a result, they have excess circulating insulin, which primes the body to store fat. Atkins contended that when people with hyperinsulinism dieted to lose weight—especially when they reduced their fat intake and increased carbohydrate consumption—their efforts were doomed to fail. He claimed that dieters could alter their metabolism and burn fat by inducing a state of ketosis (the accumulation of ketones from partly digested fats due to inadequate carbohydrate intake) that they monitored by testing their urine for the presence of ketones. Dieters who were tired of limiting portion size, weighing and measuring their foods, counting calories, and assiduously avoiding fatty foods such as steak, bacon, butter, cheese, and heavy cream embraced the low-carbohydrate diet with religious fervor.

The high-protein, low-carbohydrate diet not only was satisfying but also produced the immediate benefit of weight loss through water loss because the body flushes the waste products of protein digestion in the form of urine. Especially during the early weeks of dieting this additional weight loss delivered a psychological boost to dieters and provided the motivation to continue. Many researchers and health professionals agreed with Atkins's premise that sharply limiting carbohydrate intake can help curb the appetite by maintaining even levels of insulin and preventing the insulin surges and blood sugar drops that may trigger hunger. For example, in "The Effects of High Protein Diets on Thermogenesis, Satiety, and Weight Loss: A Critical Review" (*Journal of the American College of Nutrition*, vol. 23, no. 5, October 2004), Thomas L. Halton and Frank B. Hu of the Harvard School of Public Health observe that there is considerable evidence that high-protein diets, such as the Atkins regimen, increase satiety. David S. Weigle et al. arrive at the same conclusion in "A High-Protein Diet Induces Sustained Reductions in Appetite, Ad Libitum Caloric Intake, and Body Weight Despite Compensatory Changes in Diurnal Plasma Leptin and Ghrelin Concentrations" (*American Journal of Clinical Nutrition*, vol. 82, no. 1, July 2005). The researchers posit that the increased satiety produced by high-protein diets may help explain the weight loss produced by low-carbohydrate diets.

Atkins and his devotees were celebrating weight loss, good health, and improved mood as a result of the low-carbohydrate diet, but nutritionists and health professionals were countering by trumpeting the benefits of low-fat diets that were high in complex carbohydrates and fiber. Fat was demonized, and nutritionists pointed dieters to the USDA Food Guide Pyramid (http://www.mypyramid.gov/), which advised using fats sparingly. (The updated 2005 USDA Food Guide Pyramid continued to promote a low-fat diet and minimal use of fats and oils.) Critics of the low-carbohydrate regimen were concerned about the long-term health consequences of the high-fat diet and wondered if it might elevate cholesterol and triglyceride levels in people who by virtue of being overweight were already at increased risk for heart disease. There were also concerns that high-protein diets might cause kidney damage or bone loss over time. Rigorous research to compare the effectiveness and assess the health outcomes of low-carbohydrate and low-fat diets was not conducted until the late 1990s. Even though Atkins enjoyed tremendous celebrity, published a series of weight-loss books, and oversaw the sale of food products bearing his name, his significant contributions to the scientific understanding of nutrition and weight loss were not fully appreciated until the year preceding his death in 2003.

The 1970s also witnessed several fad diets. Robert Linn's *The Last Chance Diet—When Everything Else Has Failed* (1976) advised a protein-sparing fast, which was so dangerously deficient in essential nutrients that several deaths were attributed to it. In *The Complete Scarsdale Medical Diet Plus Dr. Tarnower's Lifetime Keep-Slim Program* (1978), Herman Tarnower (1910–1980) advocated a fat-free, high-protein diet that allowed 700 calories per day.

At the close of the 1970s, Nathan Pritikin's (1915–1985) *The Pritikin Program for Diet and Exercise* (1979) championed a nearly fat-free diet that consisted of fresh and cooked fruits and vegetables, whole grains, breads and pasta, and small amounts of lean meat, fish, and poultry, in concert with daily aerobic exercise. Advocating heart health and fitness, in 1975 Pritikin opened the Pritikin Longevity Center, where people could learn to modify not only their diet but also their lifestyle. Even though Pritikin's plan, which essentially eliminated fat from the diet, was considered by many health professionals too extreme to gain long-term adherents, Pritikin enjoyed as loyal a following as did Atkins.

During the 1980s Judy Mazel (1943–2007) resurrected the notion of specific food combinations as central to weight loss in *The Beverly Hills Diet* (1981). Mazel asserted that eating foods together, such as protein and carbohydrates, destroyed digestive enzymes and caused weight gain and poor digestion. Her diet featured an abundance of fruit, and some observers speculated that weight loss attributable to the diet resulted from the combined effects of caloric restriction and fluid loss resulting from diarrhea. Celebrity endorsements and Mazel's frequent media interviews stimulated interest in the diet.

In 1983 Jenny Craig (1932–) launched a weight-loss program that would become one of the world's two largest diet companies (the other being Weight Watchers). With 600 centers in North America, Australia, New Zealand, Puerto Rico, and Guam, the company (2010, http://www.jennycraig.com/corporate/media/profile/) that bears her name sells prepared foods, along with other weight-loss materials. The company offers telephone and online support and home delivery of food and support materials. In 2002 the company founders Jenny

Craig and Sid Craig sold their majority stake in the company to ACI Capital Co. and MidOcean Capital Partners Inc., but retained 20% interest in the company. Celebrity endorsements, including paid spokespeople such as Kirstie Alley (1951–) and Valerie Bertinelli (1960–), have helped promote the program.

The 1990s served up so-called new and revised versions of high-protein, high-fat, and low-carbohydrate diets and the low-fat diet as well as an update of Mazel's Beverly Hills diet. The cardiologist Dean Ornish (1953–) rekindled enthusiasm for low-fat eating with *Eat More, Weigh Less: Dr. Dean Ornish's Life Choice Program for Losing Weight Safely While Eating Abundantly* (1993). Atkins's 1999 update of *Dr. Atkins' New Diet Revolution*, which offered advice about how to achieve total wellness and weight loss, spent more than four years on the *New York Times* best-seller list and won over a new generation of dieters. Ornish's approach was directly opposed to Atkins's—he espoused the health benefits of vegetarianism and limiting dietary fat to just 10% of the total daily calories. However, both physicians took a holistic approach to health and weight loss by encouraging readers to engage in moderate exercise, foster social support, and reconnect with themselves to support their physical and emotional well-being.

The diet that generated the most fanfare during the 1990s was by the biochemist Barry Sears (1947–), who published *The Zone: A Dietary Road Map* (1995). Sears's high-protein, low-carbohydrate plan promised that by eating the correct ratio of protein, fat, and carbohydrates dieters would lose weight permanently, avoid disease, enhance mental productivity, achieve maximum physical performance, balance and control insulin levels, and enter "that mysterious but very real state in which your body and mind work together at their ultimate best."

From the 1980s into the 2000s, several new noncaloric sweeteners were marketed. Aspartame and acesulfame K were approved by the U.S. Food and Drug Administration (FDA) in 1981 and 1988, respectively. In 1999 the FDA approved the noncaloric sweetener sucralose for general use. Sucralose has gained popularity because it is derived from and tastes like sugar, has no aftertaste, does not promote tooth decay, and is deemed safe for use by pregnant women and diabetics, as well as by those in the general population who are trying to cut down on their sugar intake.

In 2002 the FDA approved neotame, another nonnutritive sweetener, for use as a general-purpose sweetener. Neotame is approximately 7,000 to 13,000 times sweeter than sugar and has been approved for use in food products including baked goods, nonalcoholic beverages (including soft drinks), chewing gum, confections and frostings, frozen desserts, gelatins and puddings, jams and jellies, processed fruits and fruit juices, toppings, and syrups.

In 2008 the FDA approved the sale of stevia, a naturally occurring, zero-calorie sweetener, as a sugar substitute. Stevia is sold in various forms: in combination with other naturally occurring flavors and sweeteners, such as the sugar alcohol erythritol, as well as on its own. Because it has a negligible effect on blood glucose, it is an attractive sugar alternative for people on low-carbohydrate diets.

However, some researchers think sugar substitutes may sabotage dieters by interfering with the body's own innate ability to monitor calorie consumption based on a food's flavor: sweet or savory. Susan E. Swithers, Alicia Doerflinger, and Terry L. Davidson of Purdue University indicate in "Consistent Relationships between Sensory Properties of Savory Snack Foods and Calories Influence Food Intake in Rats" (*International Journal of Obesity*, vol. 30, no. 11, November 2006) that absent sensory clues about the relative caloric value of a food, both animals and humans may overeat and as a result become overweight.

Since the turn of the 21st century, the fiery debate about the merits of low-carbohydrate and low-fat diets has intensified, with both sides citing scientific evidence to support the supremacy of one diet as the healthier and more effective weight-loss strategy. American cardiologist Arthur Agatston (1947–) offered a kind of compromise between the two regimens in *The South Beach Diet: The Delicious, Doctor-Designed, Foolproof Plan for Fast and Healthy Weight Loss* (2003). Agatston condemned simple carbohydrates, such as white flour and white sugar, citing them as the source of the continuous cravings that sabotage dieters, but did not eliminate complex carbohydrates from the diet. (Carbohydrates are classified as simple or complex. The classification depends on the chemical structure of the particular food source and reflects how quickly the sugar is digested and absorbed. Simple carbohydrates have one or two sugars, whereas complex carbohydrates have three or more.) Agatston's diet program was a modified carbohydrate plan that recommended plenty of high-fiber foods, lean proteins, and healthful fats, while cutting back on, but not entirely banishing, bread, rice, pastas, and fruits.

Marian Burros notes in "Make That Steak a Bit Smaller, Atkins Advises Today's Dieters" (*New York Times*, January 18, 2004) that the Atkins organization, which had previously advised dieters to satisfy their appetite with ample quantities of steak, bacon, eggs, heavy cream, and other saturated fats, modified its position in 2004. According to Burros, Colette Heimowitz, the director of research and education for Atkins Nutritionals, advised health professionals and dieters that just 20% of a dieter's calories should come from saturated fat. However, she and other Atkins representatives asserted that this was not a change in the diet itself but simply a revision in communicating how the diet should be followed. Diet industry observers maintained that the warning to reduce

the consumption of saturated fat was in direct response to the debut of the South Beach diet and other low-carbohydrate regimens that called for less saturated fat. Heimowitz asserted that the change was made because "we want physicians to feel comfortable with this diet, and we want people who are going to their physicians with this diet to feel comfortable."

Americans' enthusiasm for low-carbohydrate diets cooled during 2004, and Atkins Nutritionals Inc., the company that catapulted low-carbohydrate diets into a national obsession, filed for bankruptcy court protection in August 2005. Many dieters abandoned low-carbohydrate diets in favor of regimens focused on the glycemic index (GI)—a ranking system for carbohydrates according to their immediate effect on blood glucose levels, in which a numerical value is assigned to a carbohydrate-rich food based on its average increase in blood glucose.

In 2004 diet books that extolled the virtues of the low-GI diet—including Michel Montignac's *Eat Yourself Slim* (1999), Rick Gallop's *The G.I. Diet: The Easy, Healthy Way to Permanent Weight Loss* (2002), and H. Leighton Steward et al.'s *The New Sugar Busters!: Cut Sugar to Trim Fat* (2003)—became quite popular. Proponents of low-GI diets observed that the regimen not only produced weight loss but also improved overall health by reducing the risk for both Type 2 diabetes and cardiovascular disease.

Even though diet industry observers cannot predict the next craze, they are certain that a replacement for the low-carbohydrate diet will emerge. Contenders among the diets and diet books that debuted since 2005 include:

- *French Women Don't Get Fat* (2005) by Mireille Guiliano contends that the French are able to eat croissants and chocolate without becoming overweight because they take time to savor flavors and eat thoughtfully.

- *The Fat Resistance Diet* (2005) by Leo Galland advises a diet rich in fish and other low-fat protein, vegetables, fruit, nuts, and green tea to help relieve inflammation and restore sensitivity to leptin, a hormone involved in fat metabolism that sends satiety signals to the brain.

- *The Perricone Weight Loss Diet: A Simple 3-Part Plan to Lose the Fat, the Wrinkles, and the Years* (2005) by Nicholas Perricone recommends a diet composed of low- as opposed to high-GI foods and healthful (omega-3-rich) versus unhealthful fats.

- *The 3-Hour Diet: How Low Carb Makes You Fat and Timing Will Sculpt You Slim* (2005) by Jorge Cruise recommends eating frequently and timing meals and snacks to "stoke the metabolism."

- *The Diet Code: Revolutionary Weight-Loss Secrets from Da Vinci and the Golden Ratio* (2006) by Stephen

Lanzalotta promotes Mediterranean-style eating and emphasizes bread, fish, cheese, vegetables, meat, nuts, and wine.

- *The Total Wellbeing Diet* (2006) by Manny Noakes details a low-carbohydrate, high-protein diet that was developed by the Commonwealth Scientific and Industrial Research Organization to help Australians lose weight.

- *The Rice Diet Cookbook: 150 Easy, Everyday Recipes and Inspirational Success Stories from the Rice Diet Program Community* (2007) by Kitty Gurkin Rosati counters the low-carbohydrate diet trend with a low-salt diet featuring rice, vegetables, and fruit. This diet was developed in 1939 by Walter Kempner (1903–1997) at Duke University.

- *I Can Make You Thin* (2009) by Paul McKenna encourages mindful eating and exhorts people to savor every mouthful of food. McKenna suggests eliminating food cravings by tapping 10 times on various parts of one's body and humming "Happy Birthday" until cravings subside.

- *The End of Overeating: Taking Control of the Insatiable American Appetite* (2009) by David A. Kessler details why we overeat and how to focus on choosing sensible portions of healthful foods.

- *Eat This Not That! Supermarket Survival Guide: The No-Diet Weight Loss Solution* (2009) by David Zinczenko and Matt Goulding describes how to navigate the supermarket to select healthful foods.

AMERICANS' DIETS

Hazel A. B. Hiza, Lisa Bente, and Thomas Fungwe of the Center for Nutrition Policy and Promotion offer in *Nutrient Content of the U.S. Food Supply, 2005* (March 2008, http://www.cnpp.usda.gov/Publications/FoodSupply/FoodSupply2005Report.pdf) historical data about the nutrients in the U.S. food supply and trends in Americans' diets. Table 5.1 shows the consumption of macronutrients (nutrients that the body uses in relatively large amounts: carbohydrates, fats, and proteins) in selected years from 1909 to 2005. Trends include:

- An increase of 900 calories per day from 1960–69 to 2005

- An increase of 0.8 ounce (22 g) of protein per day from 1960–69 to 2005

- An increase of 1.7 ounces (47 g) of fat per day from 1960–69 to 2005

Table 5.2 shows Americans' decreased consumption of whole milk in favor of low-fat milk; increased consumption of cheese and legumes, nuts, and soy; and decreased use of grain products. It also documents the shift from butter to margarine use, a decline in total consumption of vegetables, and a dramatic increase in consumption of salad, cooking, and other edible oils.

Dietary Guidelines for Americans, 2005

Every five years the *Dietary Guidelines for Americans* are updated and revised to translate the most current

TABLE 5.1

Food energy and macronutrients per capita per day, selected years 1909–2005

Year	Food energy (kcal)	Carbohydrate (g)	Fiber (g)	Protein (g)	Fat (g)	Saturated fatty acids (g)	Monounsaturated fatty acids (g)	Polyunsaturated fatty acids (g)	Cholesterol (mg)
1909–19	3,400	487	28	96	120	50	47	13	440
1920–29	3,400	478	26	92	127	54	49	15	470
1930–39	3,300	452	25	89	129	55	50	15	450
1940–49	3,300	431	24	98	138	56	54	18	510
1950–59	3,100	391	20	93	138	55	55	19	500
1960–69	3,100	383	18	93	143	54	56	22	470
1970–74	3,200	392	19	98	145	50	58	26	450
1975–84	3,200	400	20	97	146	49	59	29	420
1985–94	3,500	453	23	106	153	50	64	31	410
1995	3,600	482	24	109	148	48	63	31	400
1996	3,600	491	25	110	147	47	63	30	400
1997	3,700	494	25	109	146	46	62	31	400
1998	3,700	495	25	110	148	48	63	30	410
1999	3,700	499	25	112	153	49	65	32	420
2000	3,900	498	25	112	173	54	76	36	420
2001	3,900	492	25	111	172	53	76	36	410
2002	4,000	486	24	110	184	56	81	39	420
2003	3,900	483	25	111	183	56	81	39	420
2004	3,900	483	25	112	179	55	79	39	420
2005	4,000	479	25	115	190	59	85	37	430

kcal = kilo calorie
g = gram
mg = milligram

SOURCE: H. A. B. Hiza, L. Bente and T. Fungwe, "Table 1. Food Energy and Macronutrients per Capita per Day in the U.S. Food Supply, Selected Years," in *Nutrient Content of the U.S. Food Supply, 2005*, U.S. Department of Agriculture, Center for Nutrition Policy and Promotion, March 2008, http://www.cnpp.usda.gov/Publications/FoodSupply/FoodSupply2005Report.pdf (accessed November 2, 2009)

TABLE 5.2

Food energy contributed from major food groups, selected years 1909–2005

Year	Meat, poultry, and fish				Dairy products					Eggs	Legumes, nuts & soy	Grain products
	Meat	Poultry	Fish	Total	Whole milk	Lowfat milk	Cheese	Other	Total			
						Percent						
1909–19	13.3	0.9	0.6	14.7	5.1	0.8	0.6	2.1	8.5	1.8	2.3	37.5
1920–29	12.9	0.9	0.5	14.3	5.6	0.7	0.7	2.8	9.7	1.9	2.4	32.0
1930–39	12.5	0.9	0.5	13.9	5.9	0.6	0.8	3.3	10.6	1.8	2.8	29.3
1940–49	14.6	1.2	0.5	16.3	7.2	0.5	1.0	3.7	12.4	2.1	3.1	26.4
1950–59	15.5	1.5	0.5	17.5	7.1	0.4	1.3	3.5	12.5	2.4	3.0	22.6
1960–69	16.2	2.2	0.6	18.9	6.1	0.7	1.6	3.1	11.6	2.1	3.0	21.1
1970–74	14.7	2.7	0.6	18.0	5.2	1.3	2.0	2.8	11.4	1.9	3.1	19.5
1975–84	13.1	3.1	0.6	16.7	3.7	1.7	2.6	2.6	10.6	1.7	3.2	21.0
1985–94	10.2	3.8	0.6	14.6	2.2	2.1	3.1	2.7	10.1	1.4	3.2	23.6
1995	8.9	4.2	0.6	13.7	1.6	2.1	3.2	2.7	9.6	1.3	3.0	24.6
1996	8.6	4.3	0.6	13.4	1.6	2.1	3.3	2.7	9.6	1.3	3.0	25.2
1997	8.4	4.3	0.6	13.3	1.5	2.1	3.3	2.7	9.6	1.3	3.1	25.2
1998	8.7	4.3	0.6	13.6	1.5	2.0	3.3	2.7	9.5	1.4	3.1	25.0
1999	8.6	4.6	0.6	13.8	1.5	2.0	3.4	2.6	9.4	1.4	3.2	24.6
2000	8.1	4.4	0.6	13.1	1.4	1.9	3.3	2.5	9.0	1.3	3.0	23.9
2001	8.0	4.3	0.6	12.9	1.4	1.8	3.3	2.2	8.7	1.4	3.0	23.9
2002	8.8	4.4	0.6	13.8	1.3	1.7	3.3	2.1	8.5	1.3	3.0	23.1
2003	8.7	4.5	0.5	13.8	1.3	1.7	3.3	2.2	8.5	1.4	3.1	23.4
2004	8.0	4.6	0.6	13.3	1.2	1.7	3.4	2.3	8.7	1.4	3.1	23.4
2005	10.1	4.6	0.6	15.2	1.2	1.7	3.4	1.3	7.6	1.3	2.9	22.9

Year	Fruits			Vegetables					Fats and oils						Sugars & sweeteners	Miscellaneous
	Citrus	Non-citrus	Total	White potatoes	Dark green/ deep yellow	Tomatoes	Other	Total	Butter	Margarine	Shortening	Lard & beef tallow	Salad, cooking & other edible oil	Total		
											Percent					
1909–19	0.2	2.7	2.9	4.0	0.9	0.4	1.3	6.5	4.4	0.6	3.1	3.8	0.7	12.6	12.9	0.3
1920–29	0.3	2.8	3.1	3.5	0.9	0.4	1.4	6.1	4.6	0.7	2.7	4.2	1.4	13.5	16.4	0.5
1930–39	0.5	2.7	3.1	3.1	0.9	0.4	1.5	6.0	4.8	0.7	3.4	4.2	2.0	15.1	16.8	0.6
1940–49	0.7	2.5	3.2	2.9	0.8	0.5	1.6	5.8	3.4	1.1	3.2	4.3	2.3	14.3	15.7	0.6
1950–59	0.8	2.4	3.1	2.7	0.5	0.5	1.5	5.2	2.5	2.3	3.8	3.8	3.4	15.9	17.2	0.6
1960–69	0.7	2.1	2.8	2.8	0.4	0.5	1.4	5.1	1.8	2.8	5.1	2.2	4.8	16.8	17.8	0.7
1970–74	1.0	2.0	3.0	2.7	0.4	0.6	1.8	5.5	1.4	3.1	5.9	1.3	6.5	18.2	18.6	0.9
1975–84	1.1	2.2	3.3	2.7	0.4	0.6	1.8	5.4	1.2	3.1	6.2	1.1	7.6	19.2	18.0	0.8
1985–94	0.9	2.4	3.3	2.5	0.4	0.6	1.6	5.1	1.2	2.7	7.0	0.8	8.1	19.8	18.0	0.9
1995	0.9	2.3	3.3	2.6	0.4	0.6	1.6	5.2	1.1	2.3	6.8	1.0	8.0	19.1	19.2	0.9
1996	1.0	2.4	3.4	2.7	0.4	0.6	1.6	5.3	1.0	2.2	6.6	1.1	7.7	18.7	19.1	1.0
1997	1.0	2.3	3.4	2.5	0.5	0.6	1.6	5.2	1.0	2.1	6.2	0.9	8.5	18.6	19.4	0.9
1998	1.1	2.4	3.4	2.5	0.4	0.6	1.6	5.1	1.1	2.0	6.1	1.2	8.1	18.5	19.5	1.0
1999	1.0	2.4	3.4	2.4	0.4	0.6	1.6	5.1	1.1	1.9	6.2	1.3	8.4	18.9	19.4	1.0
2000	1.0	2.2	3.2	2.4	0.4	0.6	1.4	4.8	1.0	1.9	8.9	1.4	9.5	22.6	18.2	1.0
2001	1.0	2.2	3.2	2.4	0.4	0.5	1.4	4.7	1.0	1.6	9.2	1.2	10.1	23.1	18.2	1.0
2002	0.8	2.1	3.0	2.3	0.3	0.5	1.4	4.6	1.0	1.5	9.3	1.3	11.0	24.0	17.7	1.0
2003	0.9	2.2	3.1	2.4	0.4	0.5	1.4	4.7	1.0	1.2	9.2	1.4	11.2	24.0	17.2	1.0
2004	0.9	2.2	3.1	2.3	0.4	0.6	1.4	4.7	1.0	1.2	9.2	1.4	11.2	23.9	17.4	1.1
2005	0.8	2.1	2.9	2.3	0.4	0.6	1.4	4.4	1.0	0.9	10.7	1.5	10.5	24.7	17.0	1.1

SOURCE: H. A. B. Hiza, L. Bente and T. Fungwe, "Table 4. Food Energy Contributed from Major Food Groups to the U.S. Food Supply, Selected Years," in *Nutrient Content of the U.S. Food Supply, 2005*, U.S. Department of Agriculture, Center for Nutrition Policy and Promotion, March 2008, http://www.cnpp.usda.gov/Publications/FoodSupply/FoodSupply2005Report.pdf (accessed November 2, 2009)

scientific knowledge about individual nutrients and food components into dietary recommendations that may be adopted by the public. The recommendations are based on the preponderance of scientific evidence for reducing the risk of chronic disease and promoting health. Even though the recommendations focus on nutritional content, they recognize that a combination of poor diet and physical inactivity can lead to chronic diseases that include cardiovascular disease, Type 2 diabetes, hypertension (high blood pressure), osteoporosis, and certain cancers.

According to the U.S. Department of Health and Human Services and the USDA, in *Dietary Guidelines for Americans, 2005* (January 2005, http://www.health.gov/dietaryguidelines/dga2005/document/pdf/DGA2005.pdf), a healthy diet includes plenty of fruits, vegetables, whole grains, and fat-free or low-fat milk and milk products, as well as lean meats, poultry, fish, beans, eggs, and nuts. A healthy diet is also low in saturated fats, trans fats (artificial fats created through the hydrogenation of oils, which solidifies the oil and limits the body's ability to regulate cholesterol), cholesterol, salt, and added sugars. Specific recommendations stipulate that fewer than 10% of calories should come from saturated fatty acids, and trans fatty acids, which are considered to be the most harmful to health, should be avoided. Cholesterol intake should be less than 300 milligrams per day. Total fat intake should not exceed 20% to 35% of calories. Preferred fat sources are fish, nuts, and vegetable oils containing polyunsaturated and monounsaturated fatty acids. Lean, low-fat, or fat-free meats, poultry, dry beans, and milk or milk products are preferable to full-fat foods.

In general, the guidelines encourage most Americans to eat fewer calories, increase their physical activity, and choose nutrient-dense foods. They advocate increased consumption of fruits, vegetables, whole grains, and fat-free or low-fat milk and milk products. For example, two cups of fruit and two and a half cups of vegetables per day are recommended for a 2,000-calorie diet, along with three or more servings of whole-grain products per day and three cups per day of fat-free or low-fat milk or equivalent milk products.

Two examples—the USDA Food Guide and the Dietary Approaches to Stop Hypertension (DASH) Eating Plan—offer instruction about how to allocate calories to various food groups. Table 5.3 shows the amounts of various food groups that are recommended each day or each week in the USDA Food Guide and in the DASH Eating Plan at the 2,000-calorie level and the equivalent amounts for different food choices in each group. Acknowledging Americans' tendencies to eat out and eat while commuting, running errands, or working, the guidelines also offer tips for making healthy choices away from home. (See Table 5.4.)

The guidelines specifically address weight management by advising Americans "to maintain body weight in a healthy range, balance calories from foods and beverages with calories expended," and "to prevent gradual weight gain over time, make small decreases in food and beverage calories and increase physical activity." For people who are overweight, the guidelines advise gradual, steady weight loss by decreasing caloric consumption while maintaining sufficient nutrients and increasing physical activity. Parents of overweight children are counseled to reduce the rate of weight gain while children grow and develop and to consult a health care provider before placing children on weight-reduction diets. Pregnant women are advised to gain weight as instructed by their health care provider, and breast-feeding mothers are reassured that modest weight loss is safe and will not harm the development of nursing infants.

HOW WEIGHT-LOSS DIETS WORK

Research demonstrates that weight loss is associated with the length of the diet, the pre-diet weight (people who are more overweight tend to lose more weight, more quickly than those who are only mildly overweight), and the number of calories consumed. Any diet that restricts caloric intake such that calories consumed are less than those expended will promote short-term weight loss. The key to weight loss through diet is adherence—if people do not stick to their diet, then they will not lose weight. More than a century ago, Banting, in describing the benefits of his low-carbohydrate diet, wrote that "the great charms and comfort of this system are that its effects are palpable within a week of trial and creates a natural stimulus to persevere for a few weeks more."

The successes achieved using regimens that restrict dieters to a single food or food group such as grapefruit, pineapple, or cabbage are probably in part attributable to the human hankering for variety. When limited to just one food, most dieters experience boredom—there is just no appeal to eating the same food at every meal, for days on end, so naturally less food is consumed. In addition, these diets generally rely on low-calorie foods, so that even if dieters were inspired to consume 15 grapefruits per day, their total daily caloric consumption would be about 1,200 calories, which is sufficient to produce weight loss for most overweight people. Similarly, diets that involve stringent portion control effectively reduce calories to produce weight loss.

Low-Calorie Diets

Traditional dietary therapy for weight loss generally seeks to create a deficit of 500 to 1,000 calories per day with the intent of promoting weight loss of between 1 to 2 pounds (0.5 to 0.9 kg) per week. Low-calorie diets for men usually range from 1,200 to 1,600 calories per day; for women, low-calorie diets contain between 1,000 and 1,200 calories per day. Table 5.5 is an example of the recommended percentages of nutrients in a low-calorie

TABLE 5.3

Sample USDA Food Guide and the Dietary Approaches to Stop Hypertension (DASH) Eating Plan at the 2,000-calorie level

Food groups and subgroups	USDA Food Guide amount[a]	DASH Eating Plan amount	Equivalent amounts
Fruit group	2 cups (4 servings)	2 to 2.5 cups (4 to 5 servings)	1/2 cup equivalent is: 1/2 cup fresh, frozen, or canned fruit 1 med fruit 1/4 cup dried fruit USDA: 1/2 cup fruit juice DASH: 3/4 cup fruit juice
Vegetable group Dark green vegetables Orange vegetables Legumes (dry beans) Starchy vegetables Other vegetables	2.5 cups (5 servings) 3 cups/week 2 cups/week 3 cups/week 3 cups/week 6.5 cups/week	2 to 2.5 cups (4 to 5 servings)	1/2 cup equivalent is: 1/2 cup of cut-up raw or cooked vegetable 1 cup raw leafy vegetable USDA: 1/2 cup vegetable juice DASH: 3/4 cup vegetable juice
Grain group Whole grains Other grains	6 ounce-equivalents 3 ounce-equivalents 3 ounce-equivalents	7 to 8 ounce-equivalents (7 to 8 servings)	1 ounce-equivalent is: 1 slice bread 1 cup dry cereal 1/2 cup cooked rice, pasta, cereal DASH: 1 oz dry cereal (1/2–1/4 cup depending on cereal type—check label)
Meat and beans group	5.5 ounce-equivalents	6 ounces or less meat, poultry, fish 4 to 5 servings per week nuts, seeds, and dry beans[b]	1 ounce-equivalent is: 1 ounce of cooked lean meats, poultry, fish 1 egg USDA: 1/4 cup cooked dry beans or tofu, 1 Tbsp peanut butter, 1/2 oz nuts or seeds DASH: 1 1/2 oz nuts, 1/2 oz seeds, 2 Tbsp peanut butter, 1/2 cup cooked dry beans
Milk group	3 cups	2 to 3 cups	1 cup equivalent is: 1 cup low-fat/fat-free milk, yogurt 1 1/2 oz of low-fat or fat-free natural cheese 2 oz of low-fat or fat-free processed cheese
Oils	27 grams (6 tsp)	8 to 12 grams (2 to 3 tsp)	1 tsp equivalent is: DASH: 1 tsp soft margarine 1 Tbsp low-fat mayo 2 Tbsp light salad dressing 1 tsp vegetable oil
Discretionary calorie allowance Example of distribution: Solid fat[c] Added sugars	267 calories 18 grams 8 tsp	~2 tsp of added sugar (5 Tbsp per week)	1 Tbsp added sugar equivalent is: DASH: 1 Tbsp jelly or jam 1/2 oz jelly beans 8 oz lemonade

Note: All servings are per day unless otherwise noted. USDA vegetable subgroup amounts and amounts of DASH (Dietary Approaches to Stop Hypertension) nuts, seeds, and dry beans are per week.
[a]The 2,000-calorie USDA Food Guide is appropriate for many sedentary males 51 to 70 years of age, sedentary females 19 to 30 years of age, and for some other gender/age groups who are more physically active.
[b]In the DASH Eating Plan, nuts, seeds, and dry beans are a separate food group from meat, poultry, and fish.
[c]The oils listed in this table are not considered to be part of discretionary calories because they are a major source of the vitamin E and polyunsaturated fatty acids, including the essential fatty acids, in the food pattern. In contrast, solid fats (i.e., saturated and trans fats) are listed separately as a source of discretionary calories.

SOURCE: "Table 1. Sample USDA Food Guide and the DASH Eating Plan at the 2,000-Calorie Level," in *Dietary Guidelines for Americans, 2005*, 6th ed., U.S. Department of Health and Human Services and U.S. Department of Agriculture, January 2005, http://www.health.gov/dietaryguidelines/dga2005/document/html/chapter2.htm (accessed November 2, 2009)

diet that aims to decrease the risk factors for hypertension and high cholesterol as well as cause weight loss.

The most successful low-calorie diets take individual food preferences into account to custom-tailor the diet. Table 5.6 and Table 5.7 show examples of how traditional American cuisine may be used to create a low-calorie diet containing 1,200 and 1,600 calories per day, respectively. Table 5.8 incorporates regional southern cuisine into a reduced-calorie diet. Table 5.9 illustrates how Asian-American cuisine may be adapted to 1,200- and 1,600-calorie-per-day diets, and Table 5.10

shows how Mexican-American cuisine may be adapted for low-calorie diets. Table 5.11 is a sample of a reduced-calorie diet that vegetarians who eat milk and eggs but no meat or fish can use to lose weight. Food exchanges, such as those shown in Table 5.12, enable dieters to enjoy a variety of foods in their reduced-calorie meals, which can prevent boredom and the tendency to abandon the diet.

Research reveals that reducing fat in the diet is an effective way to reduce calories and that when low-calorie diets are combined with low-fat diets, better

TABLE 5.4

Smart choices for eating out and on the go

It's important to make smart food choices and watch portion sizes wherever you are—at the grocery store, at work, in your favorite restaurant, or running errands. Try these tips:

- At the store, plan ahead by buying a variety of nutrient-rich foods for meals and snacks throughout the week.
- When grabbing lunch, have a sandwich on whole-grain bread and choose low-fat/fat-free milk, water, or other drinks without added sugars.
- In a restaurant, opt for steamed, grilled, or broiled dishes instead of those that are fried or sautéed.
- On a long commute or shopping trip, pack some fresh fruit, cut-up vegetables, string cheese sticks, or a handful of unsalted nuts—to help you avoid impulsive, less healthful snack choices.

SOURCE: "Don't Give in When You Eat out and Are on the Go," in *Dietary Guidelines for Americans, 2005*, 6th ed., U.S. Department of Health and Human Services and U.S. Department of Agriculture, January 2005, http://www.health.gov/dietaryguidelines/dga2005/document/media/OnTheGo.pdf (accessed November 2, 2009)

TABLE 5.5

Low-calorie Step I diet

Nutrient	Recommended intake
Calories[a]	Approximately 500 to 1,000 kcal/day reduction from usual intake
Total fat[b]	**30 percent or less of total calories**
Saturated fatty acids[c]	8 to 10 percent of total calories
Monounsaturated fatty acids	Up to 15 percent of total calories
Polyunsaturated fatty acids	Up to 10 percent of total calories
Cholesterol[c]	<300 mg/day
Protein[d]	Approximately 15 percent of total calories
Carbohydrate[e]	55 percent or more of total calories
Sodium chloride	No more than 100 mmol/day (approximately 2.4 g of sodium or approximately 6 g of sodium chloride)
Calcium[f]	1,000 to 1,500 mg/day
Fiber[e]	20 to 30 g/day

[a]A reduction in calories of 500 to 1,000 kcal/day will help achieve a weight loss of 1 to 2 pounds/week. Alcohol provides unneeded calories and displaces more nutritious foods. Alcohol consumption not only increases the number of calories in a diet but has been associated with obesity in epidemiologic studies as well as in experimental studies. The impact of alcohol calories on a person's overall caloric intake needs to be assessed and appropriately controlled.
[b]Fat-modified foods may provide a helpful strategy for lowering total fat intake but will only be effective if they are also low in calories and if there is no compensation by calories from other foods.
[c]Patients with high blood cholesterol levels may need to use the Step II diet to achieve further reductions in LDL-cholesterol levels; in the Step II diet, saturated fats are reduced to less than 7 percent of total calories, and cholesterol levels to less than 200 mg/day. All of the other nutrients are the same as in Step I.
[d]Protein should be derived from plant sources and lean sources of animal protein.
[e]Complex carbohydrates from different vegetables, fruits, and whole grains are good sources of vitamins, minerals, and fiber. A diet rich in soluble fiber, including oat bran, legumes, barley, and most fruits and vegetables may be effective in reducing blood cholesterol levels. A diet high in all types of fiber may also aid in weight management by promoting satiety at lower levels of calorie and fat intake. Some authorities recommend 20 to 30 grams of fiber daily, with an upper limit of 35 grams.
[f]During weight loss, attention should be given to maintaining an adequate intake of vitamins and minerals. Maintenance of the recommended calcium intake of 1,000 to 1,500 mg/day is especially important for women who may be at risk of osteoporosis.

SOURCE: "Table 4. Low-Calorie Step I Diet," in *The Practical Guide: Identification, Evaluation, and Treatment of Overweight and Obesity in Adults*, National Institutes of Health, National Heart, Lung, and Blood Institute, North American Association for the Study of Obesity, October 2000, http://www.nhlbi.nih.gov/guidelines/obesity/prctgd_b.pdf (accessed November 2, 2009)

weight loss is achieved than through calorie reduction alone. Furthermore, even though very-low-calorie diets that provide about 500 calories per day have been demonstrated to produce greater initial weight loss than low-calorie diets, the long-term weight loss is not different between the two regimens.

Low-Carbohydrate Diets

During 2004 and 2005 several rigorous research studies reported that low-carbohydrate diets were as effective, or even more effective, in producing short-term weight loss than low-fat diets. The low-carbohydrate diets owed much of their success to adherence—dieters were better able to stick with their diets, and as a result achieved better results. Another hypothesis about the success of low-carbohydrate regimens is that dieters do not feel as hungry as they do on other diets because protein is the most satisfying of the three macronutrients: carbohydrates, fats, and proteins.

The scientific premise of low-carbohydrate diets is that consuming certain carbohydrates can cause surges in blood sugar and insulin that not only stimulate appetite and weight gain but may also increase the risk for diabetes and heart disease. At first, low-carbohydrate diets viewed all carbohydrates as equally harmful. Increasingly, however, low-carbohydrate diets distinguished between simple and complex carbohydrates, which contain simple (single or double) or complex (three or more) sugars.

Examples of single sugars from foods include fructose, which is found in fruits, and galactose, which is found in milk products. Double sugars include lactose in dairy products; maltose, which is found in certain vegetables and in beer; and sucrose (table sugar). Examples of complex carbohydrates, which are often referred to as starches, include breads, cereals, legumes, brown rice, and pastas. Simple carbohydrates occur naturally in fruits, milk products, and vegetables and, like complex carbohydrates, contain vitamins and minerals, which distinguishes them from the refined simple sugars many nutritionists advise against (or at least recommend limiting in the diet). The simple carbohydrates most nutritionists call "empty calories" are the processed and refined sugars found in candy, table sugar, and sodas, as well as in foods such as white flour, sugar, and polished white rice.

Besides distinguishing between simple and complex carbohydrates, low-carbohydrate regimens rely on a measure known as the glycemic index (GI), which ranks foods based on how rapidly their consumption raises blood glucose levels. The GI measures how much blood sugar increases over a period of two or three hours after a meal. Carbohydrate foods that break down quickly during digestion have the highest GI. The GI may be used to determine if a particular food will trigger the problematical "carbohydrate–blood sugar–insulin cascade." High-GI

TABLE 5.6

Sample reduced calorie menus, traditional American cuisine—1,200 calories

	Calories	Fat (grams)	% Fat	Exchange for
Breakfast				
• Whole wheat bread, 1 medium slice	70	1.2	15	(1 bread/starch)
• Jelly, regular, 2 tsp	30	0	0	(1/2 fruit)
• Cereal, shredded wheat, 1/2 cup	104	1	4	(1 bread/starch)
• Milk, 1%, 1 cup	102	3	23	(1 milk)
• Orange juice, 3/4 cup	78	0	0	(1 1/2 fruit)
• Coffee, regular, 1 cup	5	0	0	(free)
Breakfast total	**389**	**5.2**	**10**	
Lunch				
• Roast beef sandwich:				
Whole wheat bread, 2 medium slices	139	2.4	15	(2 bread/starch)
Lean roast beef, unseasoned, 2 oz	60	1.5	23	(2 lean protein)
Lettuce, 1 leaf	1	0	0	(1 vegetable)
Tomato, 3 medium slices	10	0	0	
Mayonnaise, low calorie, 1 tsp	15	1.7	96	(1/3 fat)
• Apple, 1 medium	80	0	0	(1 fruit)
• Water, 1 cup	0	0	0	(free)
Lunch total	**305**	**5.6**	**16**	
Dinner				
• Salmon, 2 ounces edible	103	5	44	(2 lean protein)
• Vegetable oil, 1 1/2 tsp	60	7	100	(1 1/2 fat)
• Baked potato, 3/4 medium	100	0	0	(1 bread/starch)
• Margarine, 1 tsp	34	4	100	(1 fat)
• Green beans, seasoned, with margarine, 1/2 cup	52	2	4	(1 vegetable) (1/2 fat)
• Carrots, seasoned	35	0	0	(1 vegetable)
• White dinner roll, 1 small	70	2	28	(1 bread/starch)
• Iced tea, unsweetened, 1 cup	0	0	0	(free)
• Water, 2 cups	0	0	0	(free)
Dinner total	**454**	**20**	**39**	
Snack				
• Popcorn, 2 1/2 cups	69	0	0	(1 bread/starch)
• Margarine, 3/4 tsp	30	3	100	(3/4 fat)
Total	**1,247**	**34–36**	**24–26**	

Calories	1,247	Saturated fat, % Kcals	7	
Total carbohydrate, % Kcals	58	Cholesterol, mg	96	
Total fat, % Kcals	26	Protein, % Kcals	19	
*Sodium, mg	1,043			

Note: Calories have been rounded.
1,200: 100% RDA met for all nutrients except vitamin E 80%, vitamin B_2 96%, vitamin B_6 94%, calcium 68%, iron 63%, and zinc 73%.
*No salt added in recipe preparation or as seasoning. Consume at least 32 ounces of water.

SOURCE: "Appendix D. Traditional American Cuisine—1,200 Calories," in *The Practical Guide: Identification, Evaluation, and Treatment of Overweight and Obesity in Adults*, National Institutes of Health, National Heart, Lung, and Blood Institute, North American Association for the Study of Obesity, October 2000, http://www.nhlbi.nih.gov/guidelines/obesity/prctgd_b.pdf (accessed November 2, 2009)

foods are those that are rapidly digested and absorbed or transformed metabolically into glucose.

Examples of foods with GI scores of 70 or above are cake, cookies, doughnuts, honey, French fries, rice, baked potato, and white bread. In contrast, lentils have a GI of 29, whereas broccoli, peanuts, and spinach have GIs of less than 15. Carbohydrates that break down slowly, such as whole-grain breads and cereals, beans, leafy greens, or cruciferous vegetables (which include mustard greens, cabbage, broccoli, cauliflower, kale, and brussels sprouts), generate slower glucose release into the bloodstream and lower GI scores—50 or less. Eating low-GI foods supports weight loss by enhancing satiety (the feeling of fullness or satisfaction after eating) and thereby decreasing total food consumption.

The measurement of GI is a relatively recent practice. It began during the 1990s, following the discovery that specific carbohydrates such as potatoes and cornflakes raised blood sugar faster than others such as brown rice and oatmeal. Harvard University School of Public Health researchers used GI to calculate glycemic load—a measure that considers the food's GI and the amount of carbohydrates contained in a single serving. For example, many whole fruits, vegetables, and grains have low glycemic loads, which when consumed prompt a moderate rise in blood glucose and insulin. When the same fruits, vegetables, and grains are squeezed or pulverized into juice or flour, their glycemic load increases—effectively rendering them with the same high glycemic load of sugar water.

TABLE 5.7

Sample reduced calorie menus, traditional American cuisine—1,600 calories

	Calories	Fat (grams)	% Fat	Exchange for
Breakfast				
• Whole wheat bread, 1 medium slice	70	1.2	15.4	(1 bread/starch)
• Jelly, regular, 2 tsp	30	0	0	(1/2 fruit)
• Cereal, shredded wheat, 1 cup	207	2	8	(2 bread/starch)
• Milk, 1%, 1 cup	102	3	23	(1 milk)
• Orange juice, 3/4 cup	18	0	0	(1 1/2 fruit)
• Coffee, regular, 1 cup	5	0	0	(free)
• Milk, 1%, 1 oz	10	0.3	27	(1/8 milk)
Breakfast total	**502**	**6.5**	**10**	
Lunch				
• Roast beef sandwich:				
Whole wheat bread, 2 medium slices	139	2.4	15	(2 bread/starch)
Lean roast beef, unseasoned, 2 oz	60	1.5	23	(2 lean protein)
American cheese, low fat and low sodium, 1 slice, 3/4 oz	46	1.8	36	(1 lean protein)
Lettuce, 1 leaf	1	1	0	
Tomato, 3 medium slices	10	0	0	(1 vegetable)
Mayonnaise, low calorie, 2 tsp	30	3.3	99	(2/3 fat)
• Apple, 1 medium	8	0	0	(1 fruit)
• Water, 1 cup	0	0	0	(free)
Lunch total	**366**	**9**	**22**	
Dinner				
• Salmon, 3 ounces edible	155	7	40	(3 lean protein)
• Vegetable oil, 1 1/2 tsp	60	7	100	(1 1/2 fat)
• Baked potato, 3/4 medium	100	0	0	(1 bread/starch)
• Margarine, 1 tsp	34	4	100	(1 fat)
• Green beans, seasoned, with margarine, 1/2 cup	52	2	4	(1 vegetable) (1/2 fat)
• Carrots, seasoned, with margarine, 1/2 cup	52	2	4	(1 vegetable) (1/2 fat)
• White dinner roll, 1 medium	80	3	33	(1 bread/starch)
• Ice milk, 1/2 cup	92	3	28	(1 bread/starch) (1/2 fat)
• Iced tea, unsweetened, 1 cup	0	0	0	(free)
• Water, 2 cups	0	0	0	(free)
Dinner total	**625**	**28**	**38**	
Snack				
• Popcorn, 2 1/2 cups	69	0	0	(1 bread/starch)
• Margarine, 1/2 tsp	58	6.5	100	(1 1/2 fat)
Total	**1,613**	**50**	**28**	

Calories	1,613	Saturated fat, % kcals	8	
Total carbohydrate, % kcals	55	Cholesterol, mg	142	
Total fat, % kcals	29	Protein, % kcals	19	
*Sodium, mg	1,341			

Note: Calories have been rounded.
1,600: 100% RDA met for all nutrients except vitamin E 99%, iron 73%, and zinc 91%.
No salt added in recipe preparation or as seasoning. Consume at least 32 ounces of water.

SOURCE: "Appendix D. Traditional American Cuisine—1,600 Calories," in *The Practical Guide: Identification, Evaluation, and Treatment of Overweight and Obesity in Adults*, National Institutes of Health, National Heart, Lung, and Blood Institute, North American Association for the Study of Obesity, October 2000, http://www.nhlbi.nih.gov/guidelines/obesity/prctgd_b.pdf (accessed November 2, 2009)

After consuming a meal with a high glycemic load, blood sugar rises higher and faster than it does after eating a meal with a low glycemic load. In an effort to recover from the resulting peaks and plummets, the brain transmits a hunger signal long before the next meal is due. Wildly fluctuating blood sugar and insulin may result in overeating, which in turn causes overweight. For people who are overweight or physically inactive, another potential danger of consuming foods with high glycemic loads is that they may already be insulin resistant, and the overexertion of insulin-producing cells in the pancreas that is required to metabolize the high glycemic loads may ultimately exhaust their insulin-producing cells, leading to diabetes.

Weight-loss diets based on the GI emphasize sharply restricting high-index foods and consuming primarily low-index foods. The proponents of low-carbohydrate, low-GI food diets observe that consuming foods with low glycemic loads stabilizes blood sugar and insulin to prevent the fluctuations that can cause overeating and may increase the risk for diabetes. They also assert that reliance on low-fat diets inadvertently led to diets that were high in simple carbohydrates and indirectly promoted the observed increase in overweight and diabetes in the United States.

Low-Fat Diets

Low-fat diets reduce caloric intake by reducing fat consumption. Fat has 9 calories per gram, whereas protein

TABLE 5.8

Sample reduced calorie menus, Southern cuisine

	1,600 calories	1,200 calories
Breakfast		
• Oatmeal, prepared with 1% milk, low fat	1/2 cup	1/2 cup
• Milk, 1%, low fat	1/2 cup	1/2 cup
• English muffin	1 medium	—
• Cream cheese, light, 18% fat	1 T	—
• Orange juice	3/4 cup	1/2 cup
• Coffee	1 cup	1 cup
• Milk, 1%, low fat	1 oz	1 oz
Lunch		
• Baked chicken, without skin	2 oz	2 oz
• Vegetable oil	1 tsp	1/2 tsp
• Salad:		
Lettuce	1/2 cup	1/2 cup
Tomato	1/2 cup	1/2 cup
Cucumber	1/2 cup	1/2 cup
• Oil and vinegar dressing	2 tsp	1 tsp
• White rice	1/2 cup	1/4 cup
• Margarine, diet	1/2 tsp	1/2 tsp
• Baking powder biscuit, prepared with vegetable oil	1 small	1/2 small
• Margarine	1 tsp	1 tsp
• Water	1 cup	1 cup
Dinner		
• Lean roast beef	3 oz	2 oz
• Onion	1/4 cup	1/4 cup
• Beef gravy, water-based	1 T	1 T
• Turnip greens	1/2 cup	1/2 cup
• Margarine, diet	1/2 tsp	1/2 tsp
• Sweet potato, baked	1 small	1 small
• Margarine, diet	1/2 tsp	1/4 tsp
• Ground cinnamon	1 tsp	1 tsp
• Brown sugar	1 tsp	1 tsp
• Corn bread prepared with margarine, diet	1/2 medium slice	1/2 medium slice
• Honeydew melon	1/4 medium	1/8 medium
• Iced tea, sweetened with sugar	1 cup	1 cup
Snack		
• Saltine crackers, unsalted tops	4 crackers	4 crackers
• Mozzarella cheese, part skim, low sodium	1 oz	1 oz

Calories	1,653	Calories	1,225
Total carbohydrate, % kcals	53	Total carbohydrate, % kcals	50
Total fat, % kcals	28	Total fat, % kcals	31
*Sodium, mg	1,231	*Sodium, mg	867
Saturated fat, % kcals	8	Saturated fat, % kcals	9
Cholesterol, mg	172	Cholesterol, mg	142
Protein, % kcals	20	Protein, % kcals	21

1,600: 100% RDA met for all nutrients except vitamin E 97%, magnesium 98%, iron 78%, and zinc 90%.
1,200: 100% RDA met for all nutrients except vitamin E 82%, vitamin B₁ & B₂ 95%, vitamin B₃ 99%, vitamin B₆ 88%, magnesium 83%, iron 56%, and zinc 70%.
*No salt added in recipe preparation or as seasoning. Consume at least 32 ounces of water.

SOURCE: "Appendix D. Southern Cuisine—Reduced Calorie," in *The Practical Guide: Identification, Evaluation, and Treatment of Overweight and Obesity in Adults*, National Institutes of Health, National Heart, Lung, and Blood Institute, North American Association for the Study of Obesity, October 2000, http://www.nhlbi.nih.gov/guidelines/obesity/prctgd_b.pdf (accessed November 2, 2009)

TABLE 5.9

Sample reduced calorie menus, Asian American cuisine

	1,600 calories	1,200 calories
Breakfast		
• Banana	1 small	1 small
• Whole wheat bread	2 slices	1 slice
• Margarine	1 tsp	1 tsp
• Orange juice	3/4 tsp	3/4 tsp
• Milk 1%, low fat	3/4 cup	3/4 cup
Lunch		
• Beef noodle soup, canned, low sodium	1/2 cup	1/2 cup
• Chinese noodle and beef salad:		
Roast beef	3 oz	2 oz
Peanut oil	1 1/2 tsp	1 tsp
Soya sauce, low sodium	tsp	1 tsp
Carrots	1/2 cup	1/2 cup
Zucchini	1/2 cup	1/2 cup
Onion	1/4 cup	1/4 cup
Chinese noodles, soft type	1/4 cup	1/4 cup
• Apple	1 medium	1 medium
• Tea, unsweetened	1 cup	1 cup
Dinner		
• Pork stir-fry with vegetables:		
Pork cutlet	2 oz	2 oz
Peanut oil	1 tsp	1 tsp
Soya sauce, low sodium	1 tsp	1 tsp
Broccoli	1/2 cup	1/2 cup
Carrots	1 cup	1 cup
Mushrooms	1/4 cup	1/2 cup
• Steamed white rice	1 cup	1/2 cup
• Tea, unsweetened	1 cup	1 cup
Snack		
• Almond, cookies	2 cookies	—
• Milk 1%, low fat	1/2 cup	1/2 cup

Calories	1,609	Calories	1,220
Total carbohydrate, % kcals	56	Total carbohydrate, % kcals	55
Total fat, % kcals	27	Total fat, % kcals	27
*Sodium, mg	1,296	*Sodium, mg	1,043
Saturated fat, % kcals	8	Saturated fat, % kcals	8
Cholesterol, mg	148	Cholesterol, mg	117
Protein, % kcals	20	Protein, % kcals	21

1,600: 100% RDA net for all nutrients except zinc 95%, iron 87%, and calcium 93%
1,200: 100% RDA net for all nutrients except vitamin E 75%, calcium 84%, magnesium 98%, iron 66%, and zinc 77%
*No salt added in recipe preparation or as seasoning. Consume at least 32 ounces of water.

SOURCE: "Appendix D. Asian American Cuisine—Reduced Calorie," in *The Practical Guide: Identification, Evaluation, and Treatment of Overweight and Obesity in Adults*, National Institutes of Health, National Heart, Lung, and Blood Institute, North American Association for the Study of Obesity, October 2000, http://www.nhlbi.nih.gov/guidelines/obesity/prctgd_b.pdf (accessed November 2, 2009)

Table 5.13 shows some of the food substitutions that may be made to reduce the dietary fat content. Besides making substitutions, many fat-free or low-fat food products are available—from fat-free frozen desserts to reduced-fat peanut butter. However, dieters are often cautioned that fat-free or reduced-fat foods are not calorie-free and that their consumption will not result in weight loss when more of the reduced-fat foods are consumed than would be eaten of the full-fat versions. For example, eating twice as many baked tortilla chips would actually result in higher caloric intake than a single serving of regular tortilla chips. (See Table 5.14.)

and carbohydrates have 4 calories per gram. These diets rely on the high-fiber content of complex carbohydrates to satisfy dieters. High-fiber foods also slow the absorption of carbohydrates, so they do not provoke a rapid rise in blood sugar and insulin.

TABLE 5.10

Sample reduced calorie menus, Mexican American cuisine

	1,600 calories	1,200 calories
Breakfast		
• Cantaloupe	1 cup	1/2 cup
• Farina, prepared with 1% low fat milk	1/2 cup	1/2 cup
• White bread	1 slice	1 slice
• Margarine	1 tsp	1 tsp
• Jelly	1 tsp	1 tsp
• Orange juice	1 1/2 cup	3/4 cup
• Milk, 1%, low fat	1/2 cup	1/2 cup
Lunch		
• Beef enchilada:		
Tortilla, corn	2 tortillas	2 tortillas
Lean roast beef	2 1/2 oz	2 oz
Vegetable oil	2/3 tsp	2/3 tsp
Onion	1 T	1 T
Tomato	4 T	4 T
Lettuce	1/2 cup	1/2 cup
Chili peppers	2 tsp	2 tsp
Refried beans, prepared with vegetable oil	1/4 cup	1/4 cup
• Carrots	5 sticks	5 sticks
• Celery	6 sticks	6 sticks
• Milk, 1%, low fat	1/2 cup	—
• Water	—	1 cup
Dinner		
• Chicken taco:		
Tortilla, corn	1 tortilla	1 tortilla
Chicken breast, without skin	2 oz	1 oz
Vegetable oil	2/3 tsp	2/3 tsp
Cheddar cheese, low fat and low sodium	1 oz	1/2 oz
Guacamole	2 T	2 T
Salsa	1 T	1 T
• Corn, seasoned with	1/2 cup	1/2 cup
margarine	1/2 tsp	—
• Spanish rice without meat	1/2 cup	1/2 cup
• Banana	1 large	1/2 large
• Coffee	1 cup	1/2 cup
• Milk, 1%	1 oz	1 oz
Calories	1,638	Calories	1,239
Total carbohydrate, % kcals	56	Total carbohydrate, % kcals	58
Total fat, % kcals	27	Total fat, % kcals	26
*Sodium, mg	1,616	*Sodium, mg	1,364
Saturated fat, % kcals	9	Protein, % kcals	8
Cholesterol, mg	153	Cholesterol, mg	91
Protein, % kcals	20	Protein, % kcals	19

1,600: 100% RDA met for all nutrients except vitamin in E 97% and zinc 84%.
1,200: 100% RDNA met for all nutrients except vitamin E 71%, vitamin B₁ & B₃ 91%, vitamin B₂ & iron 90%, and calcium 92%.
*No salt in recipe preparation or as seasoning. Consume at least 32 ounces of water.

SOURCE: "Appendix D. Mexican American Cuisine—Reduced Calorie," in *The Practical Guide: Identification, Evaluation, and Treatment of Overweight and Obesity in Adults*, National Institutes of Health, National Heart, Lung, and Blood Institute, North American Association for the Study of Obesity, October 2000, http://www.nhlbi.nih.gov/guidelines/obesity/prctgd_b.pdf (accessed November 2, 2009)

TABLE 5.11

Sample reduced calorie menus, lacto-ovo vegetarian cuisine

	1,600 calories	1,200 calories
Breakfast		
• Orange	1 medium	1 medium
• Pancakes, made with 1% lowfat milk and egg whites	3 4" circles	2 4" circles
• Pancake syrup	2 T	1 T
• Margarine, diet	1 1/2 tsp	1 1/2 tsp
• Milk, 1%, lowfat	1 cup	1/2 cup
• Coffee	1 cup	1 cup
• Milk, 1%, lowfat	1 oz	1 oz
Lunch		
• Vegetable soup, canned, low sodium	1 cup	1/2 cup
• Bagel	1 medium	1/2 medium
• Processed American cheese, lowfat	3/4 oz	—
• Spinach salad:		
Spinach	1 cup	1 cup
Mushrooms	1/2 cup	1/2 cup
• Salad dressing, regular calorie	2 tsp	2 tsp
• Apple	1 medium	1 medium
• Iced tea, unsweetened	1 cup	1 cup
Dinner		
• Omelette:		
Egg whites	4 large eggs	4 large eggs
Green pepper	2 T	2 T
Onion	2 T	2 T
Mozzarella cheese, made from part skim milk, low sodium	1 oz	1/2 oz
Vegetable oil	1 T	1/2 T
• Brown rice, seasoned with	1/2 cup	1/2 cup
margarine, diet	1/2 tsp	1/2 tsp
• Carrots, seasoned with	1/2 cup	1/2 cup
Margarine, diet	1/2 tsp	1/2 tsp
• Whole wheat bread	1 slice	1 slice
• Margarine, diet	1 tsp	1 tsp
• Fig bar cookie	1 bar	1 bar
• Tea	1 cup	1 cup
• Honey	1 tsp	1 tsp
• Milk, 1%, lowfat	3/4 cup	3/4 cup
Calories	1,650	Calories	1,205
Total carbohydrate, % kcals	56	Total carbohydrate, % kcals	60
Total fat, % kcals	27	Total fat, % kcals	25
*Sodium, mg	1,829	*Sodium, mg	1,335
Saturated fat, % kcals	8	Saturated fat, % kcals	7
Cholesterol, mg	82	Cholesterol, mg	44
Protein, % kcals	19	Protein, % kcals	18

1,600: 100% RDA met for all nutrients except vitamin E 92%, vitamin B₃ 97%, vitamin B₆ 67%, iron 73%, and zinc 68%.
1,200: 100% RDA met for all nutrients except vitamin E 75%, vitamin B₁ 92%, vitamin B₃ 69%, vitamin B₆ 59%, iron 54%, and zinc 46%.
*No salt added in recipe preparation or as seasoning. Consume at least 32 ounces of water.

SOURCE: "Appendix D. Lacto-Ovo Vegetarian Cuisine—Reduced Calorie," in *The Practical Guide: Identification, Evaluation, and Treatment of Overweight and Obesity in Adults*, National Institutes of Health, National Heart, Lung, and Blood Institute, North American Association for the Study of Obesity, June 1998, http://www.nhlbi.nih.gov/guidelines/obesity/practgde.htm (accessed November 2, 2009)

Low-Fat versus Low-Carbohydrate Diets

In the absence of rigorous scientific research and studies demonstrating the long-term safety and effectiveness of low-carbohydrate and low-fat diets, many investigators and health professionals hesitate to proclaim one diet's superiority over all others. There is consensus that even though some diets may produce greater initial weight loss, most perform similarly over time.

In "Efficacy and Safety of Low-Carbohydrate Diets: A Systematic Review" (*Journal of the American Medical Association*, vol. 289, no. 14, April 9, 2003), Dena M. Bravata et al. report the results of their analysis of data about diet-induced changes in weight, serum lipids, fasting serum glucose and fasting serum insulin levels, and blood pressure among adults using low-carbohydrate diets. The investigators undertook the research in response to

TABLE 5.12

Food exchange list

Within each group, these foods can be exchanged for each other. You can use this list to give yourself more choices.

Vegetables contain 25 calories and 5 grams of carbohydrate. One serving equals:
- 1/2 cup   Cooked vegetables (carrots, broccoli, zucchini, cabbage, etc.)
- 1 cup   Raw vegetables or salad greens
- 1/2 cup   Vegetable juice

If you're hungry, eat more fresh or steamed vegetables.

Fat free and very low fat milk contains 90 calories and 12 grams of carbohydrate per serving. One serving equals:
- 8 oz   Milk, fat free or 1% fat
- 1/4 cup   Yogurt, plain nonfat or low fat
- 1 cup   Yogurt, artificially sweetened

Very lean protein choices have 35 calories and 1 gram of fat per serving. One serving equals:
- 1 oz   Turkey breast or chicken breast, skin removed
- 1 oz   Fish fillet (flounder, sole, scrod, cod, haddock, halibut)
- 1 oz   Canned tuna in water
- 1 oz   Shellfish (clams, lobster, scallop, shrimp)
- 3/4 cup   Cottage cheese, nonfat or lowfat
- 2 each   Egg whites
- 1/4 cup   Egg substitute
- 1 oz   Fat free cheese
- 1/2 cup   Beans—cooked (black beans, kidney, chickpeas, or lentils): count as 1 starch/bread and 1 very lean protein

Medium fat proteins have 75 calories and 5 grams of fat per serving. One serving equals:
- 1 oz   Beef (any prime cut), corned beef, ground beef**
- 1 oz   Pork chop
- 1 each   Whole egg (medium)**
- 1 oz   Mozzarella cheese
- 1/4 cup   Ricotta cheese
- 4 oz   Tofu (note that this is a heart-healthy choice)

**Choose these very infrequently.

Fats contain 45 calories and 5 grams of fat per serving. One serving equals:
- 1 tsp   Oil (vegetable, corn, canola, olive, etc.)
- 1 tsp   Butter
- 1 tsp   Stick margarine
- 1 tsp   Mayonnaise
- 1 T   Reduced fat margarine or mayonnaise
- 1 T   Salad dressing
- 1 T   Cream cheese
- 2 T   Lite cream cheese
- 1/8   Avocado
- 8 large   Black olives
- 10 large   Stuffed green olives
- 1 slice   Bacon

Fruits contain 15 grams of carbohydrates and 60 calories. One serving equals:
- 1 small   Apple, banana, orange, nectarine
- 1 medium   Fresh peach
- 1   Kiwi
- 1/2   Grapefruit
- 1/2   Mango
- 1 cup   Fresh berries (strawberries, raspberries, or blueberries)
- 1 cup   Fresh melon cubes
- 1/8   Honeydew melon
- 4 oz   Unsweetened juice
- 4 tsp   Jelly or jam

Lean protein choices have 55 calories and 2 to 3 grams of fat per serving. One serving equals:
- 1 oz   Chicken—dark meat, skin removed
- 1 oz   Turkey—dark meat, skin removed
- 1 oz   Salmon, swordfish, herring, catfish, trout
- 1 oz   Lean beef (flank steak, London broil, tenderloin, roast beef)*
- 1 oz   Veal, roast, or lean chop*
- 1 oz   Lamb, roast, or lean chop*
- 1 oz   Pork, tenderloin, or fresh ham*
- 1 oz   Lowfat luncheon meats (with 3 grams or less of fat per ounce)
- 1/4 cup   4.5% cottage cheese
- 2 medium   Sardines

*Limit to 1 to 2 times per week.

Starches contain 15 grams of carbohydrate and 80 calories per serving. One serving equals:
- 1 slice   Bread (white, pumpernickel, whole wheat, rye)
- 2 slice   Reduced calorie or "lite" bread
- 1/4 (1 oz)   Bagel (varies)
- 1/2   English muffin
- 1/2   Hamburger bun
- 3/4 cup   Cold cereal
- 1/3 cup   Rice, brown or white—cooked
- 1/3 cup   Barley or couscous—cooked
- 1/3 cup   Legumes (dried beans, peas, or lentils)—cooked
- 1/2 cup   Pasta—cooked
- 1/2 cup   Bulgur—cooked
- 1/2 cup   Corn, sweet potato, or green peas
- 3 oz   Baked sweet or white potato
- 3/4 oz   Pretzels
- 3 cups   Popcorn, hot-air popped or microwave (80-percent light)

SOURCE: "Appendix E. Food Exchange List," in *The Practical Guide: Identification, Evaluation, and Treatment of Overweight and Obesity in Adults*, National Institutes of Health, National Heart, Lung, and Blood Institute, North American Association for the Study of Obesity, October 2000, http://www.nhlbi.nih.gov/guidelines/obesity/prctgd_b.pdf (accessed November 2, 2009)

concerns about low carbohydrates expressed by the American Dietetic Association and the American Heart Association. Both organizations had warned that low-carbohydrate diets may lead to abnormal metabolic functioning that in turn may prompt serious medical consequences, particularly for participants with cardiovascular disease, Type 2 diabetes, hyperlipidemia (an excess of fats called lipids, chiefly cholesterol and triglycerides, in the blood), or hypertension. Specifically, it has been cautioned that low-carbohydrate diets cause the accumulation of ketones, which may result in abnormal metabolism of insulin, impaired liver and kidney function, and salt and water depletion that may cause postural hypotension (sudden drop in blood pressure when rising from sitting) as well as fatigue, constipation, and kidney stones. It has also been posited that excessive consumption of animal proteins and fats may promote hyperlipidemia and that higher dietary protein loads may impair kidney function.

Bravata et al. find that diets that restricted calorie intake and were longer in duration were associated with weight loss. They also observe that when lower-carbohydrate diets resulted in weight loss, it was likely because of the restriction of caloric intake and longer duration rather than changes in carbohydrate intake. The researchers note that at least in the short term, low-carbohydrate diets were not associated with the anticipated adverse

TABLE 5.13

Low calorie, lower fat food alternatives

Instead of...		Replace with...
• Evaporated whole milk		• Evaporated fat free (skim) or reduced fat (2%) milk
• Whole milk		• Low fat (1%), reduced fat (2%), or fat free (skim) milk
• Ice cream		• Sorbet, sherbet, lowfat or fat free frozen yogurt, or ice milk (check label for calorie content)
• Whipping cream		• Imitation whipped cream (made with fat free [skim] milk) or lowfat vanilla yogurt
• Sour cream		• Plain lowfat yogurt
• Cream cheese	**Dairy**	• Neufchatel or "light" cream cheese or fat free cream cheese
• Cheese (cheddar, Swiss, jack)	**Products**	• Reduced calorie cheese, low calorie processed cheese, etc.
		• Fat free cheese
• American cheese		• Fat free American cheese or other types of fat free cheeses
• Regular (4%) cottage cheese		• Lowfat (1%) or reduced fat (2%) cottage cheese
• Whole milk mozzarella cheese		• Part skim low-moisture mozzarella cheese
• Whole milk ricotta cheese		• Part skim milk ricotta cheese
• Coffee cream (half and half) or nondairy creamer (liquid, power)		• Low fat (1%) or reduced fat (2%) milk or nonfat dry milk power
• Ramen noodles		• Rice or noodles (spaghetti, macaroni, etc.)
• Pasta with white sauce (alfredo)	**Cereals, grains**	• Pasta with red sauce (marinara)
• Pasta with cheese sauce	**and pasta**	• Pasta with vegetables (primavera)
• Granola		• Bran flakes, crispy rice, etc.
		• Cooked grits or oatmeal
		• Whole grains (e.g., couscous, barley, bulgur, etc.)
		• Reduced fat granola
• Cold cuts or lunch meats (bologna, salami, liverwurst, etc.)		• Lowfat cold cuts (95% to 97% fat free lunch meats, lowfat pressed meats)
• Hot dogs (regular)		• Lower fat hot dogs
• Bacon or sausage		• Canadian bacon or lean ham
• Regular ground beef		• Extra lean ground beef such as ground round or ground turkey (read labels)
• Chicken or turkey with skin, duck, or goose		• Chicken or turkey without skin (white meat)
• Oil-packed tuna		• Water-packed tuna (rinse to reduce sodium content)
• Beef (chuck, rib, brisket)	**Meat, fish,**	• Beef (round, loin) (trimmed of external fat) (choose select grades)
• Pork (spareribs, untrimmed loin)	**and poultry**	• Pork tenderloin or trimmed, lean smoked ham
• Frozen breaded fish or fried fish (homemade or commercial)		• Fish or shellfish, unbreaded (fresh, frozen, canned in water)
• Whole eggs		• Egg whites or egg substitutes
• Frozen TV dinners (containing more than 13 gram of fat per serving)		• Frozen TV dinners (containing less than 13 grams of fat per serving and lower in sodium)
• Chorizo sausage		• Turkey sausage, drained well (read label)
		• Vegetarian sausage (made with tofu)
• Croissants, brioches, etc.		• Hard French rolls or soft "brown 'n serve" rolls
• Donuts, sweet rolls, muffins, scones, or pastries		• English muffins, bagels, reduced fat or fat free muffins or scones
• Party crackers		• Lowfat crackers (choose lower in sodium)
• Saltine or soda crackers (choose lower in sodium)	**Baked goods**	
• Cake (pound, chocolate, yellow)		• Cake (angel food, white, gingerbread)
• Cookies		• Reduced fat or fat free cookies (graham crackers, ginger snaps, fig bars) (compare calorie level)
• Nuts	**Snacks and**	• Popcorn (air-popped or light microwave), fruits, vegetables
• Ice cream, e.g., cones or bars	**sweets**	• Frozen yogurt, frozen fruit, or chocolate pudding bars
• Custards or puddings (made with whole milk)		• Puddings (made with skim milk)
• Regular margarine or butter		• Light-spread margarines, diet margarine, or whipped butter, tub or squeeze bottle
• Regular mayonnaise		• Light or diet mayonnaise or mustard
• Regular salad dressings	**Fats, oils, and**	• Reduced calorie or fat free salad dressings, lemon juice, or plain, herb-flavored, or wine vinegar
	salad dressings	
• Butter or margarine on toast or bread		• Jelly, jam, or honey on bread or toast
• Oils, shortening, or lard		• Nonstick cooking spray for stir-frying or sautéing
		• As a substitute for oil or butter, use applesauce or prune puree in baked goods
• Canned cream soups		• Canned broth-based soups
• Canned beans and franks	**Miscellaneous**	• Canned baked beans in tomato sauce
• Gravy (home made with fat and/or milk)		• Gravy mixes made with water or homemade with the fat skimmed off and fat free milk included
• Fudge sauce		• Chocolate syrup
• Avocado on sandwiches		• Cucumber slices or lettuce leaves
• Guacamole dip or refried beans with lard		• Salsa

SOURCE: "Appendix C. Instead of...Replace with...," in *The Practical Guide: Identification, Evaluation, and Treatment of Overweight and Obesity in Adults*, National Institutes of Health, National Heart, Lung, and Blood Institute, North American Association for the Study of Obesity, October 2000, http://www .nhlbi.nih.gov/guidelines/obesity/prctgd_b.pdf (accessed November 2, 2009)

effects on lipid levels, glucose levels, or blood pressure. Furthermore, their findings suggest that people without diabetes tolerated a lower-carbohydrate diet better than higher-carbohydrate alternatives and that this diet may be an effective means of achieving short-term weight loss without significant adverse effects on serum lipid levels, glycemic control, or blood pressure. They caution, however, that there is still inadequate evidence to recommend or condemn the use of low-carbohydrate diets among people with diabetes or for long-term use.

TABLE 5.14

Calories in fat free or reduced fat and regular food

Fat free or reduced fat	Calories	Regular	Calories
Reduced fat peanut butter, 2 T	187	Regular peanut butter, 2 T	191
Cookies		Cookies	
Reduced fat chocolate chip cookies, 3 cookies (30 g)	118	Regular chocolate chip cookies, 3 cookies (30 g)	142
Fat free fig cookies, 2 cookies (30 g)	102	Regular fig cookies, 2 cookies (30 g)	111
Ice cream		Ice cream	
Nonfat vanilla frozen yogurt (1% fat), 1/2 cup	100	Regular whole milk vanilla frozen yogurt (3–4% fat), 1/2 cup	104
Light vanilla ice cream (7% fat), 1/2 cup	111	Regular vanilla ice cream (11% fat), 1/2 cup	133
Fat free caramel topping, 2 T	103	Caramel topping, homemade with butter, 2 T	103
Low fat granola cereal, approx. 1/2 cup (55 g)	213	Regular granola cereal, approx 1/2 cup (55 g)	257
Low fat blueberry muffin, 1 small (2 1/2 inch)	131	Regular blueberry muffin, 1 small (2 1/2 inch)	138
Baked tortilla chips, 1 oz.	113	Regular tortilla chips, 1 oz.	143
Low fat cereal bar, 1 bar (1.3 oz.)	130	Regular cereal bar, 1 bar (1.3 oz.)	140

SOURCE: "Fat Free or Reduced Fat [versus] Regular," in *The Practical Guide: Identification, Evaluation, and Treatment of Overweight and Obesity in Adults*, National Institutes of Health, National Heart, Lung, and Blood Institute, North American Association for the Study of Obesity, October 2000, http://www.nhlbi.nih.gov/guidelines/obesity/prctgd_b.pdf (accessed November 2, 2009)

In "Comparison of the Atkins, Ornish, Weight Watchers, and Zone Diets for Weight Loss and Heart Disease Risk Reduction: A Randomized Trial" (*Journal of the American Medical Association*, vol. 293, no. 1, January 5, 2005), Michael L. Dansinger et al. compare the effectiveness of four popular diets: Atkins (low carbohydrates), the Zone (moderate carbohydrates), Ornish (low-fat vegetarian), and Weight Watchers (moderate fat). The researchers report that all the diets helped the subjects to achieve weight loss when they adhered to them. For those participants who adhered, weight loss and cardiac risk factor reduction were comparable for participants on the low-carbohydrate, moderate-carbohydrate, and moderate-fat plans. Low-carbohydrate and low-fat diets did, however, have different effects on cardiovascular risk profiles. Low-carbohydrate diets consistently increased HDL cholesterol, and low-fat diets consistently decreased LDL cholesterol levels.

Dansinger et al. reiterate the importance of tailoring the selection of a weight-loss diet to ensure adherence, asserting that "more research is also needed to identify practical techniques to increase dietary adherence, including techniques to match individuals with the diets best suited to their food preferences, lifestyle, and medical conditions."

In 2004 two published studies reaffirmed the safety and efficacy of low-carbohydrate diets. In the first study, "A Low-Carbohydrate, Ketogenic Diet versus a Low-Fat Diet to Treat Obesity and Hyperlipidemia: A Randomized, Controlled Trial" (*Annals of Internal Medicine*, vol. 140, no. 10, May 18, 2004), William Yancy Jr. et al. assigned 120 study participants to a low-carbohydrate, high-protein diet or a low-fat, low-cholesterol, low-calorie diet. The low-carbohydrate group was allowed unlimited calories, animal foods (meat, fowl, fish, and shellfish), and eggs, as well as 4 ounces (113 g) of hard cheese, 2 cups of salad vegetables (lettuce, spinach, or celery), and 1 cup of low-carbohydrate vegetables (broccoli, cauliflower, or squash). The low-fat, low-cholesterol, low-calorie group consumed less than 30% of daily caloric intake from fat, less than 10% of calories from saturated fat, and less than 300 milligrams of cholesterol daily. After six months, weight loss was greater in the low-carbohydrate diet group than in the low-fat diet group. Compared with the low-fat diet group, the low-carbohydrate diet group had greater decreases in serum triglyceride levels and greater increases in HDL cholesterol levels.

In the second study, "A Low-Carbohydrate, Ketogenic Diet versus a Low-Fat Diet to Treat Obesity and Hyperlipidemia: A Randomized, Controlled Trial" (*Annals of Internal Medicine*, vol. 140, no. 10, May 18, 2004), William Yancy Jr. et al. assigned 120 obese adults to either restrict carbohydrate intake to less than 1.1 ounces (30 g) per day (low-carbohydrate diet) or to restrict caloric intake by 500 calories per day with less than 30% of calories from fat (conventional diet). After one year, weight loss was greater in the low-carbohydrate diet group, and Yancy et al. find that the low-carbohydrate diet group fared better in terms of a greater decrease in triglyceride levels.

In another study, Y. Wady Aude et al. confirm in "The National Cholesterol Education Program Diet vs. a Diet Lower in Carbohydrates and Higher in Protein and Monounsaturated Fat" (*Archives of Internal Medicine*, vol. 164, no. 19, October 25, 2004) that modified low-carbohydrate diets produced greater weight loss than the U.S. National Cholesterol Education Program diet, which replaces saturated fat with carbohydrates.

However, in "Comparison of Weight-Loss Diets with Different Compositions of Fat, Protein, and Carbohydrates" (*New England Journal of Medicine*, vol. 360, no. 9, February 26, 2009), Frank M. Sacks et al. refute the notion that one type of weight-loss diet is better than another. The researchers randomly assigned 811 people to four diets that varied in terms of calories derived from protein, fat, and carbohydrates. The diets consisted of similar foods and met prevailing guidelines for heart health. The subjects were followed for two years. Among the subjects who completed the study, the average weight loss was 8.8 pounds (3.9 kg) and there were no significant differences between the four groups. Satiety, hunger, satisfaction with the diet, and attendance at group sessions were similar for all diets. Sacks et al. conclude that "reduced-calorie diets result in clinically meaningful weight loss regardless of which macronutrients they emphasize." The researchers also note that because the balance of macronutrients is not crucial for weight loss, "diets can also be tailored to individual patients on the basis of their personal and cultural preferences and may therefore have the best chance for long-term success."

Even though there is no single winner in the diet wars, research has dispelled some of the fears about the safety and effectiveness of low-carbohydrate diets. Low-carbohydrate diets appear to be safe and effective in the short term, but long-term outcomes are still unclear. Some results suggest that higher protein and fat intakes lead to lower total caloric intake by producing earlier satiety, but these diets have not been shown to alter fundamental eating behaviors, nor have they demonstrated, as many of their proponents argue, the ability to modify caloric balance such that weight loss persists when more calories are consumed than expended.

Finally, Dansinger et al. indicate that adherence to a diet for one year, rather than to a specific type of diet, is the single most important determinant of weight loss and reduction of risk of cardiovascular disease. The researchers find that the amount of weight lost was associated with the level of dietary adherence but not with the diet type. Dansinger et al. conclude that "one way to improve dietary adherence rates in clinical practice may be to use a broad spectrum of diet options, to better match individual patient food preferences, lifestyles, and cardiovascular risk profiles.... Our findings challenge the concept that 1 type of diet is best for everybody and that alternative diets can be disregarded. Likewise, our findings do not support the notion that very low carbohydrate diets are better than standard diets, despite recent evidence to the contrary."

Gabrielle M. Turner-McGrievy, Neal D. Barnard, and Anthony R. Scialli indicate in "A Two-Year Randomized Weight Loss Trial Comparing a Vegan Diet to a More Moderate Low-Fat Diet" (*Obesity*, vol. 15, no. 1, September 2007), a weight-loss maintenance study that compares vegan diets to the National Cholesterol Education Program (NCEP) diet (a low-calorie, low-fat diet that is high in carbohydrates), that a vegan diet was associated with significantly greater weight loss than the NCEP diet after the one- and two-year follow-ups.

CHAPTER 6

PHYSICAL ACTIVITY, DRUGS, SURGERY, AND OTHER TREATMENTS FOR OVERWEIGHT AND OBESITY

Lack of activity destroys the good condition of every human being, while movement and methodical physical exercise save it and preserve it.

—Plato

One credible hypothesis about the source of the epidemic of overweight and obesity in the United States is the progressive decrease in physical activity expended in daily life—for work, transportation, and household chores. Some researchers contend that the average caloric intake of Americans has not substantially increased; instead, by reducing daily physical activity, the caloric imbalance between calories consumed and expended has shifted to favor weight gain. Even though no data conclusively prove this hypothesis, there is some evidence to support it.

Among the studies that support the premise that Americans' sedentary lifestyle has precipitated the obesity epidemic is a landmark study that examined the diets of an Amish community in Ontario, Canada. In "Physical Activity in an Old Order Amish Community" (*Medicine and Science in Sports and Exercise*, vol. 36, no. 1, January 2004), David R. Bassett, Patrick L. Schneider, and Gertrude E. Huntington describe the "Amish paradox"— that despite a diet that is high in fat, calories, and refined sugar, the Amish community had a scant 4% obesity rate, compared with 31% in the general U.S. population. The researchers chose this particular Amish population because it has rejected technological advances such as automobiles and electricity, and its physically demanding lifestyle is comparable to the way Americans lived 150 years ago. (Other Amish communities that have assumed occupations less physically active than farming have obesity rates that are similar to those found in the general U.S. population.) Bassett, Schneider, and Huntington analyzed the daily routines of 98 Amish people and found that the men averaged 18,425 steps per day and the women 14,196 per day, compared with the recommended 10,000 steps per day that most Americans struggle to

achieve. The Amish men performed about 10 hours per week of vigorous exercise and the women spent 3.4 hours engaged in heavy lifting, shoveling, digging, shoeing horses, or tossing straw bales. The men devoted an additional 42.8 hours per week and the women an average of 39.2 hours to moderate physical activities such as gardening, performing farm-related chores, or doing laundry.

PHYSICAL ACTIVITY

In sharp contrast to the Amish farmers, many Americans are not physically active. The Centers for Disease Control and Prevention (CDC) defines in "How Much Physical Activity Do Adults Need?" (August 21, 2009, http://www.cdc.gov/physicalactivity/everyone/guidelines/adults.html) the minimum recommended physical activity level for adults as: (1) moderate-intensity physical activity for 150 minutes every week and muscle-strengthening activities on at least two days per week or (2) vigorous-intensity physical activity for 75 minutes or more every week and muscle-strengthening activities on at least two days per week. Regardless, Table 6.1 shows that the percent of men and women that are physically inactive during leisure time increases with age. In 2006 more than half (53.4%) of adults aged 65 and older said they were physically inactive during leisure time, compared with about one-third (34.9%) of adults aged 18 to 44. More women were more physically inactive than men of the same age across all age groups except those aged 45 to 54. Furthermore, the proportion of the U.S. population that reported no leisure-time physical activity has decreased from 31% in 1989 to 24% in 2007. (See Figure 6.1.)

The 2009 National Health Interview Survey data reveal that among adults aged 25 to 64 who engage in regular leisure-time physical activity, the gender gap is closing, with comparable percentages of men and women reporting regular physical activity. (See Figure 6.2.) Figure 6.3 shows that non-Hispanic white adults (37.2%)

TABLE 6.1

Physical activity among adults age 18 and older, by selected characteristics, 1998, 2005, and 2006

[Data are based on household interviews of a sample of the civilian noninstitutionalized population]

Characteristic	Inactive[a]			Some leisure-time activity[a]			Regular leisure-time activity[a]		
	1998	2005	2006	1998	2005	2006	1998	2005	2006
					Percent of adults				
18 years and over, age-adjusted[b, c]	40.5	40.5	39.5	30.0	29.3	29.5	29.5	30.2	31.0
18 years and over, crude[c]	40.2	40.5	39.5	30.0	29.3	29.6	29.8	30.1	30.9
Age									
18–44 years	35.2	35.9	34.9	31.4	30.5	30.4	33.5	33.7	34.6
18–24 years	32.8	33.5	34.8	30.1	29.1	27.1	37.1	37.4	38.1
25–44 years	35.9	36.7	35.0	31.8	31.0	31.6	32.4	32.4	33.4
45–64 years	41.2	41.2	39.7	30.6	29.7	30.8	28.2	29.1	29.5
45–54 years	38.9	39.5	38.2	31.4	30.1	30.7	29.8	30.4	31.1
55–64 years	44.9	43.6	41.9	29.3	29.2	30.9	25.8	27.2	27.2
65 years and over	55.4	53.9	53.4	24.7	24.9	24.5	19.9	21.3	22.0
65–74 years	49.1	47.8	48.0	26.5	27.0	25.8	24.4	25.3	26.2
75 years and over	63.3	60.6	59.6	22.4	22.6	23.1	14.3	16.8	17.3
Sex[b]									
Male	37.8	39.1	38.5	28.7	29.2	28.4	33.5	31.8	33.1
Female	42.9	41.7	40.3	31.1	29.5	30.7	26.0	28.8	29.0
Sex and age									
Male :									
18–44 years	32.0	34.4	34.2	30.7	30.5	28.8	37.2	35.1	36.9
45–54 years	37.7	40.2	39.0	29.6	29.4	28.4	32.6	30.4	32.7
55–64 years	44.5	43.4	41.1	26.9	28.0	30.6	28.6	28.7	28.2
65–74 years	45.3	44.7	46.9	23.6	27.5	25.0	31.1	27.8	28.2
75 years and over	57.4	54.1	52.1	21.6	24.0	26.6	20.9	21.9	21.4
Female:									
18–44 years	38.2	37.3	35.6	32.0	30.5	32.0	29.8	32.2	32.4
45–54 years	39.9	38.8	37.5	33.0	30.8	33.0	27.1	30.3	29.5
55–64 years	45.2	43.8	42.6	31.5	30.3	31.1	23.3	25.9	26.3
65–74 years	52.2	50.4	49.0	28.7	26.5	26.5	19.0	23.1	24.5
75 years and over	67.0	64.8	64.4	22.9	21.7	20.8	10.1	13.6	14.7
Race[b, d]									
White only	38.8	38.6	38.2	30.5	29.9	29.9	30.7	31.6	31.9
Black or African American only	52.2	54.7	48.9	25.2	24.1	26.2	22.6	21.2	24.9
American Indian or Alaska Native only	49.2	42.7	32.8	19.0	29.0	37.8	31.8	28.3	29.5
Asian only	39.4	41.0	39.8	35.2	31.3	29.7	25.4	27.6	30.5
Native Hawaiian or other Pacific Islander only	—	*	*	—	*	*	—	*	*
2 or more races	—	40.7	34.2	—	30.9	35.8	—	28.4	30.0
Hispanic origin and race[b, d]									
Hispanic or Latino	55.5	56.7	53.4	23.4	23.3	23.8	21.1	20.0	22.8
Mexican	56.7	54.9	53.9	23.9	24.3	24.2	19.4	20.8	22.0
Not Hispanic or Latino	38.8	38.1	37.3	30.7	30.1	30.4	30.5	31.8	32.3
White only	36.7	35.3	35.3	31.3	30.9	31.0	32.0	33.8	33.8
Black or African American only	52.2	54.6	49.0	25.1	24.3	26.4	22.6	21.1	24.7
Education[e, f]									
No high school diploma or GED	64.8	62.9	62.3	19.4	21.5	21.2	15.8	15.7	16.5
High school diploma or GED	47.6	50.2	47.5	28.7	28.1	29.0	23.7	21.6	23.5
Some college or more	30.2	30.7	29.2	34.3	32.4	33.3	35.5	36.8	37.6
Percent of poverty level[b, g]									
Below 100%	59.4	58.2	56.0	20.5	22.3	23.4	20.1	19.5	20.6
100%–less than 200%	52.2	52.8	50.4	26.2	25.5	25.8	21.6	21.7	23.8
200% or more	34.7	34.5	33.6	32.4	31.4	31.6	33.0	34.1	34.8

were more likely than Hispanic adults (27.7%) and non-Hispanic African-American adults (26%) to participate in regular leisure-time physical activity.

Physical Activity and Weight Loss

Increasing physical activity and exercise is an important element of regimens intended to produce weight loss, even though the addition of exercise to a diet program generally does not produce substantially greater weight loss—most weight lost is attributable to decreased caloric intake. By favorably affecting blood lipids, increased and sustained physical activity does offer many direct and indirect health benefits, including reducing risks for cardiovascular heart disease and Type 2 diabetes beyond the risk reduction possible through diet alone. Physical activity lowers low-density lipoprotein (LDL) cholesterol and triglycerides, increases high-density lipoprotein (HDL) cholesterol, reduces abdominal fat as measured by waist circumference, and may protect against a decrease in muscle mass during weight loss.

TABLE 6.1

Physical activity among adults age 18 and older, by selected characteristics, 1998, 2005, and 2006 [CONTINUED]

[Data are based on household interviews of a sample of the civilian noninstitutionalized population]

Characteristic	Inactive[a]			Some leisure-time activity[a]			Regular leisure-time activity[a]		
	1998	2005	2006	1998	2005	2006	1998	2005	2006
				Percent of adults					
Hispanic origin and race and percent of poverty level [b, d, g]									
Hispanic or Latino:									
Below 100%	68.6	65.9	65.3	18.0	21.1	19.2	13.4	13.0	15.5
100%–less than 200%	60.8	62.7	59.4	21.2	20.4	22.3	18.0	16.9	18.4
200% or more	45.6	48.6	44.3	27.6	26.3	26.7	26.8	25.1	29.0
Not Hispanic or Latino:									
White only:									
Below 100%	53.7	52.1	50.8	22.5	23.5	25.5	23.8	24.4	23.7
100%–less than 200%	49.0	47.6	46.1	27.6	27.5	26.3	23.4	24.9	27.5
200% or more	32.7	31.3	31.2	32.9	32.3	32.5	34.4	36.3	36.3
Black or African American only:									
Below 100%	64.3	65.1	58.7	17.4	18.8	21.8	18.3	16.1	19.4
100%–less than 200%	55.6	60.5	56.2	24.4	23.7	24.3	19.9	15.8	19.5
200% or more	46.0	48.1	41.2	28.7	26.6	29.4	25.3	25.3	29.5
Geographic region[b]									
Northeast	39.4	39.0	36.1	31.3	28.2	31.1	29.4	32.7	32.8
Midwest	37.3	34.3	34.7	31.7	34.3	32.7	31.0	31.4	32.6
South	46.9	47.6	44.8	27.1	25.6	27.2	26.0	26.8	28.0
West	33.9	36.9	38.1	31.6	30.6	28.9	34.6	32.5	33.0
Location of residence[b]									
Within MSA[h]	39.3	39.2	38.0	30.6	29.7	30.2	30.0	31.1	31.8
Outside MSA[h]	44.7	45.7	46.4	27.5	27.9	26.6	27.8	26.5	26.9

*Estimates are considered unreliable.

— Data not available.

[a]All questions related to leisure-time physical activity were phrased in terms of current behavior and lack a specific reference period. Respondents were asked about the frequency and duration of vigorous and light/moderate physical activity during leisure time. Adults classified as inactive reported no sessions of light/moderate or vigorous leisure-time activity of at least 10 minutes duration; adults classified with some leisure-time activity reported at least one session of light/moderate or vigorous physical activity of at least 10 minutes duration but did not meet the definition for regular leisure-time activity; adults classified with regular leisure-time activity reported three or more sessions per week of vigorous activity lasting at least 20 minutes or five or more sessions per week of light/moderate activity lasting at least 30 minutes in duration.

[b]Estimates are age-adjusted to the year 2000 standard population using five age groups: 18–44 years, 45–54 years, 55–64 years, 65–74 years, and 75 years and over. Age-adjusted estimates in this table may differ from other age-adjusted estimates based on the same data and presented elsewhere if different age groups are used in the adjustment procedure.

[c]Includes all other races not shown separately and unknown education level.

[d]The race groups, white, black, American Indian or Alaska Native, Asian, Native Hawaiian or Other Pacific Islander, and 2 or more races, include persons of Hispanic and non-Hispanic origin. Persons of Hispanic origin may be of any race. Starting with 1999 data, race-specific estimates are tabulated according to the 1997 Revisions to the Standards for the Classification of Federal Data on Race and Ethnicity and are not strictly comparable with estimates for earlier years. The five single-race categories plus multiple-race categories shown in the table conform to the 1997 Standards. Starting with 1999 data, race-specific estimates are for persons who reported only one racial group; the category 2 or more races includes persons who reported more than one racial group. Prior to 1999, data were tabulated according to the 1977 Standards with four racial groups and the Asian only category included Native Hawaiian or Other Pacific Islander. Estimates for single-race categories prior to 1999 included persons who reported one race or, if they reported more than one race, identified one race as best representing their race. Starting with 2003 data, race responses of other race and unspecified multiple race were treated as missing, and then race was imputed if these were the only race responses. Almost all persons with a race response of other race were of Hispanic origin.

[e]Estimates are for persons 25 years of age and over and are age-adjusted to the year 2000 standard population using five age groups: 25–44 years, 45–54 years, 55–64 years, 65–74 years, and 75 years and over.

[f]GED stands for General Educational Development high school equivalency diploma.

[g]Percent of poverty level is based on family income and family size and composition using U.S. Census Bureau poverty thresholds. Missing family income data were imputed for 30%–35% of adults 18 years of age and over in 1998–2006.

[h]MSA is metropolitan statistical area. Starting with 2006 data, MSA status is determined using 2000 census data and the 2000 standards for defining MSAs.

Note: Data for additional years are available.

SOURCE: "Table 74. Leisure-Time Physical Activity among Adults 18 Years of Age and over, by Selected Characteristics: United States, Selected Years 1998, 2005, and 2006," in *Health, United States, 2008,* Centers for Disease Control and Prevention, National Center for Health Statistics, 2008, http://www.cdc.gov/nchs/data/hus/hus08.pdf (accessed October 18, 2009)

Like those who have been inactive or sedentary, overweight people are advised to initiate physical activity slowly and gradually. Walking and swimming at a slow pace are ideal activities because they are enjoyable, easy to schedule, and less likely to produce injuries than many competitive sports. Table 6.2 is an example of a walking program that progressively increases physical activity. Furthermore, because amounts of activity and the resulting health benefits are functions of the duration, intensity, and frequency of the activity, the same amounts of activity may be obtained in longer sessions of moderately intense activity such as brisk walking than in shorter sessions of more strenuous activity such as running. Table 6.3 shows how a moderate amount of activity—physical activity that uses about 150 calories of energy per day for a total of about 1,000 calories per week—can be obtained in a variety of ways. The table also indicates how performing common household chores, and even self-care activities such as using a wheelchair, may be used to fulfill requirements for moderate amounts of physical activity. Changing routines to include walking up stairs rather than taking an elevator or parking farther than usual from work or school are ways to increase physical activity incrementally. Even reducing sedentary

FIGURE 6.1

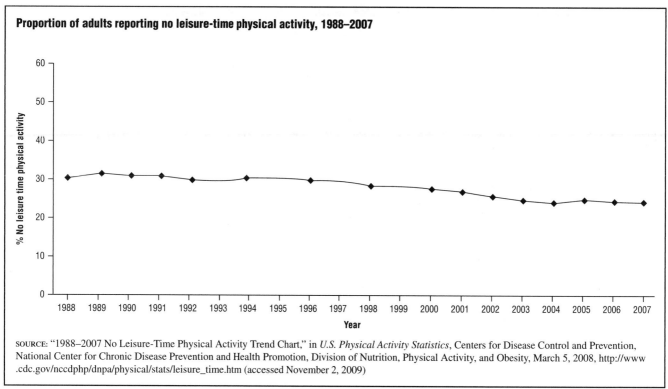

Proportion of adults reporting no leisure-time physical activity, 1988–2007

SOURCE: "1988–2007 No Leisure-Time Physical Activity Trend Chart," in *U.S. Physical Activity Statistics*, Centers for Disease Control and Prevention, National Center for Chronic Disease Prevention and Health Promotion, Division of Nutrition, Physical Activity, and Obesity, March 5, 2008, http://www .cdc.gov/nccdphp/dnpa/physical/stats/leisure_time.htm (accessed November 2, 2009)

time, such as hours spent in front of the television or computer, can serve to increase energy expenditure.

Table 6.3 also shows the relationship between the intensity and duration of physical activities by comparing the amount of time an adult must spend performing each activity to expend 150 calories. It is interesting to note that just five additional minutes of walking at a moderate pace expends the same number of calories as walking at a brisk pace.

In "Effect of Exercise Intensity on Abdominal Fat Loss During Calorie Restriction in Overweight and Obese Postmenopausal Women: A Randomized, Controlled Trial" (*American Journal of Clinical Nutrition*, vol. 89, no. 4, April 2009), Barbara J. Nicklas et al. examine the weight-loss benefits of even moderate exercise. The researchers assigned 112 women to one of three regimes: calorie restriction (CR) only, CR plus moderate-intensity aerobic exercise, or CR plus vigorous-intensity exercise. Nicklas et al. find that the average weight loss was not significantly different across the three groups. However, women in the CR only group lost more lean muscle mass than did the exercisers, suggesting that exercise more effectively produces fat loss and preserves lean muscle mass.

In another study, Cris A. Slentz et al. find in "Effects of the Amount of Exercise on Body Weight, Body Composition, and Measures of Central Obesity: STRRIDE—A Randomized Controlled Study" (*Archives of Internal Medicine*, vol. 164, no. 1, January 12, 2004) a close relationship between exercise and weight loss—increasing

amounts of exercise yielded greater benefits. The study randomly assigned 182 sedentary, overweight adults aged 40 to 65 to one of four groups: a control group with no exercise; supervised low-dose/moderate-intensity exercise equivalent to walking 12 miles (19.3 km) per week; low-dose/vigorous-intensity exercise equivalent to jogging 12 miles (19.3 km) per week; or high-dose/vigorous-intensity exercise equivalent to jogging 20 miles (32.2 km) per week. The subjects were advised to maintain their weight and not to change their diet. Slentz et al. followed the subjects for eight months and then measured weight, body fat, waist circumference, and lean muscle mass.

Weight change was a 3.5% loss in the high-dose/ vigorous-intensity group and about a 1% loss in the two low-dose exercise groups, compared with a 1.1% gain in the control group. Increases in lean body mass were 1.4% in the two vigorous-intensity groups and 0.7% in the low-intensity group. Body fat mass increased by 0.5% in the control group and decreased by 2% in the low-dose/moderate-intensity group, by 2.6% in the low-dose/vigorous-intensity group, and by 4.9% in the high-dose/vigorous-intensity group. Waist circumference increased by 0.8% in the control group and decreased by 1.6% in the low-dose/moderate-intensity group, by 1.4% in the low-dose/vigorous-intensity group, and by 3.4% in the high-dose/vigorous-intensity group. The three exercise groups also had significantly decreased waist and hip circumference measurements compared with the control group.

FIGURE 6.2

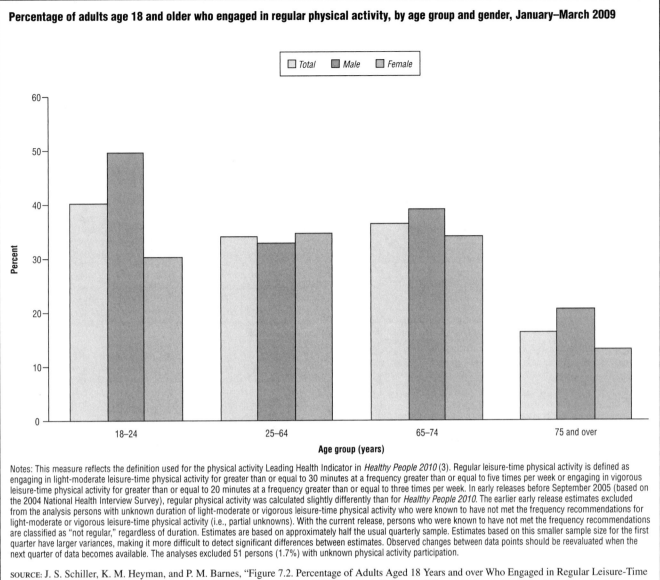

Percentage of adults age 18 and older who engaged in regular physical activity, by age group and gender, January–March 2009

Notes: This measure reflects the definition used for the physical activity Leading Health Indicator in *Healthy People 2010* (3). Regular leisure-time physical activity is defined as engaging in light-moderate leisure-time physical activity for greater than or equal to 30 minutes at a frequency greater than or equal to five times per week or engaging in vigorous leisure-time physical activity for greater than or equal to 20 minutes at a frequency greater than or equal to three times per week. In early releases before September 2005 (based on the 2004 National Health Interview Survey), regular physical activity was calculated slightly differently than for *Healthy People 2010*. The earlier early release estimates excluded from the analysis persons with unknown duration of light-moderate or vigorous leisure-time physical activity who were known to have not met the frequency recommendations for light-moderate or vigorous leisure-time physical activity (i.e., partial unknowns). With the current release, persons who were known to have not met the frequency recommendations are classified as "not regular," regardless of duration. Estimates are based on approximately half the usual quarterly sample. Estimates based on this smaller sample size for the first quarter have larger variances, making it more difficult to detect significant differences between estimates. Observed changes between data points should be reevaluated when the next quarter of data becomes available. The analyses excluded 51 persons (1.7%) with unknown physical activity participation.

SOURCE: J. S. Schiller, K. M. Heyman, and P. M. Barnes, "Figure 7.2. Percentage of Adults Aged 18 Years and over Who Engaged in Regular Leisure-Time Physical Activity, by Age Group and Sex: United States, January–March 2009," in *Early Release of Selected Estimates Based on Data from the January–March 2009 National Health Interview Survey*, Centers for Disease Control and Prevention, National Center for Health Statistics, September 2009, http://www.cdc.gov/nchs/data/nhis/earlyrelease/200909_07.pdf (accessed November 2, 2009)

RESEARCHERS RECONSIDER THE ROLE OF EXERCISE IN WEIGHT LOSS AND MAINTENANCE. According to Deborah F. Tate et al., in "Long-Term Weight Losses Associated with Prescription of Higher Physical Activity Goals: Are Higher Levels of Physical Activity Protective against Weight Regain?" (*American Journal of Clinical Nutrition*, vol. 85, no. 4, April 2007), regular exercise and high levels of physical activity help maintain weight loss over time. However, does strenuous exercise really cause weight loss?

In an effort to answer this question, Neil A. King et al. asked 35 overweight people to exercise vigorously enough to burn 500 calories per day for 12 weeks and reported their findings in "Individual Variability Following 12 Weeks of Supervised Exercise: Identification and Characterization of Compensation for Exercise-Induced Weight Loss" (*International Journal of Obesity*, vol. 32, no. 1, January 2008). Even though many of the subjects lost weight during the study, five gained weight—and there was not much variability between dietary changes made by subjects who lost as much as 30 pounds (13.6 kg), those who lost just a few pounds, and those who gained weight. King et al. suggest their results demonstrate that there is considerable variability in the body's compensatory responses to exercise. In other words, moderate exercise may cause some people to lose weight, whereas others find their weight is unchanged or even increases.

In "Exercise Training Prevents Regain of Visceral Fat for 1 Year Following Weight Loss" (*Obesity*, October 8, 2009),

FIGURE 6.3

Percentage of adults age 18 and older who engaged in regular physical activity, by race/ethnicity, January–March 2009

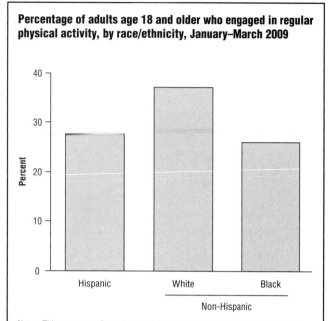

Notes: This measure reflects the definition used for the physical activity Leading Health Indicator in *Healthy People 2010* (3). Regular leisure-time physical activity is defined as engaging in light-moderate leisure-time physical activity for greater than or equal to 30 minutes at a frequency greater than or equal to five times per week or engaging in vigorous leisure-time physical activity for greater than or equal to 20 minutes at a frequency greater than or equal to three times per week. In early releases before September 2005 (based on the 2004 National Health Interview Survey), regular physical activity was calculated slightly differently than for *Healthy People 2010*. The earlier early release estimates excluded from the analysis persons with unknown duration of light-moderate or vigorous leisure-time physical activity who were known to have not met the frequency recommendations for light-moderate or vigorous leisure-time physical activity (i.e., partial unknowns). With the current release, persons who were known to have not met the frequency recommendations are classified as "not regular," regardless of duration. Estimates are based on approximately half the usual quarterly sample. Estimates based on this smaller sample size for the first quarter have larger variances, making it more difficult to detect significant differences between estimates. Observed changes between data points should be reevaluated when the next quarter of data becomes available. The analyses excluded 51 persons (1.7%) with unknown physical activity participation. Estimates are age-sex adjusted using the projected 2000 U.S. population as the standard population and using five age groups: 18–24 years, 25–34 years, 35–44 years, 45–64 years, and 65 years and over.

SOURCE: J. S. Schiller, K. M. Heyman, and P. M. Barnes, "Figure 7.3. Age-Sex-Adjusted Percentage of Adults Aged 18 Years and over Who Engaged in Regular Leisure-Time Physical Activity, by Race/Ethnicity: United States, January–March 2009," in *Early Release of Selected Estimates Based on Data from the January–March 2009 National Health Interview Survey*, Centers for Disease Control and Prevention, National Center for Health Statistics, September 2009, http://www.cdc.gov/nchs/data/nhis/earlyrelease/200909_07.pdf (accessed November 2, 2009)

Gary R. Hunter et al. look at the effects of specific forms of exercise—aerobic training and resistance training—on the gain of visceral fat (fat around the internal organs in the abdomen, which is associated with increased risk of developing heart disease and other health problems) during the year following weight loss. Study subjects were randomly assigned to aerobic training, resistance training, or no exercise training, and computed tomography (a type of imaging study) was used to measure visceral fat. The researchers find that the aerobic exercisers and resistance exercisers gained less weight than the nonexercisers. Furthermore, both groups of exercisers did not gain signifi-

TABLE 6.2

A sample walking program

	Warm up	Exercising	Cool down	Total time
Week 1				
Session A	Walk 5 min.	Then walk briskly 5 min.	Then walk more slowly 5 min.	15 min.
Session B	Repeat above pattern			
Session C	Repeat above pattern			

Continue with at least three exercise sessions during each week of the program.

Week 2	Walk 5 min.	Walk briskly 7 min.	Walk 5 min.	17 min.
Week 3	Walk 5 min.	Walk briskly 9 min.	Walk 5 min.	19 min.
Week 4	Walk 5 min.	Walk briskly 11 min.	Walk 5 min.	21 min.
Week 5	Walk 5 min.	Walk briskly 13 min.	Walk 5 min.	23 min.
Week 6	Walk 5 min.	Walk briskly 15 min.	Walk 5 min.	25 min.
Week 7	Walk 5 min.	Walk briskly 18 min.	Walk 5 min.	28 min.
Week 8	Walk 5 min.	Walk briskly 20 min.	Walk 5 min.	30 min.
Week 9	Walk 5 min.	Walk briskly 23 min.	Walk 5 min.	33 min.
Week 10	Walk 5 min.	Walk briskly 26 min.	Walk 5 min.	36 min.
Week 11	Walk 5 min.	Walk briskly 28 min.	Walk 5 min.	38 min.
Week 12	Walk 5 min.	Walk briskly 30 min.	Walk 5 min.	40 min.

Week 13 on: Gradually increase your brisk walking time to 30 to 60 minutes, three or four times a week. Remember that your goal is to get the benefits you are seeking and enjoy your activity.

SOURCE: "A Sample Walking Program," in *The Practical Guide: Identification, Evaluation, and Treatment of Overweight and Obesity in Adults*, National Institutes of Health, National Heart, Lung, and Blood Institute, North American Association for the Study of Obesity, October 2000, http://www.nhlbi.nih.gov/guidelines/obesity/prctgd_b.pdf (accessed November 2, 2009)

cant visceral fat compared with the nonexercisers, who experienced a 38% increase in visceral fat. According to Hunter et al., "As little as 80 min/week aerobic or resistance training had modest positive effects on preventing weight regain following a diet-induced weight loss. More importantly, both aerobic and resistance training prevented regain of potentially harmful visceral fat."

MEDICATION

Pharmacotherapy for weight loss involves the use of prescription drugs as one of several strategies including diet, physical activity, behavioral therapy, counseling, and participation in group-support programs that in combination can work to effect weight loss. Adding weight-loss medications to a comprehensive treatment program consisting of diet, physical activity, and counseling can increase weight loss by 5 to 20 pounds (2.3 to 9.1 kg) during the first six months of treatment. The decision to add prescription drugs to a treatment program takes into account the individual's body mass index (BMI; body weight in kilograms divided by height in meters squared), other medical problems, and coexisting risk factors. Table 6.4 shows the therapies that are appropriate for people with differing BMIs and takes into account the presence of comorbidities (the coexistence of two or more diseases) such as diabetes, severe obstructive sleep apnea, or heart disease.

TABLE 6.3

Examples of moderate amounts of physical activity

Common chores	Sporting activities	
Washing and waxing a car for 45–60 minutes	Playing volleyball for 45–60 minutes	**Less vigorous more time***
Washing windows or floors for 45–60 minutes	Playing touch football for 45 minutes	
Gardening for 30–45 minutes	Walking 1 3/4 miles in 35 minutes (20 min/mile)	
Wheeling self in wheelchair for 30–40 minutes	Basketball (shooting baskets) for 30 minutes	
Pushing a stroller 1 1/2 miles in 30 minutes	Bicycling 5 miles in 30 minutes	
Raking leaves for 30 minutes	Dancing fast (social) for 30 minutes	
Walking 2 miles in 30 minutes (15 min/mile)	Water aerobics for 30 minutes	
Shoveling snow for 15 minutes	Swimming laps for 20 minutes	
Stairwalking for 15 minutes	Basketball (playing a game) for 15–20 minutes	
	Jumping rope for 15 minutes	**More vigorous, less time**
	Running 1 1/2 miles in 15 minutes	

Note: A moderate amount of physical activity is roughly equivalent to physical activity that uses approximately 150 calories of energy per day, or 1,000 calories per week.
*Some activities can be performed at various intensities; the suggested durations correspond to expected intensity of effort.

SOURCE: "Appendix H. Examples of Moderate Amounts of Physical Activity," in *The Practical Guide: Identification, Evaluation, and Treatment of Overweight and Obesity in Adults*, National Institutes of Health, National Heart, Lung, and Blood Institute, North American Association for the Study of Obesity, October 2000, http://www.nhlbi.nih.gov/guidelines/obesity/prctgd_b.pdf (accessed November 2, 2009)

TABLE 6.4

A guide to selecting weight loss treatment by body mass index (BMI)

Treatment	BMI category				
	25–26.9	27–29.9	30–34.9	35–39.9	≥40
Diet, physical activity, and behavior therapy	With comorbidities	With comorbidities	+	+	+
Pharmacotherapy		With comorbidities	+	+	+
Surgery				With comorbidities	

- Prevention of weight gain with lifestyle therapy is indicated in any patient with a BMI ≥25 kg/m², even without comorbidities, while weight loss is not necessarily recommended for those with a BMI of 25–29.9 kg/m² or a high waist circumference, unless they have two or more comorbidities.
- Combined therapy with a low-calorie diet (LCD), increased physical activity, and behavior therapy provide the most successful intervention for weight loss and weight maintenance.
- Consider pharmacotherapy only if a patient has not lost 1 pound per week after 6 months of combined lifestyle therapy.

The + represents the use of indicated treatment regardless of comorbidities.

SOURCE: "Table 3. A Guide to Selecting Treatment," in *The Practical Guide: Identification, Evaluation, and Treatment of Overweight and Obesity in Adults*, National Institutes of Health, National Heart, Lung, and Blood Institute, North American Association for the Study of Obesity, October 2000, http://www.nhlbi.nih.gov/guidelines/obesity/prctgd_b.pdf (accessed November 2, 2009)

Most drugs used for weight loss are anorexiants (appetite suppressants), which act on neurotransmitters (chemical substances that convey impulses from one nerve cell to another) in the brain. Anorexiant drugs vary depending on which neurotransmitters they affect: some affect catecholamines such as dopamine and norepinephrine; others affect serotonin; and a third class of drugs acts on more than one neurotransmitter. The drugs act by increasing the secretion of dopamine, norepinephrine, or serotonin, by inhibiting reuptake of neurotransmitters, or by a combination of both mechanisms. For example, sibutramine inhibits the reuptake of norepinephrine and serotonin.

Another class of weight-loss drugs blocks the absorption of fat. Orlistat, which was approved by the U.S. Food and Drug Administration (FDA) in 1999, decreases fat absorption in the digestive tract by about one-third. Because it also inhibits absorption of water and vitamins, some users suffer from cramping and diarrhea.

The determination of which type of drug to prescribe is based on individual patient characteristics—sibutramine works best for people who are preoccupied with food and feel constantly hungry, orlistat may be effective for those who are unwilling to reduce fat from their diet, and phentermine may help reduce food cravings. Even though drug therapy has not demonstrated remarkable effectiveness, only modestly enhancing weight loss over diet alone, consumer demand for weight-loss drugs is high. In February 2007 the FDA approved the over-the-counter (nonprescription) sale of orlistat.

Several weight-loss drugs that appeared effective and were popular among consumers have been withdrawn from the U.S. market due to the number and severity of adverse side effects associated with their use. During the 1990s a combination of two drugs—phentermine and fenfluramine, commonly known as "phen-fen"—was prescribed for long-term use (more than three months); however, rare but unacceptable side effects, including serious damage to the heart valves, prompted the withdrawal of fenfluramine and a similar drug, dexfenfluramine, in September 1997. Phentermine is still approved for short-term use.

Rimonabant acts on the endocannabinoid system to block the so-called munchie receptor, which is believed to stimulate appetite among people who smoke marijuana. Because it blocks cravings, rimonabant was used to aid in weight loss. The drug was originally approved for use in Europe, but the FDA refused to grant marketing approval for it in the United States, largely due to reports of adverse side effects with its use, which were addressed in *Rimonabant Briefing Document* (June 13, 2007, http://www.fda.gov/ohrms/dockets/AC/07/briefing/2007-4306b1-fda-backgrounder.pdf). In November 2008 marketing of rimonabant was suspended in the United Kingdom due to safety concerns, and in January 2009 the European Medicines Agency withdrew its approval of the drug. Data revealed that people taking rimonabant had twice the risk of psychiatric disorders, compared with those taking placebo.

In "Effective Obesity Treatments" (*American Psychologist*, vol. 62, no. 3, April 2007), Lynda H. Powell, James E. Calvin III, and James E. Calvin Jr. of the Rush University Medical Center evaluate the results of published studies of the efficacy (effectiveness) of obesity treatments and conclude that "drug interventions result in modest weight loss with minimal risks but disproportionate clinical benefit. Combinations of lifestyle, drug, and, where appropriate, surgical interventions may be the most efficacious approach to achieving sustained weight loss for the widest diversity of patients."

Research Focuses on New Weight-Loss Drugs

By January 2010 only two weight-loss drugs, orlistat and sibutramine, were FDA-approved for long-term use, and evidence indicates that many users experience so-called rebound weight gain when the use of either of these drugs is discontinued. Regardless, approximately three dozen new drugs were in various stages of development during 2009.

Andrew Pollack reports in "Medicine's Elusive Goal: A Safe Weight-Loss Drug" (*New York Times*, October 16, 2009) that three drug companies hope to obtain FDA approval to market promising new antiobesity drugs. The new formulations combine two drugs, and in clinical trials subjects using them lost between 3% and 10% of their body weight in one year. The most significant challenge in developing effective weight-loss drugs is ensuring their safety, especially because people may have to use them over the course of several years to produce the desired weight loss.

In "Effects of Liraglutide in the Treatment of Obesity: A Randomised, Double-Blind, Placebo-Controlled Study" (*Lancet*, vol. 374, no. 9701, November 7, 2009), Arne Astrup et al. report the results of a study comparing the effect of a new drug, liraglutide, with orlistat or placebo on body weight. Over 560 subjects received liraglutide or placebo by injection or took an oral dose of orlistat. All the subjects reduced their intake by 500 calories per day and increased their physical activity. Subjects taking liraglutide lost significantly more weight than did those on orlistat or the placebo. Liraglutide also reduced blood pressure; however, nausea and vomiting occurred more often in subjects on liraglutide than in those taking the placebo.

According to Gabriele E. Sonnenberg, Glenn Matfin, and Rickey R. Reinhardt, in "Drug Treatments for Obesity: Where Are We Heading and How Do We Get There?" (*British Journal of Diabetes and Vascular Disease*, vol. 7, no. 3, 2007), more effective drug therapy will likely target multiple systems, such as the gastrointestinal (digestive) system as well as the endocrine and neurological pathways. There is also enthusiasm for the development of a drug that increases the body's metabolic rate because it might enable people to forgo severely restricted diets and still realize weight loss.

Nonprescription Weight-Loss Aids

The withdrawal of fenfluramine from the market prompted many consumers to seek alternative weight-loss aids, including herbal preparations that were marketed as dietary supplements and available over the counter. Some preparations combined ephedra, caffeine, and other ingredients. Ephedra (also known by its traditional Chinese medicine name, *ma huang*) is a naturally occurring substance that comes from botanicals. Products containing ephedra and ephedrine have been promoted to accelerate weight loss, increase energy, and improve athletic performance. The principal active ingredient in ephedrine is an amphetamine-like compound that stimulates the nervous system and heart. Because ephedrine has some anorectic and thermogenic properties, it may induce weight loss in some people, and some studies show that when ephedrine is combined with caffeine, the combination may lead to even more weight loss.

During 2003 the FDA and the National Institutes of Health (NIH) investigated reports of adverse effects linked to ephedra use. In *Ephedra and Ephedrine for Weight Loss and Athletic Performance Enhancement: Clinical Efficacy and Side Effects* (February 2003, http://www.ahrq.gov/downloads/pub/evidence/pdf/ephedra/ephedra.pdf), Paul Shekelle et al. of the RAND Corporation conclude that there is only limited evidence of health benefits resulting from ephedra use. These benefits do not outweigh the serious risks posed by its association with heart palpitations, psychiatric and upper gastrointestinal effects, tremors, and insomnia, especially in formulations in which it was combined with caffeine or taken with other stimulants. Shekelle et al. reviewed 16,000 adverse events and identified one seizure, two deaths, four heart attacks, five psychiatric cases, and nine strokes in which ephedra appeared to be the causative agent.

In another study, "The Relative Safety of Ephedra Compared with Other Herbal Products" (*Annals of Internal Medicine*, vol. 138, no. 6, March 18, 2003), Stephen Bent et al. compare the risk for adverse events attributable to ephedra and other herbal products. The researchers find that even though ephedra products made up only 0.8% of all dietary supplement sales in 2001, they accounted for 64% of adverse events associated with dietary supplements. Bent et al. conclude that "the risk for an adverse reaction after the use of ephedra is substantially greater than with other herbal products."

According to the press release "FTC Charges Direct Marketers of Ephedra Weight Loss Products with Making Deceptive Efficacy and Safety Claims" (July 1, 2003, http://www.ftc.gov/opa/2003/07/ephedra.shtm), in July 2003 the Federal Trade Commission (FTC) charged marketers of weight-loss products that contain ephedra with making deceptive efficacy and safety claims. The FTC deemed as examples of "false advertising claims that the ephedra supplements cause rapid, substantial, and permanent weight-loss without diet or exercise, and that 'clinical studies' or 'medical research' prove these claims. The FTC also challenges claims that the ephedra weight-loss products are '100% safe,' 'perfectly safe,' or have 'no side effects.'"

The press release "FDA Announces Plans to Prohibit Sales of Dietary Supplements Containing Ephedra" (http://www.hhs.gov/news/press/2003pres/20031230.html) notes that on December 30, 2003, the U.S. Department of Health and Human Services and the FDA notified manufacturers of dietary supplements containing ephedra that the sale of these dietary supplements would be banned 60 days following publication of the yearend notice. That same day the FDA issued an alert to consumers advising them to stop using ephedra products immediately.

In early 2004 dieters flocked to health food stores and Internet sites selling dietary supplements and bought entire inventories of supplements containing ephedra in anticipation of the ban of its sale. Many of the supplements' fans asserted that the ban was prompted by the publicity surrounding the ephedra-related death of the Baltimore Orioles pitcher Steve Bechler (1979–2003). In February 2003 Bechler collapsed from heatstroke at the Orioles' spring training camp in Florida. Two weeks later the FDA ordered warning labels be placed on products containing ephedra and set in motion plans to ban its sale.

Many health professionals and consumer watchdog agencies applauded the FDA action. However, they also observed that the FDA first proposed warning labels and a dosage curb for ephedra in 1997, but the supplement industry effectively blocked the move. The December 2003 action was a historic occasion—it was the first time the FDA completed the steps necessary to ban the sale of a dietary supplement.

WEIGHT-LOSS DRUG IS AVAILABLE WITHOUT A PRESCRIPTION. In February 2007 orlistat was approved for nonprescription sales, and in 2008 consumers began buying 60-milligram capsules sold under the trade names Alli and Xenical. The introduction of orlistat as an over-the-counter product made it the only FDA-approved product for weight loss since phenylpropanolamine was withdrawn by the FDA. Phenylpropanolamine is an amphetamine-like drug that constricts blood vessels and is used in some nasal decongestants. Because it has an appetite suppressant effect, it was used in diet pills that were sold without a prescription until 2005, when the FDA removed it from over-the-counter sales because it increased the risk of stroke. According to the FDA, in "Early Communication about an Ongoing Safety Review Orlistat (Marketed as Alli and Xenical)" (August 24, 2009, http://www.fda.gov/Drugs/DrugSafety/), in 2009 it analyzed 32 reports of serious liver injuries in users of orlistat and an undisclosed number of suspected cases of liver injury possibly related to the drug. The FDA advised orlistat users to consult their health care professional if they have symptoms such as weakness, fatigue, fever, brown urine, or yellowing of the skin or whites of the eyes, which may indicate the presence of liver problems. The FDA did not advise health care professionals to change their prescribing practices with orlistat.

SURGERY

Weight-loss surgery is considered a treatment option only for people for whom all other treatment methods have failed and who suffer from clinically severe obesity—BMI of 40 or greater or BMI of 35 or greater in the presence of comorbidities. (Clinically severe obesity was formerly known as morbid obesity, indicating its potential to cause disease.) Two types of surgical procedures have been demonstrated effective in producing weight loss maintained for five years: restrictive techniques, which restrict gastric volume, and malabsorptive procedures, which not only limit food intake but also alter digestion. An example of the first type is banded gastroplasty, in which an inflatable band that can be adjusted to different diameters is placed around the stomach. (See Figure 6.4.) The Roux-en-Y gastric bypass is an example of the second type. On average, patients maintain a weight loss of 25% to 40% of their preoperative body weight after these procedures.

The surgery not only improves patients' quality of life by causing weight loss and the resolution of many

FIGURE 6.4

Surgical weight loss procedures

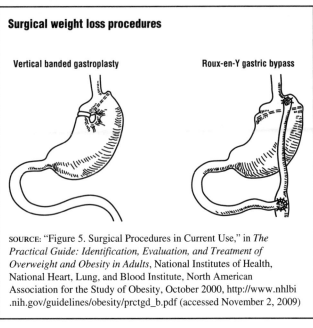

Vertical banded gastroplasty   Roux-en-Y gastric bypass

SOURCE: "Figure 5. Surgical Procedures in Current Use," in *The Practical Guide: Identification, Evaluation, and Treatment of Overweight and Obesity in Adults*, National Institutes of Health, National Heart, Lung, and Blood Institute, North American Association for the Study of Obesity, October 2000, http://www.nhlbi .nih.gov/guidelines/obesity/prctgd_b.pdf (accessed November 2, 2009)

weight-related conditions such as sleep apnea, joint pain, and diabetes, but also reduces their risk of death. Lars Sjöström et al. find in "Effects of Bariatric Surgery on Mortality in Swedish Obese Subjects" (*New England Journal of Medicine*, vol. 357, no, 8, August 23, 2007), a study following 2,010 bariatric surgery patients and a control group consisting of 2,037 obese subjects who did not have surgery, that bariatric surgery was associated with a reduction in overall mortality (death).

Because the surgical procedures are not without risk, physicians generally recommend surgery only when the risks of obesity far outweigh the risks associated with the surgery. The National Heart, Lung, and Blood Institute (NHLBI) explains that surgical complications vary, depending on the weight and overall health of the surgical patient. According to Daniel Leslie, Todd A. Kellogg, and Sayeed Ikramuddin, in "Bariatric Surgery Primer for the Internist: Keys to the Surgical Consultation" (*Medical Clinics of North America*, vol. 91, no. 3, May 2007), young people without comorbidities and a BMI equal to or less than 50 have the lowest reported mortality rates— less than 1%. Not unexpectedly, those with a BMI equal to or greater than 60 with comorbidities such as diabetes or high blood pressure have higher mortality rates.

People who undergo weight-loss surgeries require lifelong medical monitoring. After surgery, they are no longer able to eat in the way to which they were accustomed. Those who have undergone gastric bypass experience "dumping syndrome" with symptoms such as sweating, palpitations, lightheadedness, and nausea when they ingest significant amounts of calorie-dense food, and most become conditioned not to eat such foods. Patients who have had gastric restriction surgery are unable to eat

more than a limited amount of food at a single sitting without vomiting, so they must eat several small meals per day to maintain adequate nutrition. Those who do not adhere to a prescribed regimen of vitamins and minerals may develop vitamin and iron deficiencies. There are also postoperative and long-term complications of surgery such as wound infections, hernias at the incision site, and gallstones. Generally, however, patients fare extremely well, experiencing dramatic improvement and even complete resolution of diabetes, hypertension (high blood pressure), and infertility, as well as improved mobility, self-esteem, and overall quality of life.

The article "Gastric Bypass Surgery May Cause Post-op Nutrient Deficiencies" (Reuters Health Information, October 15, 2007) notes that besides the possibility of nutritional deficiencies, bypass surgery may also cause a condition known as "small intestinal bacterial overgrowth," which interferes with nutrient absorption. Deficiencies in vitamin D, calcium, and zinc may in turn increase the risk of developing other serious conditions such as hypothyroidism (deficiency of the thyroid hormone, which is produced by the thyroid gland) and osteoporosis.

In "Death Rates and Causes of Death after Bariatric Surgery for Pennsylvania Residents, 1995 to 2004" (*Archives of Surgery*, vol. 142, no. 10, October 2007), a study of 16,683 patients who had undergone bariatric surgery, Bennet I. Omalu et al. report an excessive number of patient deaths attributable to coronary artery disease and suicide. Heart disease was the leading cause of death and was responsible for 20% of deaths that occurred 30 days or more after the surgery. This rate is nearly three times higher than in the general population. Another 7% of deaths were attributable to suicide or drug overdose, and the researchers speculate that continued obesity and/or weight regain might have contributed to both the heart disease and suicide deaths.

Number of Weight-Loss Surgeries Soars

Nanci Hellmich states in "Study: Gastric Bypass Reduces Death Risk in the Morbidly Obese" (*USA Today*, August 22, 2007) that 23,100 bariatric procedures were performed in 1997. By 2008 this number increased to 220,000, according to the American Society for Metabolic and Bariatric Surgery in the fact sheet "Metabolic and Bariatric Surgery" (July 2009, http://www.asmbs.org/ Newsite07/media/asmbs_fs_surgery.pdf). For thousands of patients weight-loss surgery has eliminated debilitating diseases and improved their quality of life. With the number of candidates for bariatric surgery increasing, the number of procedures is expected to continue to grow, even in view of data that reveal that the risks may be greater than previously believed.

In "Understanding Patients' Value of Weight Loss and Expectations for Bariatric Surgery" (*Obesity Surgery*, vol. 16, no. 4, April 2006), Christina C. Wee et al. find that even the risk of death does not dissuade many patients from undergoing bariatric surgery. In an effort to quantify the value people place on modest weight loss, the researchers interviewed 44 patients planning to undergo bariatric surgery. The subjects were asked to imagine a treatment that would guarantee them effortless weight loss of varying amounts of weight. For each amount, they were asked if they would be willing to accept a risk of death to achieve it. If so, how much of a risk of death?

Wee et al. find that significantly more patients were willing to risk death to achieve their "dream" weight than to lose 10% or 20% of their total body weight. The researchers conclude that "patients appeared to value weight loss highly but had unrealistic expectations for bariatric surgery."

Many of the overweight and obese participants in the survey also said they would give up some of their remaining years of life if they could live those years weighing slightly less. Thirty-one percent of obese patients and 8.3% of overweight patients said they would trade up to 5% of their remaining life to be 10% thinner. Wee et al. conclude that many people, especially those who are obese, value modest weight loss and suggest that physicians emphasize the benefits of modest weight loss when counseling their patients.

AND BENEFITS OFTEN OUTWEIGH RISKS. David R. Flum et al. find in "Perioperative Safety in the Longitudinal Assessment of Bariatric Surgery" (*New England Journal of Medicine*, vol. 361, no. 5, July 30, 2009), a study of 4,776 bariatric surgery patients, that in the short term (30 days after the surgical procedures were performed) "the overall risk of death and other adverse outcomes after bariatric surgery was low and varied considerably according to patient characteristics," such as higher BMI and coexisting medical conditions and the type of bariatric surgery performed. Flum et al. conclude that "bariatric surgery appears to be the only intervention that consistently results in substantial, sustained weight loss. The safety of such surgery is an important consideration, and our study shows that the incidence of death and adverse events within 30 days after bariatric surgery is low but is varied among different risk groups."

According to Malcolm K. Robinson, in the editorial "Surgical Treatment of Obesity—Weighing the Facts" (*New England Journal of Medicine*, vol. 361, no. 5, July 30, 2009), newer bariatric surgery techniques carry fewer risks than the older ones did and laparoscopic surgeries, which are performed through smaller incisions than traditional open surgeries and entail shorter hospital stays, have been proven effective. Robinson also observes that bariatric surgery "reduces medication use, outpatient visits, and hospitalizations over time. This ultimately may make surgery less costly than the current, less effective nonsurgical treatments of obesity."

COUNSELING AND BEHAVIORAL THERAPY

Weight-loss counseling and behavioral therapy aim to assist people to develop the skills needed to identify and modify eating and activity behaviors and to change thinking patterns that undermine weight-control efforts. Behavioral strategies include self-monitoring of weight, food intake, and physical activity; identifying and controlling stimuli that provoke overeating; problem identification and problem solving; and using family and social support systems to reinforce weight-control efforts. Counseling and behavioral therapy are often perceived as necessary components of comprehensive weight-loss treatment, but are also viewed as labor intensive because educating and supporting people seeking to lose weight is time consuming. The effort also requires the active participation of everyone who may be involved in treatment—the affected individuals, their families, physicians, nurses, nutritionists, dieticians, exercise instructors, and mental health professionals. In view of the considerable resources that must be allocated to deliver counseling and behavioral therapy, it is important to know if these approaches promote weight loss effectively.

Kathleen M. McTigue et al. considered the evidence supporting the efficacy of counseling and behavioral therapy as well as other treatment methods and reported their findings in "Screening and Interventions for Obesity in Adults: Summary of the Evidence for the U.S. Preventive Services Task Force" (*Annals of Internal Medicine*, vol. 139, no. 11, December 2, 2003). The researchers report that counseling to promote change in diet, exercise, or both, and behavioral therapy to help patients acquire the skills, motivations, and support to change diet and exercise patterns enabled obese patients to achieve modest but clinically significant and sustained (one to two years) weight loss. Furthermore, they observe that because control groups also frequently received some form of counseling, education, or support, they might have underestimated the effectiveness of counseling. Not unexpectedly, more intensive programs, with more frequent contact, were generally more successful, as were those incorporating behavioral therapy.

Interestingly, McTigue et al. find that treating patients on an individual basis rather than on a group basis did not appear to affect outcomes. This finding offers credence to the theory that the benefits of mutual aid and peer support provided by group programs may be as powerful as the personalized, one-to-one attention afforded patients in individual counseling sessions. If this is true, then group programs might be a laborsaving, cost-effective alternative to individual weight-loss counseling.

McTigue et al. conclude that "all obesity therapies carry promise and burden, which must be balanced in clinical decision-making. Counseling approaches appear the least harmful and produce modest, clinically important weight loss, but entail cost in time and resources. Pharmacotherapy promotes modest additional weight loss, but long-term drug use may be needed to sustain this benefit with unknown long-term adverse events and appreciable cost. Only surgical options consistently result in large amounts of long-term weight reduction; however, they carry a low risk for severe complications and are expensive. Body size, health status, and prior weight-loss history may all influence obesity treatment."

Michael L. Dansinger et al. of Tufts–New England Medical Center in Boston, Massachusetts, reviewed 46 studies that looked at the effects of dietary counseling to determine its effect on long-term weight change. The review "Meta-analysis: The Effect of Dietary Counseling for Weight Loss" (*Annals of Internal Medicine*, vol. 147, no. 1, July 3, 2007) reveals that dietary counseling interventions produced an average net weight loss of approximately 2 BMI units (6%) at 12 months, compared with usual care. In addition, it found that typically about half of the initial weight loss was regained after three years. Dansinger et al. also find diminishing net treatment effects with increasing duration of intervention—the initial weight difference observed between people who received counseling and those who did not narrowed considerably over the subsequent four years.

Comparing Weight-Loss Using a Self-Help Program and a Commercial Program

Stanley Heshka et al. report the results of their research to determine the efficacy of commercial weight-loss programs in "Weight Loss with Self-Help Compared with a Structured Commercial Program" (*Journal of the American Medical Association*, vol. 289, no. 14, April 9, 2003). Their study randomly assigned one group of obese men and women to a self-help program consisting of two 20-minute counseling sessions with a nutritionist and access to self-help resources such as public library materials, Web sites, and telephone numbers of health organizations that offered free weight-control information. The other group was assigned to attend Weight Watchers, a commercial weight-loss program consisting of weekly meetings, a food plan, an exercise plan consistent with NIH-recommended physical activity guidelines, a behavior modification plan, regular weight monitoring, and printed educational materials.

The subjects were evaluated regularly during the course of the two-year study at 12, 26, 52, 78, and 104 weeks. The primary outcome measure used to evaluate the effectiveness of the programs was change in body weight; however, BMI, waist circumference, and body fat as quantified by bioimpedance analysis (electrical resistance) were also recorded. Other secondary measures were blood pressure, total cholesterol, HDL cholesterol, triglycerides, insulin, and quality of life.

After one year of participation in the study, subjects in the commercial program had greater weight loss than those in the self-help group. Similarly, waist circumference and BMI decreased more in the commercial group than in the self-help group. Blood pressure and serum insulin showed greater improvement in the commercial group, compared with the self-help group at year one, but only insulin was significantly different at year two. Total cholesterol and the HDL/total cholesterol ratio improved in both groups. The self-help group was able to lose approximately 2.8 to 3.1 pounds (1.3 to 1.4 kg) per person for the first year; however, these subjects had returned to their pretreatment weight by the end of the second year. The commercial group maintained a weight loss of 9.5 to 11 pounds (4.3 to 5 kg) per person at the end of the first year and each was 5.9 to 6.6 pounds (2.7 to 3 kg) lower than the initial weight at the end of the second year. Subjects who attended 78% or more of the commercial group sessions maintained a mean (average) weight loss of almost 11 pounds (5 kg) at the end of the two-year study. Heshka et al. conclude that even though the structured commercial weight-loss program provided only modest weight loss, it was more effective than brief counseling and self-help for overweight and obese adults over a two-year period.

Weight-Loss Counseling to Change Behavior

The NIH designed a practical protocol, known as an algorithm, for obtaining and organizing information necessary for effective weight-loss counseling. The algorithm is based on the "five As":

- Assessing obesity risk
- Asking about readiness to lose weight
- Advising about a weight-control program
- Assisting to establish appropriate intervention
- Arranging for follow-up

The NHLBI recommends in *Practical Guide to the Identification, Evaluation, and Treatment of Overweight and Obesity in Adults* (October 2000, http://www.nhlbi.nih.gov/guidelines/obesity/prctgd_c.pdf) that health care professionals consider a variety of psychosocial, environmental, and health-related issues when performing a behavioral assessment of an individual for whom weight loss is indicated. These issues include:

- Whether the individual is seeking to lose weight on his or her own or in response to pressure from family members, an employer, or a physician. This is an important consideration because people who feel coerced into seeking weight-loss treatment are not as likely to achieve success as those who seek it on their own initiative.

- Identifying the source of the individual's desire to lose weight to better understand his or her motivation and goals. Because many people have suffered from overweight or obesity for years before seeking treatment, pinpointing the stimulus to lose weight can assist the health care professional to motivate and support the individual's weight-loss efforts.

- Assessing the individual's stress level to determine if external stressors such as family-, financial-, or work-related problems might prevent the individual from concentrating on weight loss. It is also important to determine if the individual is suffering from depression or other mental health problems because it is usually advisable to treat mood disorders or other mental health problems before embarking on a weight-loss program.

- Evaluating the individual for the presence of an eating disorder such as binge eating that may coexist with overweight or obesity. People suffering from eating disorders are more likely to require psychological treatment and nutritional counseling to ensure the success of weight-loss programs than those who do not have eating disorders.

- Determining the individual's understanding of the lifestyle and other changes required for weight loss. The success of treatment hinges on the individual's ability to successfully make the required changes, so it is vital to develop a treatment plan that includes realistic activities such as gradually increasing physical activity that the individual agrees are attainable.

- Setting and agreeing on realistic weight-loss goals and objectives. If an obese individual has unrealistic expectations about the amount of weight that will be lost, then he or she may become discouraged and abandon efforts to lose weight. Health professionals should temper unrealistic expectations by informing individuals about the considerable health and lifestyle benefits of even modest weight loss.

Successful weight loss is more likely to occur when health care professionals—physicians, nurses, nutritionists, dieticians, and mental health professionals—actively involve people seeking to lose weight in a collaborative effort to establish short-term goals and attain them. Shaping is a behavioral technique in which a series of short-term objectives are identified that ultimately leads to a treatment goal, such as incrementally increasing physical activity from 10 minutes per day to 45 minutes per day over time. Self-monitoring is the practice of observing and recording behaviors such as caloric intake, food choices, amounts consumed, and emotional or other triggers to eat

as well as physical activity performed and daily or weekly monitoring of body weight.

Finally, the NHLBI encourages health professionals to "acknowledge the challenging nature of weight control by adopting problem-solving responses to goals that are not fully met. Emphasize that examining the circumstances of unmet goals can lead to new and more effective strategies.... Emphasize that weight control is a journey, not a destination, and that some missteps are inevitable opportunities to learn how to be more successful."

Weight-Loss Counseling Online

An expanding array of diet, counseling, and support group programs are available on the Internet; however, little research has compared them or determined their efficacy. In "A Randomized Trial Comparing Human E-Mail Counseling, Computer-Automated Tailored Counseling, and No Counseling in an Internet Weight Loss Program" (*Archives of Internal Medicine*, vol. 166, no. 15, August 2006), Deborah F. Tate, Elizabeth H. Jackvony, and Rena R. Wing sought to determine whether computer-generated feedback, delivered via the Internet, would prove to be a viable alternative to human counseling via e-mail. They compared the effects of custom-tailored computer-automated interactions with an Internet program that provided weight-loss counseling from a human via e-mail.

Participants were randomly selected to be in one of three treatment groups: human e-mail counseling, computer-automated feedback, or no counseling. All the subjects received one weight-loss group session, coupons for meal replacements, and access to an interactive Web site, but the human e-mail counseling and computer automated feedback groups also had access to an electronic diary and a message board. The human e-mail counseling group received weekly e-mail feedback from a counselor, the computer-automated feedback group received automated, custom-tailored messages, and the control group did not receive any counseling. Recommendations included calorie-restricted diets of between 1,200 and 1,500 calories per day, daily exercise equivalent to walking for 30 minutes, and instructions about how to use meal replacement products. All the participants were encouraged to self-monitor their diet and exercise using diaries and calorie books. Both groups accessed the same Web site, which featured weekly reporting and graphs of weight, weekly e-mail prompts to report weight, weekly weight-loss tips via e-mail, recipes, and a weight-loss e-buddy network system that enabled users to interact with other dieters with similar characteristics via e-mail.

The primary outcome measure used to compare the groups was change in body weight from baseline and at three and six months. Both the human and automated e-counseling groups had greater reductions in weight than the control group at each weigh-in. Tate, Jackvony, and Wing conclude that automated computer feedback was as effective as human e-mail counseling.

In "Minimal In-Person Support as an Adjunct to Internet Obesity Treatment" (*Annals of Behavioral Medicine*, vol. 33, no. 1, February 2007), Nicci Micco et al. of the University of Vermont, Burlington, confirm the efficacy of online counseling for weight loss. The researchers compared the weight loss of people using Internet-only behavioral weight-loss treatment with people using the same program and having monthly in-person meetings. Over 120 subjects were randomly assigned to either an Internet-only or an Internet and in-person treatment plan. All the subjects participated in a 12-month behavioral weight-loss program conducted over the Internet. The online groups met weekly for the first six months and biweekly for the remaining six months. The Internet and in-person group had access to the same Web site as the Internet-only group but once a month subjects had an in-person meeting instead of an online chat. Micco et al. find that there were no significant differences in weight loss between the two groups and conclude that "dynamic, socially supportive, and interactive elements of the Web site may have obviated the need for further interpersonal behavioral counseling."

Complementary and Alternative Therapies

Many complementary and alternative medicine practices such as yoga, Dahn (a holistic mind-body training method), and mindful eating, which teaches greater awareness of bodily sensations such as hunger and satiety and helps people to identify "emotional eating," have been used to promote weight loss. However, acupuncture (the Chinese practice of inserting extremely thin, sterile needles into any of 360 specific points on the body) and hypnosis are the only alternative medical practices that have been studied as potential treatments for obesity. Several studies report that acupuncture does not appear to have any benefit greater than a placebo.

Hypnosis is an altered state of consciousness. It is a state of heightened awareness and suggestibility and enables focused concentration that may be used to alter perceptions of hunger and satiety and to modify behavior. Hypnosis is considered a mainstream treatment for addictions and overeating. Regardless, there are conflicting data about its effectiveness—some studies find that it adds little, if any, benefit beyond that of placebo, whereas others conclude that hypnosis may have some initial benefit for people seeking weight loss, but that it has little sustained effect.

In "Complementary Therapies for Reducing Body Weight: A Systematic Review" (*International Journal of Obesity*, vol. 29, no. 9, September 2005), Max H. Pittler and Edzard Ernst review the published literature describing a variety of complementary and alternative medicine therapies for weight loss. The researchers find that subjects receiving hypnotherapy lost more weight than subjects in a control group that did not receive hypnotherapy; that the addition of hypnotherapy to cognitive behavioral therapy led to a small reduction in body weight; and that patients in a small hypnotherapy group aimed at stress management lost significantly more weight than those in a control group.

According to E. Paul Cherniack of the Miami Veterans Affairs Medical Center, in "Potential Applications for Alternative Medicine to Treat Obesity in an Aging Population" (*Alternative Medicine Review*, vol. 13, no. 1, March 2008), herbal medications and dietary supplements such as conjugated linoleic acids, chitosan, Garcinia cambogia, and Citrus aurantium are being used to promote weight loss. Cherniack observes that these herbal preparations and supplements have demonstrated some benefit but have not yet been rigorously tested. As a result, health care professionals cannot definitively recommend their use. He avers that these remedies as well as acupuncture and hypnotherapy be evaluated in well-designed clinical trials to confirm whether they can play a role in combating obesity.

MIGHT WEIGHT LOSS BE HARMFUL?

Successful weight-loss treatments generally result in reduced blood pressure, reduced triglycerides, reduced total cholesterol and LDL cholesterol, and increased HDL cholesterol. Weight loss of as little as 5% to 10% of initial weight produces measurable health benefits and may prevent illnesses among people at risk. These findings suggest that treatment should not exclusively focus on the medical consequences of obesity, but that obesity itself should be treated. The NIH guidelines recommend weight loss for people with a BMI greater than 30 and for people with a BMI greater than 25 with two or more obesity-related risk factors. The guidelines also recommend that for people with a BMI between 25 and 30 without other risk factors, the focus should be on prevention of further weight gain, rather than on weight loss.

In "Weight Cycling and Mortality among Middle-Aged or Older Women" (*Archives of Internal Medicine*, vol. 169, no. 9, May 11, 2009), Alison E. Field, Susan Malspeis, and Walter C. Willett of the Harvard School of Public Health report that the health risks of weight cycling (the repeated loss and regain of body weight) are not as serious as previously assumed. Field et al. analyzed the relationship between mortality, intentional weight loss, and mild or severe weight cycling. Subjects who said they had intentionally lost at least 20.1 pounds (9.1 kg) at least three times were classified as severe weight cyclers, and those who had intentionally lost at least 9.9 pounds (4.5 kg) at least three times were classified as mild weight cyclers. Field et al. find that during the 12 years of follow-up there was no increase in mortality associated with either mild or severe weight cyclers.

Is It Better to Be Overweight?

Two studies indicate that there is less risk associated with overweight than previously thought. The first, Katherine M. Flegal et al.'s "Excess Deaths Associated with Underweight, Overweight, and Obesity" (*Journal of the American Medical Association*, vol. 293, no. 15, April 20, 2005), indicates that increased risk of death from obesity was mostly among the extremely obese, a group accounting for 8% of the total American population. The researchers also find that extreme thinness carried a slight increase risk of death. Flegal et al.'s study does not explain how or why being slightly overweight affords protection, but they speculate that it is because most people die when they are over 70 years of age. Being mildly overweight in old age may be protective, because it gives rise to more muscle and bone.

The second study, "Secular Trends in Cardiovascular Disease Risk Factors According to Body Mass Index in U.S. Adults" (*Journal of the American Medical Association*, vol. 293, no. 15, April 20, 2005) by Edward W. Gregg et al., examines 40-year trends in cardiovascular disease (CVD) risk factors by BMI groups among adults aged 20 to 74 years. The researchers find that except for diabetes, CVD risk factors have declined considerably over the past 40 years in all BMI groups. Even though obese people still have higher risk-factor levels than lean people, the levels of these risk factors are much lower than in previous decades. Gregg et al. observe that obese people in the 21st century have better CVD risk-factor profiles than their leaner counterparts did 20 to 30 years ago; however, they suggest that other factors, such as effective treatment to reduce cholesterol and blood pressure as well as the decreased prevalence of smoking, might explain the improved profiles of obese people.

The health risks and consequences of obesity are well understood, but the risk of mortality associated with overweight remains unclear. In "BMI and Mortality: Results from a National Longitudinal Study of Canadian Adults" (*Obesity*, vol. 18, no. 1, January 2010), Heather M. Opana et al. estimate the relationship between BMI and mortality in a representative sample of 11,326 adults. The researchers find that overweight (BMI 25 to 30) was associated with a significantly decreased risk of death, whereas underweight (BMI less than 18.5) was associated with a significantly increased risk of death, as was class II obesity (BMI greater than 35). Interestingly, class I obesity (BMI 30 to 35) was found to not have an increased risk of mortality. Opana et al. conclude that "when compared to the acceptable BMI category, overweight appears to be protective against mortality."

CHAPTER 7
THE ECONOMICS OF OVERWEIGHT AND OBESITY

The economic impact of obesity is considerable. According to Eric A. Finkelstein et al., in "Annual Medical Spending Attributable to Obesity: Payer- and Service-Specific Estimates" (*Health Affairs*, vol. 28, no. 5, September–October 2009), annual medical care expenditures attributable to overweight and obesity doubled in less than a decade (from 1998 to 2006) and may be as high as $147 billion per year. During this period obesity (a body mass index [BMI; body weight in kilograms divided by height in meters squared] of greater than 30) increased by 39%, prompting an 89% increase in health care costs attributable to obesity. This $147 billion represents spending for direct health care costs, which are those incurred for diagnostic and treatment services and for preventive measures. Examples of direct health care costs are physician office visits, hospital and nursing home charges, prescription drug costs, and special hospital beds to accommodate obese patients. The indirect costs of overweight and obesity are measured in terms of decreased earnings: lost wages and lower productivity resulting from the inability to work because of illness or disability, as well as the value of future earnings lost by premature mortality (death).

There are other economic consequences and personal costs of obesity: obese workers may earn less than their healthy-weight counterparts because of job discrimination. Many insurance companies, particularly in the life insurance sector, charge higher premiums with increasing degrees of overweight. When obesity compromises physical functioning and limits activities of daily living, affected individuals may require assistance from home health aides, durable medical equipment such as walkers or wheelchairs, or other costly adaptations to accommodate disability.

THE HIGH COST OF OVERWEIGHT AND OBESITY

The National Center for Chronic Disease Prevention and Health Promotion calculates and compares in *Chronic*

Disease Prevention (August 7, 2009, http://www.cdc.gov/nccdphp/press/index.htm#3) the economic burden of several chronic diseases including overweight and obesity. Table 7.1 shows that the health costs resulting from obesity ($117 billion) in 2000 were greater than those resulting from tobacco use ($96 billion). Because obesity has been linked to all the other chronic conditions described in Table 7.1 except tobacco use, it may be argued that some percentage of the costs attributed to arthritis, cancer, diabetes, heart disease, and stroke are also attributable to obesity. It is important to remember that estimates of the medical care costs, direct and indirect as well as total cost of overweight and obesity in the United States, vary depending on how the conditions are defined, whether overweight and obesity are considered together or separately, and which costs and obesity-related conditions are included in the estimates and projections.

Finkelstein et al. estimate that the direct cost of overweight and obesity in 2006 was 9.1% of the total U.S. health care expenditures, up from 6.5% in 1998. Of this 9.1%, 3.7% was attributable to overweight and 5.3% to obesity. An obese person incurred about 42% more costs than a healthy-weight person, which translates into $1,429 more (per obese person) per year for medical care. The majority of these dollars are spent treating obesity-related diseases and disorders.

According to Finkelstein et al., the estimated increase associated with being overweight was 14.5% ($247) and ranged from 11.4% ($53) for out-of-pocket spending to 15.1% ($271) for Medicaid (the state and federally funded entitlement program that pays for medical care for people unable to afford it) spending. The average increase in annual medical spending associated with obesity was 37.4% ($732) and ranged from 26.1% ($125) for out-of-pocket spending to 36.8% ($1,486) for Medicare (the federally administered system of health insurance for people aged 65 and older and people with disabilities)

TABLE 7.1

Economic and health burden of chronic disease, selected years 1979–2008

Disease/risk factors	Morbidity (illness)	Mortality (death)	Direct cost/indirect cost
Arthritis	Arthritis affects 1 in 5, or 46 million, US adults, making it one of the most common chronic conditions. Nearly 19 million US adults report activity limitations because of arthritis each year. By 2030, nearly 67 million US adults are projected to have doctor-diagnosed arthritis and more than one-third of these adults will have limited activity as a result.	From 1979–1998, the annual number of arthritis and other related rheumatic conditions (AORC) deaths rose from 5,537 to 9,367. In 1998, the crude death rate from AORC was 3.48 per 100,000 population.	The total costs attributable to arthritis and other rheumatic conditions (AORC) in the United States in 2003 was approximately $128 billion ($80.8 billion in medical care expenditures and $47 billion in earnings losses) This equaled 1.2% of the 2003 U.S. gross domestic product.
Cancer	More than 1.3 million people in the U.S. are diagnosed with cancer each year.	Cancer is the second leading cause of death in the United States. In 2005, more than 559,000 Americans died of cancer.	The National Institute of Health estimates that the overall costs for cancer in the year 2008 at $228 billion in medical costs.
Diabetes	More than 23.6 million Americans have diabetes, and about 5.7 million don't know that they have the disease.	Diabetes is the seventh leading cause of death. Over 200,000 people die each year of diabetes-related complications.	The estimated economic cost of diabetes in 2007 was $174 billion. Of this amount, $116 billion was due to direct medical costs and $58 billion to indirect costs such as lost workdays, restricted activity, and disability due to diabetes.
Heart disease and stroke	More than 80 million Americans currently live with a cardiovascular disease.	Cardiovascular diseases, including heart disease and stroke, are the first and third leading causes of death for both men and women in the United States. They account for more than one-third (35.3%) of all U.S. deaths.	The cost of heart disease and stroke in the United States in 2009 is projected to be more than $475 billion including direct and indirect costs.
Overweight/obesity	More than one third of U.S. adults-more than 72 million people-and 16% of U.S. children are obese.	The latest study from CDC scientists estimates that about 112,000 deaths are associated with obesity each year in the United States.	In 2000, obesity-related health care costs totaled an estimated $117 billion.
Tobacco	An estimated 43.4 million adults in the United States smoke cigarettes.	Each year, an estimated 443,000 people die prematurely from smoking or exposure to secondhand smoke, and another 8.6 million have a serious illness caused by smoking.	The economic burden of tobacco use is enormous: more than $96 billion in medical expenditures and another $97 billion in indirect costs.

SOURCE: "Quick Facts: Economic and Health Burden of Chronic Disease," in *Chronic Disease Prevention*, Centers for Disease Control and Prevention, National Center for Chronic Disease Prevention and Health Promotion, August 7, 2009, http://www.cdc.gov/nccdphp/press/index.htm#3 (accessed November 3, 2009)

and 39.1% ($864) for Medicaid. Obesity was responsible for nearly $40 billion of increased medical spending through 2006, including $7 billion in Medicare prescription drug costs.

Finkelstein et al. observe that the lifetime costs of overweight and obesity borne by the government are likely to be greater than the lifetime costs imposed by smokers. Furthermore, the results of this study reveal that obese people who live to age 65 have much larger annual Medicare expenditures than their normal-weight peers. According to Catharine Paddock, in "Obesity Healthcare Costs US 147 Billion Dollars a Year, New Study" (*Medical News Today*, July 28, 2009), Eric A. Finkelstein asserts that because medical care spending attributable to overweight and obesity rivals spending attributable to smoking, "the medical costs attributable to obesity are almost entirely a result of costs generated from treating the diseases that obesity promotes," and suggests "that as long as obesity prevails to the extent that it does today, it will continue to be a significant burden on health care."

The Impact of Obesity Costs on a State Economy

In "Paying for Obesity: A Changing Landscape" (*Pediatrics*, vol. 123, supp. 5, June 2009), Lisa A. Simpson and Julie Cooper report that the costs of obesity to states through their Medicaid budgets are considerable, "with estimates ranging from $23 million in Wyoming to $3.5 billion in New York in 2003." Most states use one of three strategies to pay for obesity-related medical care:

• Medicaid-focused interventions that include reimbursement and/or specific weight-management programs or incentives, which vary from state to state. In some states health professionals are "paid at least as well for obesity and its related comorbidities as for other conditions they treat," while in other states claims for obesity-related care, especially nutritional counseling, are rejected.

• Public employee benefit programs with obesity-prevention and weight-loss programs that help states to reduce the cost impact of overweight and obese workers. Arkansas and Kentucky are among the states that have implemented weight-education programs for state employees.

- Insurance-coverage mandates—by 2008 at least seven states required insurance coverage for one or more obesity-related services.

Eldo E. Frezza, Mitchell S. Wachtel, and Bradley T. Ewing developed an economic model intended to assess the impact of obesity on a state's economy. They evaluated the cost of obesity in terms of lost business output, employment, and income for the state of New Mexico and reported their findings in "The Impact of Morbid Obesity on the State Economy: An Initial Evaluation" (*Surgery for Obesity Related Diseases*, vol. 2, no. 5, September–October 2006). The researchers find that obesity cost the state more than 7,300 jobs, and its economic effect exceeded $1.3 billion—the impact on labor accounted for nearly $200 million and reduced state and local tax revenues by $48 million—accounting for 2.5% of New Mexico's gross state product.

Obesity Increases Health Expenditures

In "Differences in Disease Prevalence as a Source of the U.S.-European Health Care Spending Gap" (*Health Affairs*, vol. 26, no. 6, November–December 2007), Kenneth E. Thorpe, David H. Howard, and Katya Galactionova examine spending in the United States and Europe for the 10 most costly medical conditions. Their analysis reveals that nearly twice as many adults in the United States than in Europe are obese—33% of Americans, compared with 17% of people in 10 of the largest European countries—which results in higher numbers of Americans being afflicted with cancer, diabetes, and other chronic conditions. The treatment of obesity-related chronic diseases adds $100 billion to $150 billion to U.S. annual health expenditures.

Hospital Costs of Childhood and Adolescent Obesity

Because most research about obesity-related medical care costs focus on costs incurred as a result of treating adults, Leonardo Trasande et al. decided to look at the economic consequences of childhood obesity and reported their findings in "Effects of Childhood Obesity on Hospital Care and Costs, 1999–2005" (*Health Affairs*, vol. 28, no. 4, July–August 2009). Using data from a nationally representative sample of admissions to U.S. hospitals from 1999 to 2005, the researchers note trends in obesity-associated hospitalizations, charges, and costs. Trasande et al. find that hospitalizations attributable to obesity nearly doubled between 1999 and 2005 and that the resulting costs rose from $125.9 million in 2001 to $237.6 million in 2005. The researchers also report that Medicaid assumed a large share of the cost of hospitalizations for obesity-related conditions, such as diabetes and hypertension (high blood pressure), and that private payers paid a greater portion of hospital costs related to the direct treatment of obesity, such as nutritional counseling, drug therapy, and weight-loss surgery.

In "Incremental Hospital Charges Associated with Obesity as a Secondary Diagnosis in Children" (*Obesity*, vol. 15, no 7, July 2007), Susan J. Woolford et al. of the University of Michigan indicate that even when obesity was the secondary diagnosis resulting in a hospital stay, obese children's lengths of stay were longer and their hospital costs were significantly higher than those of healthy-weight children. For example, hospital charges were significantly higher for discharges with obesity as a secondary diagnosis versus those without, such as for appendicitis ($14,134 versus $11,049), asthma ($7,766 versus $6,043), and pneumonia ($12,228 versus $9,688).

Insurance Coverage for Obesity Treatment

Even though the Medicare and Medicaid programs spend billions on obesity-related illnesses, neither entitlement program covers treatment for obesity itself. Medicaid does not cover obesity treatment, and under Medicare hospital and physician services for obesity are generally excluded. Historically, Medicare has covered treatment when obesity results from a disease such as hypothyroidism (deficiency of the thyroid hormone, which is produced by the thyroid gland) or Cushing's disease (a condition in which excess cortisol, a hormone released in response to stress, is secreted by the pituitary gland) and when weight loss is medically necessary to treat a disease such as diabetes, hypertension, or heart disease. It also provides coverage for surgical treatment of obesity when it is medically appropriate and the surgery is to correct an illness that caused the obesity or was aggravated by the obesity.

Until 2004 Medicare justified excluding coverage for obesity treatment by asserting that obesity is not a disease. However, in October 2004 the Centers for Medicare and Medicaid Services (CMS), which administers Medicare, indicated in *CMS Manual System: Pub. 100-03 Medicare National Coverage Determinations* (http://www.cms.hhs.gov/transmittals/downloads/R23NCD.pdf) that it eliminated language ("obesity itself cannot be considered an illness") from its policy that had been used to deny coverage for weight-loss treatment. Even though the CMS did not technically name obesity a disease, this language allows consumers and health professionals to seek Medicare reimbursement for weight-loss programs and treatment. Industry observers speculate that private insurance companies will follow Medicare's lead and will extend coverage for weight-loss treatments.

The Medicare Prescription Drug, Improvement, and Modernization Act of 2003 excludes drugs used for weight loss. However, the CMS explains in "Medicare Program; Policy and Technical Changes to the Medicare

Prescription Drug Benefit" (*Federal Register*, vol. 73, no. 73, April 15, 2008) that weight-loss drugs may be covered by Medicare when they are prescribed for a "medically accepted indication" such as clinically severe obesity. Regardless, in *Your Guide to Medicare Prescription Drug Coverage* (May 2009, http://www.medicare.gov/Publications/Pubs/pdf/11109.pdf), the CMS explains that even though some plans may choose to cover weight-loss drugs, Medicare drug plans are not required to cover them.

In view of the high prevalence of obesity among the populations covered by Medicaid (the poor and minorities) and the significant Medicaid expenditures for obesity-related illnesses, many health care industry observers believe it is shortsighted that some states specifically exclude coverage of antiobesity products in their Medicaid programs. For example, Morgan Downey of the American Obesity Association (AOA) indicates in "Insurance Coverage for Obesity Treatments" (May 2, 2005, http://obesity1.tempdomainname.com/treatment/insurance2.shtml) that 10 states (Illinois, Indiana, Nevada, New Hampshire, New York, Ohio, Oklahoma, South Carolina, South Dakota, and Wyoming) do not cover antiobesity pharmaceuticals through Medicaid. Thirteen states (California, Delaware, Hawaii, Kentucky, Maine, Massachusetts, Mississippi, Montana, New Mexico, Oregon, Rhode Island, Vermont, and Virginia) cover orlistat, sibutramine, and phentermine (drugs that treat obesity) in their Medicaid programs; however, in some states coverage is limited to people with clinically severe obesity, Type 2 diabetes, or hyperlipidemia (an excess of fats called lipids, chiefly cholesterol and triglycerides, in the blood). Some health care analysts and advocacy groups, including the AOA, contend that it is difficult to reconcile this limited coverage of obesity in light of Medicaid coverage for inpatient and outpatient alcohol detoxification and rehabilitation, chemical dependency treatment and drug rehabilitation, and services for sexual impotence.

According to the AOA, many health insurance plans do not provide reimbursement for weight-loss treatment. Furthermore, few private insurance indemnity plans or managed-care organizations (e.g., health maintenance organizations and preferred-provider organizations) appear to cover the costs of obesity treatment independent of whether the service is a medically supervised weight-loss program, a surgery, or a prescription drug. The AOA notes that most employer-funded health insurance plans do not pay for obesity treatment or services, including medications, diet supplements, weight-control programs, or bariatric surgeries.

The Pharmacy Benefit Management Institute (PBMI), an independent organization that is not affiliated with any employee benefits program or pharmaceutical manufacturer, periodically surveys employers to determine the extent, cost, and coverage of their pharmacy benefits and publishes the survey data and trends in *Prescription Drug Benefit Cost and Plan Design Report*. The PBMI explains in *2009–2010 Prescription Drug Benefit Cost and Plan Design Report* (2009, http://www.benefitdesignreport.com/Portals/0/15558_BDR_LowResR1.pdf) that in 2009 it queried 417 companies that provided coverage to more than 7 million beneficiaries. The institute finds that a significant majority (67.4%) of employers continued to exclude weight-loss drugs from their coverage in 2009. Still, the percent of employers excluding weight-loss drug coverage had decreased from the previous two years: 82.7% in 2007 and 71% in 2008. Over one-third (38.1%) of employers surveyed offered complete, unlimited coverage of weight-loss programs and services.

The reluctance to cover antiobesity drugs is driven by concern about cost, in that many payers may determine that the rising prevalence of obesity and its comorbidities require higher prescription drug costs than drug treatment of obesity itself. For example, the article "Study: Metabolic Syndrome Brings Big Costs" (Associated Press, May 6, 2005) reports that Medco Health Solutions, a national prescription benefit management company, found that Americans with metabolic syndrome account for $4 out of every $10 spent on prescription drugs for adults. (Metabolic syndrome is the name given to conditions that often occur together—such as obesity, diabetes, high blood pressure, and high triglycerides—and that can lead to cardiovascular disease.) Drug treatment of metabolic syndrome skyrocketed 36% between 2002 and 2004, and prescription costs for adults with metabolic syndrome averaged $4,116 in 2004, which was 4.2 times the average.

In "Will the New Fat-Fighter Drugs Be More Worthy of Coverage?" (*Managed Care*, November 2009), Tom Reinke observes that "health plans and employers rarely cover the current FDA-approved weight loss medications, favoring diet and exercise programs." Reinke opines that as new weight-loss medications become available and prove to be safe and effective, health plans and health insurance companies may need to revise their policies about coverage for these drugs.

OVERWEIGHT WORKERS MAY PAY MORE FOR HEALTH INSURANCE COVERAGE. New federal regulations, which were reported in "Nondiscrimination and Wellness Programs in Health Coverage in the Group Market; Final Rules" (*Federal Register*, vol. 71, no. 239, December 13, 2006) and which took effect on July 1, 2007, for some groups and on January 1, 2008, for others, permit companies to charge overweight employees more for their health insurance than their healthy-weight peers.

The article "Charging Overweight Employees Beginning to Gain Credence as Healthcare Reduction Tactic" (*Small Business Digest*, August 13, 2007) reports that in 2007 more employers were considering different rates for employees who are considered overweight. The article cites the results of a survey of 135 executives, 62% of whom said they felt obese workers should pay higher benefits costs. This was a significant increase from the 2005 survey, which found that less than half (48%) of executives supported charging obese workers more for their health insurance coverage.

Even some states favor charging obese public employees more for their health coverage. For example, the article "State to Hit Obese Workers with 'Fat Fee'" (Associated Press, August 26, 2008) indicates that in August 2008 Alabama's public employee health plan became the first to approve higher premiums for overweight. The fee went into effect January 2010. In "Manchin Distances Himself from Overweight PEIA Proposal" (*Charleston [WV] Gazette*, October 28, 2009), Phil Kabler reports that in October 2009 the West Virginia Public Employees Insurance Agency voted to make the proposal to charge higher premiums to overweight employees. Other states, including North Carolina, have followed suit.

Obese People Pay More for Health Care

David Arterburn, Matthew L. Maciejewski, and Joel Tsevat analyze in "Impact of Morbid Obesity on Medical Expenditures in Adults" (*International Journal of Obesity*, vol. 29, no. 3, March 2005) the records of 16,262 adults from the 2000 Medical Expenditure Panel Survey to determine the effects of morbid obesity (BMI greater than 40) on health care expenditures. The per capita health care expenditures were calculated for BMI categories, based on self-reported height and weight, and adjusted for age, gender, race, income, educational level, health insurance type, marital status, and smoking status. The researchers find that adults with clinically severe obesity had health care costs that were nearly twice those of their normal-weight peers and conclude that "the economic burden of morbid obesity among US adults is substantial. Further research is needed to identify interventions to reduce the incidence and prevalence of morbid obesity and improve the health and economic outcomes of morbidly obese adults."

In "Fat Tax" (*New York Times*, August 12, 2009), David Leonhardt describes measures that go further than charging overweight and obese workers more for health insurance and health care services. Leonhardt explains if it were up to Delos M. Cosgrove, the chief of the Cleveland Clinic in Cleveland, Ohio, "he would . . . stop hiring obese people." Cosgrove asserts that the U.S. antiobesity campaign lacks the urgency of previous public health initiatives such as smoking cessation. He states, "We should declare obesity a disease and say we're going to help you get over it." Cosgrove's approach—making value judgments and limiting people's choices—is

unlikely to be enacted by U.S. companies, but Leonhardt observes that the impulse driving Cosgrove's approach indicates that "not even one of the nation's most prestigious hospitals can do much to reduce obesity."

FUNDING OBESITY RESEARCH

Since the 1970s considerable progress has been made in identifying the causes of obesity and developing treatments. Despite the enhanced understanding of the origins of obesity, increasing numbers of Americans continue to become overweight and obese. The AOA, along with myriad medical professional organizations and advocacy groups, contends that public funding for obesity research is woefully inadequate in view of the size and scope of this public health problem. Besides insufficient National Institutes of Health (NIH) funding for obesity research, the AOA cites inequities in research grants awarded by the NIH—even though more grants have been awarded to obesity research than in past years, obesity still receives a disproportionately small share of grant funding.

Table 7.2 shows NIH funding for a variety of diseases and research areas for fiscal years (FYs) 2005 to 2008 as well as estimates for FYs 2009 and 2010. Funding for obesity research has increased very slightly, from $664 million in FY 2008 to a projected $687 million in FY 2010.

WEIGHING THE PRICE BUSINESS PAYS

Obese employees incur substantially higher health care costs than normal-weight employees. Obesity significantly increases health expenditures and absenteeism. In "The Costs of Obesity among Full-Time Employees" (*American Journal of Health Promotion*, vol. 20, no. 1, September–October 2005), Eric A. Finkelstein, Ian C. Fiebelkorn, and Guijing Wang find that about 30% of the total costs result from increased absenteeism. In addition, even though workers with clinically severe obesity represent just 3% of the employed population, they account for 21% of the costs due to obesity. The researchers report that overweight and obesity-related costs ranged from $175 per year for overweight male employees to $2,485 per year for obese female employees. The costs of obesity alone (excluding overweight) for a company with 1,000 employees were estimated at a staggering $285,000 per year.

According to the Conference Board, in *Weights and Measures: What Employers Should Know about Obesity* (April 2008), U.S. companies pay $45 billion per year for medical care costs to treat obesity-related diseases, lower productivity, and absenteeism. The Conference Board states that obesity is associated with a 36% increase in spending on health care services, more than smoking or problem drinking. It also observes that 40% of U.S. companies have weight-reduction or weight-management

TABLE 7.2

Estimates of funding for various research, conditions, and disease categories, fiscal years 2005–10

Research/disease areas (dollars in millions and rounded)	Fiscal year 2005 actual	Fiscal year 2006 actual	Fiscal year 2007 actual (NIH historical method)	Fiscal year 2007 actual (NIH revised method)	Fiscal year 2008 actual	Fiscal year 2009 estimated	Fiscal year 2010 estimated
Acute respiratory distress syndrome	$72	$74	$48	$87	$82	$84	$85
Agent Orange & Dioxin	$20	$17	$18	$15	$13	$14	$14
Aging	$2,415	$2,431	$2,462	$1,879	$1,965	$2,019	$2,045
Alcoholism	$512	$511	$521	$443	$452	$466	$473
Allergic rhinitis (hay fever)	$3	$4	$5	$7	$6	$6	$6
ALS	$42	$44	$39	$40	$43	$44	$45
Alzheimer's disease	$656	$643	$645	$411	$412	$423	$428
American Indians / Alaska natives	$140	$155	$141	$159	$142	$147	$149
Anorexia	$14	$15	$12	$8	$7	$7	$7
Anthrax	$183	$150	$105	$160	$134	$137	$139
Antimicrobial resistance	$217	$221	$269	$209	$228	$234	$237
Aphasia	$3	$15	$14	$20	$22	$22	$23
Arctic	$22	$17	$19	$25	$22	$23	$23
Arthritis	$368	$355	$339	$222	$232	$238	$241
Assistive technology	$138	$182	$184	$192	$215	$221	$224
Asthma	$289	$283	$294	$252	$246	$252	$256
Ataxia telangiectasia	$10	$9	$11	$14	$13	$13	$13
Atherosclerosis	$322	$337	$347	$468	$460	$472	$477
Attention deficit disorder (ADD)	$107	$116	$107	$61	$60	$62	$63
Autism	$102	$108	$127	$93	$118	$122	$141
Autoimmune disease	$589	$598	$587	$759	$762	$783	$790
Basic behavioral and social science	$1,065	$1,062	$1,104	$1,119	$1,149	$1,182	$1,198
Batten disease	$9	$8	$8	$5	$5	$5	$6
Behavioral and social science	$3,044	$3,001	$3,060	$3,157	$3,215	$3,316	$3,362
Biodefense	$1,696	$1,766	$1,735	$1,735	$1,736	$1,777	$1,793
Bioengineering	$1,318	$1,546	$1,469	$2,610	$2,853	$2,932	$2,973
Biotechnology	$10,889	$9,974	$9,814	$5,344	$5,179	$5,390	$5,468
Brain cancer	$157	$178	$193	$204	$194	$200	$205
Brain disorders	$4,784	$4,732	$4,670	$3,592	$3,729	$3,835	$3,888
Breast cancer	$700	$718	$707	$729	$726	$748	$769
Burden of illness	$433	$508	$524	$60	$48	$49	$50
Cancer	$5,639	$5,575	$5,643	$5,549	$5,570	$5,748	$6,016
Cardiovascular	$2,333	$2,349	$2,370	$1,942	$2,027	$2,081	$2,103
Cerebral palsy	$23	$18	$16	$30	$28	$29	$29
Cervical cancer	$96	$97	$96	$67	$69	$71	$73
Charcot-Marie-tooth disease	-	$7	$7	$9	$12	$13	$13
Child abuse and neglect research	$40	$38	$38	$41	$30	$31	$32
Childhood leukemia	$60	$53	$55	$50	$39	$40	$41
Chronic fatigue syndrome	$5	$5	$4	$4	$4	$4	$3
Chronic liver disease and cirrhosis	$410	$408	$379	$253	$241	$248	$251
Chronic obstructive pulmonary disease	$63	$67	$91	$72	$75	$78	$79
Climate change	$57	$50	$47	$4	$4	$4	$4
Clinical research	$8,719	$8,785	$9,116	$9,862	$9,629	$9,931	$10,086
Clinical trials	$2,863	$2,767	$2,949	$3,422	$3,562	$3,663	$3,719
Colorectal cancer	$284	$269	$282	$273	$274	$282	$290
Complementary and alternative medicine	$306	$301	$299	$426	$430	$443	$450
Conditions affecting unborn children	$108	$103	$110	$81	$81	$83	$84
Contraception/reproduction	$340	$335	$314	$460	$473	$486	$492
Cooley's anemia	$42	$42	$34	$22	$22	$22	$22
Cost effectiveness research	$134	$143	$155	$50	$49	$50	$51
Crohn's disease	$59	$64	$69	$47	$51	$52	$52
Cystic fibrosis	$89	$85	$82	$78	$90	$93	$94
Dental/oral and craniofacial disease	$415	$413	$417	$484	$463	$476	$483
Depression	$329	$335	$345	$398	$402	$412	$418
Diabetes	$1,055	$1,038	$1,037	$1,069	$1,080	$1,104	$1,110
Diagnostic radiology	$788	$712	$694	$1,046	$1,095	$1,125	$1,142
Diethylstilbestrol (DES)	$9	$8	$6	$5	$4	$4	$4
Digestive diseases	$1,237	$1,252	$1,234	$1,460	$1,426	$1,466	$1,487
Digestive diseases—(gallbladder)	$7	$7	$6	$6	$7	$7	$7
Digestive diseases—(peptic ulcer)	$18	$17	$23	$15	$14	$14	$14
Down syndrome	$15	$14	$16	$16	$17	$17	$18
Drug abuse (NIDA Only)	$1,006	$990	$1,001	$1,001	$1,007	$1,033	$1,045
Duchenne/ Becker muscular dystrophy	$17	$18	$23	$23	$22	$23	$23
Dystonia	$19	$19	$16	$18	$15	$16	$16
Emerging infectious diseases	$1,872	$1,857	$1,816	$1,733	$2,098	$2,156	$2,179
Emphysema	$21	$17	$21	$30	$29	$29	$30

programs, and an additional 24% planned to launch such programs during 2008. The National Business Group on Health, a consortium of large employers that researches and develops solutions to health-service delivery challenges, states in the fact sheet "Healthy Weight, Healthy Lifestyles: Primary Fact Sheet for the Institute on the

TABLE 7.2

Estimates of funding for various research, conditions, and disease categories, fiscal years 2005–10 [CONTINUED]

Research/disease areas (dollars in millions and rounded)	Fiscal year 2005 actual	Fiscal year 2006 actual	Fiscal year 2007 actual (NIH historical method)	Fiscal year 2007 actual (NIH revised method)	Fiscal year 2008 actual	Fiscal year 2009 estimated	Fiscal year 2010 estimated
Endometriosis	$10	$12	$12	$12	$15	$15	$16
Epilepsy	$105	$103	$105	$145	$145	$150	$152
Estrogen	$183	$153	$164	$283	$245	$252	$256
Eye disease and disorders of vision	$715	$705	$714	$800	$796	$818	$827
Facioscapulohumeral muscular dystrophy	$2	$2	$4	$3	$3	$3	$3
Fetal alcohol syndrome	$28	$29	$34	$32	$34	$35	$35
Fibroid tumors (uterine)	$15	$15	$14	$20	$16	$17	$17
Fibromyalgia	$10	$9	$9	$11	$12	$13	$13
Food safety	$329	$316	$278	$230	$244	$250	$253
Fragile X syndrome	$22	$20	$27	$22	$26	$27	$28
Frontotemporal dementia (FTD)	$29	$33	$31	$17	$17	$18	$18
Gene therapy	$355	$356	$325	$250	$249	$255	$259
Gene therapy clinical trials	$31	$32	$31	$12	$16	$16	$17
Genetic testing	$422	$417	$395	$402	$383	$395	$402
Genetics	$4,840	$4,878	$4,878	$7,000	$6,872	$7,066	$7,173
Global warming climate change	$24	$58	$56	$1	$1	$1	$1
Health disparities	$2,699	$2,766	$2,744	$2,744	$2,614	$2,691	$2,725
Health effects of climate change	$159	$157	$164	$258	$286	$295	$300
Health services	$940	$929	$1,023	$730	$743	$779	$792
Heart disease	$2,087	$2,087	$2,126	$1,126	$1,217	$1,249	$1,263
Heart disease-coronary heart disease	$397	$398	$382	$379	$367	$377	$381
Hematology	$1,122	$1,114	$1,128	$881	$894	$919	$935
Hepatitis	$179	$177	$174	$176	$180	$185	$187
Hepatitis-A	$5	$3	$2	$6	$6	$6	$6
Hepatitis-B	$39	$36	$42	$53	$53	$54	$55
Hepatitis-C	$121	$122	$108	$100	$93	$95	$96
HIV/AIDS	$2,921	$2,902	$2,906	$2,906	$2,928	$3,010	$3,055
Hodgkin's disease	$18	$21	$17	$12	$16	$17	$17
Homelessness	$24	$21	$18	$14	$13	$13	$13
Homicide and legal interventions	$12	$11	$8	$1	*	—	—
HPV and/or cervical cancer vaccines	$16	$14	$20	$16	$19	$19	$20
Human fetal tissue	$24	$23	$19	**	$40	$41	$42
Human genome	$1,084	$1,065	$1,099	$1,246	$1,259	$1,297	$1,317
Huntington's disease	$48	$48	$53	$49	$51	$53	$53
Hyperbaric oxygen	$2	$2	$2	$3	$4	$4	$4
Hypertension	$371	$395	$390	$231	$263	$270	$273
Immunization	$1,438	$1,438	$1,342	$1,713	$1,734	$1,779	$1,804
Infant mortality/ (LBW)	$504	$478	$464	$227	$246	$253	$256
Infectious diseases	$3,188	$3,132	$3,059	$3,433	$3,575	$3,678	$3,725
Infertility	$40	$40	$51	$65	$73	$75	$76
Inflammatory bowel disease	$70	$72	$80	$74	$81	$83	$83
Influenza	$164	$207	$271	$280	$204	$209	$212
Injury—childhood injuries	$26	$28	$27	$28	$26	$27	$27
Injury—trauma-(head and spine)	$241	$233	$219	$164	$150	$155	$157
Injury—traumatic brain injury	$87	$85	$82	$73	$59	$61	$62
Injury—unintentional childhood injury	$22	$25	$21	$17	$15	$16	$16
Injury (total) accidents/adverse effects	$353	$355	$403	$299	$299	$308	$312
Interstitial cystitis	$26	$25	$23	$10	$10	$10	$10
Kidney disease	$427	$434	$450	$531	$523	$536	$540
Lead poisoning	$15	$15	$15	$13	$9	$9	$9
Liver cancer	$82	$88	$90	$103	$89	$91	$93
Liver disease	$454	$450	$423	$589	$562	$577	$584
Lung	$1,025	$978	$1,013	$1,169	$1,211	$1,244	$1,262
Lung cancer	$289	$266	$249	$164	$169	$175	$179
Lupus	$89	$97	$84	$113	$126	$129	$130
Lyme disease	$27	$24	$22	$26	$22	$22	$23
Lymphoma	$177	$170	$158	$186	$193	$199	$204
Macular degeneration	$58	$60	$70	$135	$135	$138	$140
Malaria	$104	$98	$104	$112	$132	$136	$141
Malaria vaccine	$44	$35	$36	$31	$32	$33	$33
Mental health	$1,848	$1,824	$1,853	$2,061	$2,086	$2,142	$2,173
Mental retardation (intellectual and developmental disabilities (IDD))	$192	$188	$204	$305	$350	$360	$365
Methamphetamine	$43	$45	$45	$66	$67	$69	$70
Mind and body	$152	$136	$133	$571	$567	$583	$591
Minority health	$2,404	$2,423	$2,407	$2,407	$2,396	$2,474	$2,508
Mucopolysaccharidoses (MPS)	$10	$10	$10	$8	$7	$7	$7

Costs and Health Effects of Obesity" (February 1, 2006, http://www.businessgrouphealth.org/pdfs/obesity_factsheet .pdf) that higher health care utilization rates, such as 45% more inpatient hospital days, produce higher health care expenditures—36% higher for inpatient and outpatient care and 77% higher for prescription drug spending.

TABLE 7.2

Estimates of funding for various research, conditions, and disease categories, fiscal years 2005–10 [CONTINUED]

Research/disease areas (dollars in millions and rounded)	Fiscal year 2005 actual	Fiscal year 2006 actual	Fiscal year 2007 actual (NIH historical method)	Fiscal year 2007 actual (NIH revised method)	Fiscal year 2008 actual	Fiscal year 2009 estimated	Fiscal year 2010 estimated
Multiple sclerosis	$110	$110	$98	$149	$169	$173	$176
Muscular dystrophy	$40	$40	$47	$58	$56	$58	$59
Myasthenia gravis	$5	$9	$6	$10	$9	$10	$10
Myotonic dystrophy	$6	$7	$8	$9	$9	$9	$9
Nanotechnology	$165	$192	$215	$257	$304	$311	$326
Networking and information technology R&D	$509	$423	$507	$959	$911	$936	$950
Neurodegenerative	$1,215	$1,217	$1,166	$1,579	$1,621	$1,668	$1,690
Neurofibromatosis	$17	$16	$13	$12	$14	$15	$15
Neuropathy	$51	$54	$59	$118	$121	$124	$126
Neurosciences	$4,902	$4,830	$4,809	$5,102	$5,224	$5,372	$5,444
Nutrition	$1,072	$1,039	$1,075	$1,327	$1,391	$1,429	$1,444
Obesity	$519	$594	$661	$595	$664	$681	$687
Organ transplantation	$358	$363	$358	$187	$175	$180	$181
Orphan drug	$1,228	$1,255	$1,158	$653	$645	$664	$678
Osteogenesis imperfecta	$9	$5	$5	$8	$5	$5	$5
Osteoporosis	$191	$169	$164	$167	$183	$188	$190
Otitis media	$15	$17	$15	$20	$18	$19	$19
Ovarian cancer	$106	$102	$103	$89	$96	$99	$102
Paget's disease	$6	$6	$4	$1	$1	$1	$1
Pain conditions—chronic	$229	$220	$224	$277	$279	$287	$291
Parkinson's disease	$225	$208	$187	$143	$152	$156	$158
Pediatric	$3,210	$3,161	$3,173	$2,622	$2,771	$2,864	$2,906
Pediatric AIDS	$279	$276	$262	$262	$241	$255	$260
Pediatric research initiative	$145	$141	$171	**	$209	$212	$215
Pelvic inflammatory disease	$4	$4	$3	$4	$3	$3	$3
Perinatal—birth—preterm (LBW)	$394	$374	$351	$181	$197	$203	$206
Perinatal—neonatal respiratory distress syndrome	$10	$8	$9	$23	$18	$19	$19
Perinatal period—conditions originating in perinatal period	$429	$407	$387	$413	$449	$461	$467
Pick's disease	$1	$1	$1	$3	$2	$3	$3
Pneumonia	$154	$145	$132	$105	$93	$95	$96
Pneumonia & influenza	$317	$351	$405	$382	$295	$303	$307
Polycystic kidney disease	$25	$32	$36	$33	$41	$42	$42
Prevention	$7,100	$6,815	$6,729	$4,596	$4,623	$4,752	$4,822
Prostate cancer	$373	$348	$345	$295	$290	$299	$307
Psoriasis	$6	$8	$10	$22	$8	$8	$8
Regenerative medicine	$591	$614	$575	$697	$723	$743	$753
Rehabilitation	$325	$324	$344	$379	$403	$415	$421
Rett syndrome	$6	$5	$6	$6	$9	$10	$10
Reye's syndrome	$1	$1	$1	$0	$0	-	-
Rural health	$199	$202	$208	$173	$170	$175	$178
Schizophrenia	$353	$364	$358	$220	$249	$256	$259
Scleroderma	$11	$11	$12	$12	$20	$21	$21
Septicemia	$42	$49	$49	$93	$95	$98	$99
Sexually transmitted diseases/herpes	$252	$264	$288	$282	$245	$251	$255
Sickle cell disease	$91	$91	$94	$78	$80	$83	$83
Sleep research	$189	$199	$190	$219	$225	$232	$235
Smallpox	$187	$149	$122	$142	$94	$97	$98
Smoking and health	$533	$517	$534	$324	$310	$319	$325
Spina bifida	$10	$11	$9	$14	$15	$16	$16
Spinal cord injury	$89	$66	$64	$90	$80	$82	$84
Spinal muscular atrophy	$15	$15	$11	$11	$10	$10	$10
Stem cell research	$609	$643	$657	$968	$938	$963	$977
Stem cell research—embryonic—human	$40	$38	$42	$74	$88	$91	$92
Stem cell research—embryonic—non-human	$97	$110	$106	$120	$150	$154	$155
Stem cell research—nonembryonic—human	$199	$206	$203	$226	$297	$305	$311
Stem cell research—nonembryonic—non-human	$273	$289	$306	$400	$497	$511	$518
Stem cell research—umbilical cord blood/placenta	$18	$19	$22	$44	$46	$47	$48
Stem cell research—umbilical cord blood/ placenta—human	$15	$16	$19	$38	$38	$39	$39
Stem cell research—umbilical cord blood/ placenta—non-human	$3	$4	$2	$9	$9	$9	$9
Stroke	$342	$342	$340	$288	$296	$305	$310

About 8% of private employer medical claims are attributable to overweight and obesity, and in 2004 obesity-related disabilities cost employers an average of $8,720 per claimant per year for wage indemnity.

In "Obesity and Workers' Compensation: Results from the Duke Health and Safety Surveillance System" (*Archives of Internal Medicine*, vol. 167, no. 8, April 23, 2007), Truls Østbye, John M. Dement, and Katrina

TABLE 7.2

Estimates of funding for various research, conditions, and disease categories, fiscal years 2005–10 [CONTINUED]

Research/disease areas (dollars in millions and rounded)	Fiscal year 2005 actual	Fiscal year 2006 actual	Fiscal year 2007 actual (NIH historical method)	Fiscal year 2007 actual (NIH revised method)	Fiscal year 2008 actual	Fiscal year 2009 estimated	Fiscal year 2010 estimated
Substance abuse	$1,508	$1,490	$1,523	$1,636	$1,763	$1,811	$1,836
Sudden infant death syndrome	$84	$77	$81	$25	$29	$30	$30
Suicide	$34	$32	$43	$52	$39	$40	$41
Teenage pregnancy	$26	$21	$16	$24	$21	$21	$22
Temporomandibular muscle/joint disorder (TMJD)	$20	$17	$15	$18	$19	$20	$20
Tobacco	$531	$515	$536	$325	$311	$320	$326
Topical microbicides	$66	$88	$99	$92	$102	$104	$105
Tourette's syndrome	$13	$13	$11	$9	$8	$9	$9
Transmissible spongiform encephalopathy (TSE)	$37	$35	$43	$50	$44	$45	$45
Transplantation	$545	$551	$534	$544	$519	$533	$540
Tuberculosis	$158	$150	$166	$188	$142	$145	$147
Tuberculosis vaccine	$26	$22	$17	$23	$18	$19	$19
Tuberous sclerosis	$9	$9	$12	$20	$20	$21	$21
Urologic diseases	$576	$536	$526	$535	$534	$550	$562
Uterine cancer	$39	$28	$22	$24	$16	$16	$17
Vaccine related	$1,450	$1,449	$1,358	$1,659	$1,632	$1,675	$1,698
Vaccine related (AIDS)	$511	$566	$597	$597	$556	$557	$557
Vector-borne diseases	$447	$464	$424	$478	$417	$428	$433
Violence against women	$22	$20	$24	$49	$45	$46	$47
Violence research	$121	$113	$106	$190	$183	$188	$191
West Nile virus	$43	$85	$69	$81	$39	$40	$41
Women's health	$3,551	$3,498	$3,470	$3,470	$3,514	$3,627	$3,683
Youth violence	$69	$67	$60	$123	$115	$119	$120

SOURCE: "Estimates of Funding for Various Research, Condition, and Disease Categories (RCDC)," U.S. Department of Health and Human Services, National Institutes of Health, May 7, 2009, http://report.nih.gov/rcdc/categories/ (accessed November 7, 2009)

M. Krause of the Duke University Medical Center seek to determine the relationship between BMI and the number and types of workers' compensation claims, associated costs, and lost workdays. The researchers find that employees with BMIs greater than or equal to 40 had twice the rate of compensation claims as healthy-weight coworkers. Among obese workers, the number of lost workdays was nearly 13 times higher, indemnity claims costs were 11 times higher, and medical claims costs were seven times higher, compared with their healthy-weight coworkers.

Rhonda K. Hill et al. of the Arkansas Center for Health Improvement in Little Rock, Arkansas, confirm in "Self-Reported Health Risks Linked to Health Plan Cost and Age Group" (*American Journal of Preventive Medicine*, vol. 36, no. 6, June 2009) that along with other high-risk workers, such as tobacco users, overweight and obese people have medical bills $2,050 greater per year than workers without health risks. The researchers looked at 77,774 workers in Arkansas's state employee plan and compared medical costs incurred by workers with different BMIs. Hill et al. find that medical costs rose with increasing age and were highest among people with more than one risk factor, such as workers who were obese, smoked, and were inactive.

Obesity-Related Disability

According to Darius N. Lakdawalla, Jayanta Bhattacharya, and Dana P. Goldman, in "Are the Young Becoming More Disabled?" (*Health Affairs*, vol. 23, no. 1, 2004), obesity is a key cause of the more than 50% increase in disability rates over the last two decades, particularly among younger Americans. After analyzing data from the National Health Interview Survey, an annual nationwide government survey of about 36,000 households, the researchers identify disability trends among people aged 18 to 69 between 1984 and 2000 and find significant growth in reported disability rates among those under the age of 50 but not among older adults.

Lakdawalla, Bhattacharya, and Goldman report that "obesity accounts for about half of the increased disability among those ages 18–29." For those 30 to 39 years old, the number reporting disabilities increased from 118 per 10,000 people in 1984 to 182 per 10,000 people in 1996. Among people 40 to 49 years old, the number rose from 212 per 10,000 people to 278 per 10,000 people during this same period. Among people aged 50 to 59, disability rose only among those who were obese. The number of disability cases resulting from musculoskeletal problems and diabetes grew more rapidly than those from other problems during the length of the study, and the proportion that was diabetes-related doubled. Lakdawalla, Bhattacharya, and Goldman caution that this increase in the disability rate could translate into higher health care costs in the future. Because people with disabilities generally use more medical services, should this trend persist, it could generate additional costs to the nation's already enormous health care bill.

Soham Al Snih et al. of the University of Texas Medical Branch in Galveston, Texas, looked at the relationship between obesity, disability, and mortality by following the health of 12,725 adults aged 65 and older. In "The Effect of Obesity on Disability vs. Mortality in Older Americans" (*Archives of Internal Medicine*, vol. 167, no. 8, April 23, 2007), the researchers report that over the course of 11 years, 3,570 subjects became disabled and 2,019 died. Subjects with a low BMI (less than 18.5, which is considered underweight) and obese subjects (BMI greater than 30) were significantly more likely to experience disability and death. Snih et al. conclude that "disability-free life expectancy is greatest among subjects with a BMI of 25 to less than 30."

In "Smoking Kills, Obesity Disables: A Multistate Approach of the US Health and Retirement Survey" (*Obesity*, vol. 17, no. 4, April 2009), Mieke Reuser, Luc G. Bonneux, and Frans J. Willekens estimate life expectancy with and without disability at age 55 for different BMIs. Compared with high normal weight (BMI of 23 to 24.9), mild obesity (BMI of 30 to 34.9) decreased disability-free life expectancy by 2.7 years in men and 3.6 years in women.

THE HIGH COST OF LOSING WEIGHT

The AOA estimates in the fact sheet "Consumer Protection" (May 2, 2005, http://obesity1.tempdomainname.com/subs/fastfacts/Obesity_Consumer_Protect.shtml) that at any given moment approximately 40% of women and 25% of men are trying to lose weight and that 45 million Americans diet each year. Americans spend about $30 billion per year to lose or prevent weight gain. The market research firm Marketdata forecasts in *U.S. Weight Loss and Diet Control Market (10th Edition)* (February 2009) that substantial annual growth in the U.S. weight-loss industry will produce revenues in excess of $68 billion in 2010.

Along with commercial weight-loss centers, medically supervised weight-loss programs, and prescription diet drugs, products such as diet books, audio and video programs, Web-based diet and nutrition services, low-calorie and low-carbohydrate food products, meal replacements, and over-the-counter (nonprescription) appetite suppressants compete for consumer dollars. As the low-carbohydrate diet craze subsides, more dieters are turning to structured commercial programs such as Weight Watchers, LA Weight Loss, and Jenny Craig. In *Weight Reduction Services* (November 2009), First Research Inc. estimates that the 1,300 weight-loss centers in the United States had an annual revenue of $2 billion in 2009. The report observes that the 50 largest companies accounted for 80% of this staggering $2 billion and that the four largest—Weight Watchers,

Jenny Craig, NutriSystem, and the online program eDiets—brought in 60% of this revenue.

According to Marketdata, the most affluent dieters, primarily in big cities, are purchasing home-delivered diet foods, which is a market that grew in excess of $1 billion in 2008. About 30 companies, including Nutri-System, Jenny Direct, Medifast, Diet to Go, 5 Squares, BistroMD, Atkins at Home, eDiets Meal Delivery, Chefs Diet, Freshology, Sunfare, Seattle Sutton's Healthy Eating, HMR at Home, In the Zone, and Personal Chef to Go, cater to this market. The cost averages $726 per month for home-delivered diet food, and dieters can spend as much as $1,200 per month. Demand for these services grew an estimated 3.7% in 2008 and was projected to rise 12% to 13% by 2012.

Medical and Behavioral Treatments

The greatest proportion of outlays for weight loss are for food products and commercial weight-loss programs, but Kathleen M. McTigue et al. observe in "Screening and Interventions for Obesity in Adults: Summary of the Evidence for the U.S. Preventive Services Task Force" (*Annals of Internal Medicine*, vol. 139, no. 11, December 2, 2003) that medical and behavioral treatment options for obesity involve considerable cost. The researchers state, "Intensive counseling programs require significant time and staffing commitment. Based on average U.S. wholesale price, a 1-year supply of orlistat (120 mg 3 times daily) is $1,445.40 and of sibutramine (15 mg daily) is $1464.78." It is important to note that consumers generally purchase prescription drugs at retail rather than at wholesale prices, so their costs are considerably higher than those reported by McTigue et al.

According to William E. Encinosa et al. of the Agency for Healthcare Research and Quality, in "Recent Improvements in Bariatric Surgery Outcomes" (*Medical Care*, vol. 47, no. 5, May 2009), weight-loss surgery costs declined between 2002 and 2006, from $29,563 to $27,905 for patients without complications and from $41,807 to $38,175 for patients who experienced complications. Even hospital payments for those readmitted because of complications decreased from $80,001 to $69,960. Some of the decline in costs may be related to volume—between 2001 and 2005 weight-loss surgeries grew by 115%. Encinosa et al. opine that the decrease in cost was also due to a move to the less invasive laparoscopic technique, which requires shorter hospital stays, and to an increase in procedures that use gastric banding without bypass.

Long-Term Savings

Even though surgical treatment of obesity is a relatively recent phenomenon, research reveals that its costs are offset by a reduction in future utilization of health care services and a resultant reduction in health care costs. In "The Clinical Effectiveness and Cost-Effectiveness of Bariatric (Weight Loss) Surgery for Obesity: A Systematic Review and Economic Evaluation" (*Health Technology Assessment*, vol. 13, no. 41, September 2009), a review of research assessing the clinical effectiveness and cost effectiveness of bariatric surgery for obesity, Julien Picot et al. conclude that, overall, bariatric surgery is cost effective in comparison to nonsurgical treatment for people with moderate to severe obesity. However, the researchers do observe that nearly all the studies they reviewed suffered from methodological problems that may compromise the extent to which their result may be generalized to the entire population of obese adults. For example, some studies included one-year postsurgery models and others used 5-year postsurgery economic models, and some did not consider the probabilities of developing or reversing obesity-related diseases with or without the surgical intervention.

Other research confirms cost savings, but in "Obesity, Weight Management, and Health Care Costs: A Primer" (*Disease Management*, vol. 10, no. 3, June 2007), a review of the available evidence, Keith H. Bachman of the Kaiser Permanente's Care Management Institute in Oakland, California, cautions that "the cost-effectiveness of obesity-related interventions is highly dependent on the risk status of the treated population, as well as the length, cost, and effectiveness of the intervention. Bariatric surgery offers high initial costs and uncertain long-term cost savings. From the perspective of a payor, obesity management services are as cost-effective as other commonly offered health services, though not likely to offer cost savings."

In "A Study on the Economic Impact of Bariatric Surgery" (*American Journal of Managed Care*, vol. 14, no. 9, September 2008), Pierre-Yves Cremieux et al. evaluate the third-party payer's return on investment for weight-loss surgery. The researchers matched 3,651 bariatric surgery patients to control subjects with clinically severe obesity who did not undergo the surgery and compared their health care costs. The mean (average) weight-loss surgery cost the payer between $17,000 and $26,000, and Cremieux et al. estimate that "all costs [were] recouped within 2 years for laparoscopic surgery patients and within 4 years for open surgery patients." The study also reveals that the bariatric surgery costs were recouped more quickly in 2005 than they were in 2002. In 2005 it took six years to recoup the costs of open bariatric surgery, compared with just two years in 2005 for laparoscopic bariatric surgery. Cremieux et al. attribute this improvement to "surgical experience, improved technology, and dedicated facilities."

CATERING TO AN EXPANDING MARKET

Along with increased costs, many businesses have discovered that they must literally expand their products and services to meet the needs of overweight and obese consumers. Scott Mayerowitz describes in "Living Large: Products for the Obese" (ABC News, January 5, 2009) a wide array of products—from heavy-duty weight scales, portable chairs, and seatbelt extenders, to super-sized robes and towels—that are designed to meet the needs of obese Americans.

According to the Franklin Furniture Institute of Mississippi State University, in *Tipping the Scales: Weighing the Bariatric Furniture Market* (October 2009, http://www.ffi.msstate.edu/pdf/bariatric_furniture.pdf), the market for furniture that can accommodate extra weight is an unmet need and is estimated to be as great as $400 million per year. The institute describes adults aged 40 to 59 with BMIs of 30 or greater as the target market for seating, beds, and furniture frames that can withstand additional weight and pressure.

According to Deborah Yao, in "Stores Target Plus-Size Market" (Associated Press, April 24, 2006), the market research firm NPD Group reports that from March 2005 to February 2006 sales of plus-sized women's apparel rose by nearly 7% to $19 billion. In the article "Demand for Plus-Size Girls' Apparel Expanding" (Reuters, October 9, 2007), Marshal Cohen, an analyst with the NPD Group, opines that the children's plus-sized market could eventually grow to 18% of the total children's apparel market of more than $35 billion. The article "Expanding Plus-Size and Big-and-Tall Clothing Market Estimated to Reach $107 Billion by 2012" (PRNewswire, June 26, 2007) notes that another market research firm, Packaged Facts, predicts that the plus-sized clothing market will grow by 41% from 2006 to 2012, with commensurate growth in sales, from $47.1 billion in 2006 to almost $65 billion in 2012.

Hot Topic, a California-based company that specializes in clothing for teenagers and young women, launched in 2001 a chain of six stores called Torrid that offer fashion-forward plus-sized clothing for young women. Hot Topic (2009, http://investorrelations.hottopic.com/phoenix.zhtml?c=120007&p=irol-homeProfile&t=&id=&) notes that in FY 2008 it had 159 Torrid stores in 36 states that offered an array of clothing and lingerie for young women who wear larger sizes. The company also reports that it opened 11 new stores in FY 2008 and closed three.

In "0 Is the New 8" (*Boston Globe*, May 5, 2006), Kate M. Jackson observes that size inflation and the practice of "vanity sizing" is widespread. Jackson states, "It's no secret that retailers have been playing to women's vanity for years by downsizing the sizes on garment labels.... Manufacturers are simply making women's clothing larger and labeling them with smaller sizes. As a result, what was a size 8 in the 1950s had become a 4 by the 1970s and 00 today."

Demand for larger, sturdier hospital beds and stretchers to accommodate extremely heavy patients, special imaging equipment such as computed tomography (CT) and magnetic resonance imaging (MRI) scanners to accommodate obese patients, bigger blood pressure cuffs, recliners constructed to hold 350 pounds (159 kg), automobiles that comfortably seat obese drivers and passengers, and devices that enable people who cannot bend over to put on their socks and shoes have prompted the design and manufacture of these and other specialty products. Even morticians have observed and responded to the obesity epidemic. Warren St. John reports in "On the Final Journey, One Size Doesn't Fit All These Days" (*New York Times*, September 28, 2003) that when the founders of Goliath Casket Company in Lynn, Indiana, opened their business in the late 1980s, they sold just one triple-wide casket, which measures 44 inches (112 cm) across, compared with the 24-inch (61-cm) standard model, per year. By 2003 the company was shipping about five triple-wide caskets per month. David A. Hazelett, the president of Astral Industries, another coffin builder in Indiana, acknowledges the issue and adds that the problem affects every aspect of the funeral industry. Hazelett explains that "the standard-size casket is meant to go in the standard-size vault, and the standard-size vault is meant to go into the standard-size cemetery plot." St. John reports that hearse manufacturers have increased the width of their vehicles' rear doors, cemeteries have increased their standard burial plot size to accommodate wider vaults, and mausoleums have constructed larger crypts to accommodate oversized coffins.

According to Daniel Connolly, in "Obesity Creates Need for Oversized Caskets" (*Birmingham Post-Herald*, April 20, 2005), Mike Hauser, the marketing director of Ridout funeral homes and cemeteries, explains that newer parts of the company's cemeteries are being laid out with wider spaces for graves to accommodate larger bodies. In the case of an extremely large casket and vault, families that purchased a family plot can allow the grave to take up two spaces rather than one. Connolly notes that the Batesville Casket Company in Indiana, one of the nation's largest casket makers, introduced 13 new oversized models in 2004; by 2005 it offered a total of 53 oversized models. Connolly states that the Goliath Casket Company has also continued to increase the size of its offerings. Besides the 44-inch (112-cm) coffin, it makes caskets that are 48 and 52 inches (122 and 132 cm) wide. The caskets are constructed with extra supports intended for body weights between 650 and 1,200 pounds (295 and 544 kg). The 52-inch-wide casket is slightly wider than a standard pickup bed. In 2008 the company sold 12 of its largest models, and in 2009 another 20 were sold.

Naturally, these oversized accommodations carry additional costs, and as a result some families opt for cremation. For the most severely obese, cremation may not, however, be an option. According to St. John, Jack Springer, the executive director of the Cremation Association of North America, explains that most crematoria are not equipped to handle bodies weighing more than 500 pounds (227 kg).

CHAPTER 8
POLITICAL, LEGAL, AND SOCIAL ISSUES OF OVERWEIGHT AND OBESITY

This isn't rocket science. People want to eat healthy diets, but they tend to eat whatever's convenient and affordable. If we want to reduce obesity, we need to make eating fruits and vegetables convenient and affordable for all Americans. Reducing obesity—especially for children—would be one of the biggest steps we could take towards this better health future. And if everyone in this room throws their weight behind helping Americans lower theirs, I think we [will] make it happen.

—Kathleen Sebelius, U.S. Secretary of Health and Human Services, at the Weight of the Nation conference (July 28, 2009)

THE GLOBAL POLITICS OF OBESITY

At the international level, the World Health Organization (WHO) has developed an aggressive strategy to combat an escalating global epidemic of overweight and obesity throughout the world. In the resolution *Global Strategy on Diet, Physical Activity, and Health* (October 2005, http://www.who.int/dietphysicalactivity/strategy/eb11344/strategy_english_web.pdf), the WHO exhorts individuals and populations to:

- Achieve energy balance and a healthy weight

- Limit energy intake from total fats and shift fat consumption away from saturated fats to unsaturated fats and towards the elimination of trans fatty acids

- Increase consumption of fruits and vegetables and legumes, whole grains and nuts

- Limit the intake of free sugars

- Limit salt (sodium) consumption from all sources and ensure that salt is iodized

- Engage in at least 30 minutes of regular, moderate-intensity physical activity on most days

The WHO asserts that "government is crucial in achieving lasting change in public health" and believes that governments should take the lead in initiating and developing the strategy and ensuring that it is imple-

mented. The WHO also recommends sharply limiting the marketing of food to children and using tax and pricing policies to influence food consumption. According to the WHO, these measures are necessary to reverse the rising rates of obesity-related illnesses (heart disease, diabetes, and cancer), which are forecast to account for nearly three-quarters of deaths worldwide by 2020.

The WHO strategy was developed by an international team of experts using the latest scientific evidence available and has been commended by public health officials throughout the world. It is not, however, favored by some food manufacturers because among its proposals are restrictions on advertising unhealthful foods to children and the imposition of taxes and farm subsidy changes aimed at increasing prices of sugary and high-fat foods. For example, the International Sugar Organization strenuously objects to the recommendation that sugar amounts to no more than 10% of food and drink calories consumed per day, calling instead for a 25% cap. Table 8.1 shows that the total U.S. consumption of caloric sweeteners spiked in 1999, but that the overall use of caloric sweeteners has not varied significantly between 1997 and 2008.

On January 2, 2004, the United States (http://www.commercialalert.org/bushadmincomment.pdf) expressed its opposition to the WHO strategy and demanded significant changes to the initiative. William R. Steiger (1969–), the director of the Office of Global Health Affairs and special assistant to the secretary for international affairs at the U.S. Department of Health and Human Services, questioned the validity of some of the dietary recommendations. In a 28-page critique of the WHO strategy, Steiger wrote, "There is also an unsubstantiated focus on 'good' and 'bad' foods, and a conclusion that specific foods are linked to non-communicable diseases and obesity." Steiger put forth the U.S. position that all foods can be part of a healthy and balanced diet and called for

TABLE 8.1

Total estimated deliveries of caloric sweeteners for domestic food and beverage use, by calendar year, 1966–2008

Calendar year	Sugar[a] Raw value	Sugar[a] Refined basis	HFCS	Corn sweeteners Glucose syrup	Corn sweeteners Dextrose	Corn sweeteners Total	Honey	Other edible	Total caloric sweeteners[b]
				1,000 short tons, dry basis					
1966	10,235	9,565	0	952	415	1,367	98	69	11,099
1967	10,474	9,789	3	984	428	1,415	89	50	11,342
1968	10,656	9,959	15	1,031	444	1,489	90	70	11,608
1969	10,950	10,234	33	1,061	459	1,553	101	61	11,949
1970	11,163	10,433	56	1,102	471	1,629	103	51	12,216
1971	11,345	10,603	86	1,163	482	1,731	93	52	12,478
1972	11,487	10,736	121	1,257	485	1,863	105	52	12,756
1973	11,429	10,681	218	1,384	489	2,092	95	53	12,922
1974	10,945	10,229	295	1,480	486	2,262	75	43	12,609
1975	10,302	9,628	527	1,515	473	2,515	108	43	12,294
1976	10,893	10,180	782	1,514	452	2,748	100	44	13,072
1977	11,099	10,373	1,057	1,517	429	3,003	100	44	13,519
1978	10,889	10,177	1,198	1,551	410	3,159	120	45	13,501
1979	10,756	10,052	1,660	1,519	399	3,578	117	44	13,791
1980	10,189	9,522	2,158	1,472	393	4,024	94	50	13,690
1981	9,769	9,130	2,626	1,486	390	4,501	96	46	13,773
1982	9,153	8,554	3,090	1,479	392	4,961	104	46	13,665
1983	8,812	8,236	3,655	1,523	398	5,577	116	47	13,975
1984	8,428	7,877	4,399	1,552	408	6,359	108	47	14,391
1985	8,003	7,479	5,386	1,607	418	7,411	104	48	15,043
1986	7,731	7,225	5,498	1,632	430	7,561	121	50	14,957
1987	8,103	7,573	5,792	1,679	441	7,912	104	55	15,644
1988	8,136	7,604	5,998	1,747	452	8,197	100	54	15,955
1989	8,304	7,761	5,960	1,587	438	7,985	95	53	15,894
1990	8,615	8,051	6,202	1,700	455	8,358	103	53	16,565
1991	8,622	8,058	6,376	1,776	463	8,615	116	53	16,842
1992	8,826	8,249	6,652	1,943	461	9,056	126	53	17,483
1993	8,886	8,305	7,086	2,050	481	9,617	135	56	18,112
1994	9,072	8,478	7,398	2,093	502	9,993	126	54	18,651
1995	9,258	8,652	7,676	2,176	528	10,380	120	57	19,209
1996	9,400	8,785	7,788	2,216	537	10,541	131	57	19,514
1997	9,481	8,861	8,240	2,364	511	11,116	129	58	20,163
1998	9,594	8,966	8,552	2,358	502	11,411	130	59	20,566
1999	9,912	9,264	8,897	2,281	488	11,666	147	60	21,138
2000	9,901	9,253	8,845	2,230	476	11,551	157	61	21,022
2001	9,839	9,195	8,920	2,205	469	11,595	134	61	20,986
2002	9,746	9,109	9,045	2,224	473	11,741	153	62	21,065
2003	9,479	8,859	8,849	2,209	449	11,507	146	63	20,575
2004	9,678	9,045	8,779	2,292	487	11,558	130	64	20,797
2005	10,000	9,346	8,756	2,261	481	11,497	156	66	21,064
2006	9,975	9,323	8,702	2,053	463	11,218	174	66	20,782
2007	10,005	9,351	8,479	2,067	448	10,994	141	67	20,553
2008	10,778	10,073	8,080	2,036	419	10,535	150	69	20,826

Notes: Per capita deliveries of sweeteners by U.S. processors and refiners and direct-consumption imports to food manufacturers, retailers, and other end users represent the per capita supply of caloric sweeteners. The data exclude deliveries to manufacturers of alcoholic beverages. Actual human intake of caloric sweeteners is lower because of uneaten food, spoilage, and other losses.
HFCS = high fructose corn syrup

SOURCE: "Table 49. U.S. Total Estimated Deliveries of Caloric Sweeteners for Domestic Food and Beverage Use, by Calendar Year," in *Sugar and Sweeteners: Recommended Data*, U.S. Department of Agriculture, Economic Research Service, November 4, 2009, http://www.ers.usda.gov/Briefing/Sugar/ Data.htm (accessed November 9, 2009)

"greater personal responsibility in battling obesity." According to the WHO spokesperson David Porter, Steiger was the only member of the international scientific community to contest the proposed population nutrient intake goals.

U.S. opposition to the WHO strategy has been criticized as a clear effort to appease U.S. food and sugar suppliers. Some WHO scientists and consumer advocacy groups suggest the U.S. objections—specifically those about the recommendations to limit sugar consumption and to reconsider food advertising aimed at young children—aim to protect industries that have recently been under attack rather than to improve public health. However, the food industry itself has publicly pledged to support the WHO strategy. The Grocery Manufacturers of America, the world's largest association of food and drink companies, which includes PepsiCo Inc. and Hershey Foods Corp., said it was committed to working with the WHO to combat obesity.

In "The Sweet and Lowdown on Sugar" (*New York Times*, January 23, 2004), Kelly Brownell and Marion Nestle compare the food industry's self-serving attempts to delay action on the WHO strategy to efforts made by the tobacco industry to defend the harmlessness of cigarettes. They assert that "by making its position on the W.H.O. indistinguishable from that of the food industry, the Bush administration undermines the efforts of more forward-thinking food companies and threatens public health. Its action underscores the need for government to create a wall between itself and the food industry when establishing nutrition and public health policy. Recommendations to cut back on sugars may not please food companies, but it's time to stop trading calories for dollars."

The WHO strategy did not become official until it was endorsed by member states at the United Nations (UN) summit in May 2004. The strategy is not binding, but it is considered a guiding document for public health efforts on the issue worldwide. Even though the draft gained broad international support in 2004, the WHO agreed to U.S. demands for additional time to comment on the final resolution. Nutritionists, public health agencies, and medical professional associations responded with shock and dismay that the United States had succeeded in stalling the global obesity-control plan. Despite U.S. efforts to delay its adoption at the 57th World Health Assembly, the WHO Global Strategy on Diet, Physical Activity, and Health was endorsed by resolution WHA57.17 (http://www.who.int/dietphysicalactivity/strategy/eb11344/strategy_english_web.pdf).

The strategy provides member states with a range of policy options to address two of the major risks responsible for the heavy and growing burden of chronic diseases attributable to unhealthy diet and physical inactivity. It explains how healthier diets and physical activity can help prevent and control these diseases. The strategy describes roles of WHO member states, UN agencies, civil society, educators, and the private sector to help reduce the occurrence of obesity. It recommends obesity-prevention measures, including effective food and agriculture policies, fiscal policies, surveillance systems, consumer education, and nutrition labeling. The strategy also emphasizes the need for countries to develop national strategies with a long-term, sustainable perspective on making healthy choices at both the individual and community levels.

Is Sugar the New Tobacco?

The WHO named sugar as the principal culprit in the current epidemic of obesity and obesity-related diseases, diabetes, and cardiovascular heart disease. The WHO approach to food is not, however, comparable to its strategy to combat tobacco use. The food strategy aims to provide member states and other interested stakeholders with a range of recommendations and policy options to promote healthier diets and more physical activity. It is up to member states to decide how these should be

further developed and implemented at the national level. Because the strategy was endorsed at the World Health Assembly, member states are responsible for determining which specific policy options are appropriate to their circumstances. The WHO will then provide technical support for the implementation of programs, as requested by member states.

AMERICANS CRAVE SUGAR

The Food and Agricultural Organization of the United Nations (January 2010, http://faostat.fao.org/site/339/default.aspx) reports that the United States ranked ninth globally in terms of sugarcane production in 2007. However, the United States remains a leader in global sugar consumption, and Stephen Haley of the U.S. Department of Agriculture (USDA) estimates in *Sugar and Sweeteners Outlook* (January 14, 2010, http://usda.mannlib.cornell.edu/usda/ers/SSS//2010s/2010/SSS-01-14-2010.pdf) that the demand for sugar remained strong in 2010. Table 8.2 shows monthly estimates of U.S. sugar supply and use during fiscal year 2010. Sugar is the most subsidized U.S. crop. At a rate of nearly $500 per acre annually, U.S. sugar producers receive $1.4 billion in federal subsidies each year. U.S. sugar prices are artificially inflated because of import restrictions that protect producers from foreign competition. Americans pay as much as four times more for domestic sugar than they would if foreign competitors were permitted to market sugar in the United States. Critics of these subsidies observe that the sugar industry makes generous contributions to members of Congress of both parties.

Sugar (sucrose, dextrose, fructose, corn syrup, or maltodextrin) is a key ingredient of many processed food products. Table 8.3 lists the names of added sugars that may be the principal ingredients of processed foods. The Center for Science in the Public Interest (CSPI) reports in "Added-Sugars Consumption" (2007, http://www.cspinet.org/reports/sugar/addedsugar.html) that Americans' sugar consumption has been steadily increasing since the mid-1980s. The average American consumes at least 64 pounds (29 kg) of sugar per year, and the average teenage boy at least 109 pounds (49 kg). American adults get 16% of their calories from added sugars, children aged 6 to 11 get 18% of their calories from added sugars, and teenagers aged 12 to 19 get 20% of their calories from added sugars. The CSPI also observes that people with diets high in added sugars consume lower levels of fiber, fewer vitamins, and less folate, magnesium, and calcium, among other nutrients. By displacing vital nutrients and foods in the diet, added sugars may increase the risk of osteoporosis, cancer, high blood pressure, heart disease, and other health problems.

The health food industry has been warning the public about the perils of the overconsumption of refined sugars

TABLE 8.2

Monthly estimates of fiscal year 2010 sugar supply and use, May–October 2009

	May 2009	June 2009	July 2009	August 2009	Sept. 2009	Oct. 2009
	\multicolumn{6}{c}{1,000 short tons, raw value}					
Beginning stocks*	1,192	1,202	1,102	1,252	1,307	1,224
Total production	**8,075**	**8,025**	**8,025**	**8,275**	**8,025**	**8,025**
Beet sugar	4,550	4,550	4,650	4,850	4,700	4,700
Cane sugar	3,525	3,475	3,375	3,425	3,325	3,325
Florida	1,750	1,750	1,650	1,800	1,700	1,700
Louisiana	1,400	1,400	1,400	1,300	1,300	1,300
Texas	165	165	165	165	165	165
Hawaii	210	160	160	160	160	160
Puerto Rico	0	0	0	0	0	0
Total imports	**1,807**	**1,807**	**1,807**	**1,757**	**2,087**	**2,162**
Tariff-rate quota imports	1,232	1,232	1,232	1,182	1,182	1,257
Other program imports	400	400	400	400	400	400
Non-program imports	175	175	175	175	505	505
Mexico	165	165	165	165	495	495
Total supply	**11,074**	**11,034**	**10,934**	**11,284**	**11,419**	**11,411**
Exports	200	200	200	200	200	200
Adjustments	0	0	0	0	0	0
Total deliveries	**10,585**	**10,375**	**10,375**	**10,375**	**10,375**	**10,375**
Domestic food and beverage	10,350	10,140	10,140	10,140	10,140	10,140
Other use	235	235	235	235	235	235
Total use	**10,785**	**10,575**	**10,575**	**10,575**	**10,575**	**10,575**
Ending stocks	289	459	359	709	844	836
Stocks/use ratio	2.68	4.34	3.40	6.71	7.98	7.91

*As of May 2004, includes all stocks held by processors, millers, and refiners, including stocks held for others.

SOURCE: "Table 26. Monthly Estimates of Fiscal 2010 U.S. Sugar Supply and Use," in *Sugar and Sweeteners: Recommended Data*, U.S. Department of Agriculture, Economic Research Service, November 4, 2009, http://www.ers.usda.gov/Briefing/Sugar/Data.htm (accessed November 9, 2009)

TABLE 8.3

Names for added sugars that appear on food labels

A food is likely to be high in sugars if one of these names appears first or second in the ingredient list or if several names are listed.

Brown sugar	Invert sugar
Corn sweetener	Lactose
Corn syrup	Malt syrup
Dextrose	Maltose
Fructose	Molasses
Fruit juice concentrate	Raw sugar
Glucose	Sucrose
High-fructose corn syrup	Syrup
Honey	Table sugar

SOURCE: "Box 21. Names for Added Sugars That Appear on Food Labels," in *Nutrition and Your Health: Dietary Guidelines for Americans*, 5th ed., U.S. Department of Health and Human Services and U.S. Department of Agriculture, 2000, http://www.health.gov/dietaryguidelines/dga2000/document/choose.htm (accessed November 9, 2009)

for more than 30 years, and mainstream nutritionists and public health professionals have joined the ranks of those calling for reduced sugar consumption. Along with ending sugar subsidies, they want to sharply limit the advertising of sugary products to children, ban the sale of soft drinks in schools, and conduct widespread community public health education programs to inform Americans about the health risks of consuming excessive amounts of refined sugars.

According to Rachel K. Johnson et al., in "Dietary Sugars Intake and Cardiovascular Health: A Scientific Statement from the American Heart Association" (*Circulation*, vol. 120, no. 11, September 2009), the American Heart Association issued a statement in September 2009 that offers guidance about limiting the consumption of added sugars and describes the relationship between excess sugar consumption and metabolic abnormalities, health problems, and shortfalls in essential nutrients. The statement indicates that most women should consume no more than 100 calories (about 25 grams or 6 teaspoons) of added sugars per day. Most men should consume no more than 150 calories (about 37.5 grams or 9 teaspoons) each day.

THE U.S. WAR ON OBESITY GAINS MOMENTUM

Besides generating international debate, the issue of obesity is receiving considerable attention from lawmakers, public health officials, and politicians throughout the United States. In *A Time for Action: Policy Recommendations from PHAI's Fifth Conference on Public Health, Law, and Obesity* (November 21, 2008, http://phaionline.org/wp-content/uploads/2008/10/phai_obesity_recommendations.pdf), the Public Health Advocacy Institute (PHAI), a nonprofit legal research center that focuses on public health law, offers 47 recommendations for the administration of President Barack Obama (1961–) to combat obesity. The recommendations include:

- Develop and support an array of federal policies to increase access to healthy food at the state and local levels, including: an Innovations Fund to support grocery store development, new cooperatives, local entrepreneurship, and requirements for electronic payment access in all retail food environments, including farmers markets

- Impose federal taxes (sales or excise) on purchases of unhealthy foods and beverages and earmark the revenue for obesity programs

- Promote and fund innovative farm-to-school and farm-to-community programs across the nation to support local farmers and increase access to locally grown food

- Eliminate all "competitive foods" from schools; restrict food sold and served in schools to the National School Lunch and School Breakfast Programs

- Establish and implement financial incentives for schools to improve and promote enhanced nutrition standards in the National School Lunch and Breakfast Programs, and the Child and Adult Care Food Program

- Improve school food by legislating national standards for all food and beverages in schools based on U.S. Dietary Guidelines and production standards consistent with sustainable farming methods in the 2009 reauthorization of the federal Child Nutrition Bill

- Establish strict federal regulations limiting food and beverage advertising to children, including the Internet

- Provide federal support in the form of funding, technical assistance, and public and food industry education to implement and evaluate state and local menu labeling laws

- Increase federal National Institutes of Health funding for nutrition research

- Encourage states and localities to continue to develop and test innovative strategies to prevent and reverse the obesity epidemic; hence avoid including preemption provisions in federal laws that could impact the obesity epidemic

Skirmishes in the war on obesity do not center on whether there is a problem, but on how best to address it. Participants on one side characterize the food industry, advertisers, and the media as complicit, in that they entice consumers with seductive advertising and sugary, high-calorie treats. Their opponents believe consumers should exercise personal responsibility and make their own choices about food and exercise.

In "Tackling the Politics of Obesity" (*Atlantic*, July 27, 2009), Marc Ambinder asserts that even though the food industry has conditioned Americans to crave unhealthy, inexpensive foods, obesity researchers are unwilling to confront the industry about this practice. Ambinder observes that part of this resistance may stem from the fact that it is difficult to "demonize the food industry for lowering their prices, making the food supply safer than it ever was, and feeding more people." He further notes that even if it was possible to dramatically alter Americans' food choices, the United States would have to "roughly double the production of fruits and vegetables to keep up with demand."

In "The Ironic Politics of Obesity" (*Science*, vol. 299, no. 5608, February 7, 2003), Marion Nestle of New York University asserts that the war on obesity is unlikely to be won because healthful eating is not in the best interest of U.S. industry and because government agencies are beset by conflicts of interest. Nestle condemns the lack of government leadership, observing that the USDA offers confusing and conflicting advice to consumers. To fulfill its mission to promote U.S. agricultural products, the USDA simultaneously exhorts consumers to eat more, while issuing advice about diet, which for many overweight Americans means "eat less." This conflict of interest has produced vague federal dietary guidelines that advise Americans to "aim for a healthy weight [and] choose beverages and foods to moderate your intake of sugars." Nestle calls for "small taxes on junk foods and soft drinks (to raise funds for anti-obesity campaigns); restrictions on food marketing to children, especially in schools and on television; calorie labels on fast foods; and changes in farm subsidies to promote the consumption of fruits and vegetables."

In contrast, the WHO strategy does not stipulate any specific tax or subsidy. However, it observes that several countries have adopted fiscal measures to promote the availability of and access to various foods, and to increase or decrease consumption of certain types of foods. The strategy notes that public policies can influence prices through measures such as tax policies and subsidies. It also acknowledges that decisions on policy options are the responsibility of individual member states, depending on their particular circumstances.

The PHAI contends that food industry processing and marketing practices have encouraged excessive food consumption. The PHAI Obesity Project considers the existing state of regulation, legislation, and litigation related to the food industry's contribution to obesity and the potential for new legal strategies to effectively reduce this contribution.

In 2005 California scored a legislative victory that prohibits the state's public elementary and middle schools from selling soda from vending machines and bans the sale of soda in the state's public high schools. John David Graham (1956–), a former Harvard University professor of public health and administrator of the Office of Information and Regulatory Affairs, Office of Management and Budget, successfully campaigned to require food manufacturers to disclose the trans-fat content of their products on nutrition labels. (Trans fats are formed by the partial hydrogenation of vegetable oil—the process used to make vegetable oil more solid. Trans fats raise low-density lipoprotein cholesterol levels and may lower high-density lipoprotein cholesterol.) As of January 1, 2006, the U.S. Food and Drug Administration (FDA) required the disclosure of the trans-fat content of food that is sold in the United States.

The Nutrition Facts Label: How Accurate Is It?

Despite the requirement for accurate food labeling, FDA oversight has not been entirely successful in its efforts to prevent inaccurate or misleading information on food labels. The U.S. Government Accountability Office (GAO) finds in *Food Labeling: FDA Needs to Better Leverage Resources, Improve Oversight, and Effectively Use Available Data to Help Consumers Select Healthy Foods* (September 2008, http://www.gao.gov/new.items/d08597.pdf) that the FDA has not been able to track, monitor, and conduct label reviews on even a small fraction of the thousands of foods entering the United States from foreign countries. The GAO concludes that the FDA's oversight and enforcement efforts are not adequate to address the increasing numbers of domestic or imported food products. In addition, FDA efforts to ensure that companies correct labeling violations are also lacking.

In the press release "GAO Says FDA Fails to Ensure Accuracy and Truthfulness of Food Labels" (October 10, 2008 , http://www.cspinet.org/new/200810101.html), the CSPI describes the formal complaints that it has filed with the FDA, requesting that action be taken to correct misleading claims. Ilene Ringel Heller, a CSPI senior staff attorney, laments the FDA's inability to safeguard the accuracy of label claims: "It's astounding that FDA lacks reliable mechanisms to ensure that the Nutrition Facts label is accurate and that health-related claims are trustworthy. FDA needs to reorganize its labeling division and be given a new mandate from Congress to modernize food labels. Millions of Americans are counting on label information to protect their health."

Can and Should Laws Change Americans' Diets?

The American legal professor John F. Banzhaf III (1940–), who campaigned against tobacco, advocates using the legal system to create change in Americans' diets. He exhorts attorneys to bring lawsuits against fast-food purveyors and junk-food manufacturers to increase consumer awareness of the role the food industry plays in promoting obesity. Banzhaf was interviewed in Morgan Spurlock's (1970–) documentary film *Super Size Me*

(2004), which focuses on the fast-food industry's promotion of unhealthy eating and the director's experience subsisting on a diet of fast food for 30 days.

The Center for Consumer Freedom is an advocacy group that is supported by restaurant and food companies and that represents major corporations such as RJR Nabisco. The center marshals lawyers, publicists, and lobbyists to respond to antiobesity crusaders and derides lawsuits and legislation aimed at limiting consumers' rights to choose the foods they want to consume. It also pokes fun at CSPI mandates to offer consumers nutritional data and the self-appointed "food police" (legislators, public health officials, and others) that is intent on modifying Americans' diets. It is credited with helping defeat a measure that would have required chain restaurants to offer nutritional data about their products. In "Study: Why Food and Drink Bans Won't Solve Childhood Obesity" (April 26, 2007, http://www.consumerfreedom.com/article_detail.cfm/article/182), the center staunchly opposes banning or restricting food and drink sales in schools, and asserts that physical inactivity as opposed to the overconsumption of foods high in sugar, fat, and calories is the primary cause of childhood obesity. Furthermore, the center opines in "Soda Scam Goes Hollywood" (November 6, 2009, http://www.consumerfreedom.com/news_detail.cfm/h/4028-soda-scam-goes-hollywood) that soda and sweet drinks do not disproportionately contribute to obesity and argues against a proposed tax on these beverages.

The American Obesity Association Action Plan

The American Obesity Association (AOA; May 2, 2005, http://obesity1.tempdomainname.com/subs/about.shtml) has an ambitious agenda for the government and private sector that enumerates specific funding priorities, programs, and services to prevent, treat, and educate Americans. It calls for:

- Recognizing obesity as a disease—to expand research and foster a national commitment to combating obesity comparable in scope and funding for cancer, human immunodeficiency virus (HIV), acquired immunodeficiency syndrome (AIDS), and smoking

- Making obesity a public health priority—working with the media and policy makers to improve understanding of obesity, to fight stigma and discrimination, and to effectively address the epidemic

- Supporting the prevention of obesity—advocating for a federal Human Physical Activity Impact statement that enables policy makers to evaluate the impact of public projects on physical activity in communities

- Preventing and treating childhood and adolescent obesity—support for research about the roles of the school in nutrition education and physical activity

- Including coverage for obesity treatment in health insurance—including a Medicare prescription benefit to enable older adults and disabled people to gain access to antiobesity medications

- Support for consumer protection agencies' efforts to identify and eliminate frauds and deceptive practices directed against people with obesity

- Advancing new treatments of obesity—the AOA organized a coalition of 15 pharmaceutical companies to work with the FDA on guidelines for developers of weight-loss drugs

- Supporting the obesity community—providing a national, multidisciplinary Provider Directory that enables prospective patients to find health care providers in their area and a Career Resource Center for prospective employers and job seekers

At the close of 2009, at least two key AOA objectives had been realized. In October 2004 the AOA celebrated the decision by the Centers for Medicare and Medicaid Services to eliminate language from its policy that said obesity is not a disease. Laura Kann, Nancy D. Brener, and Howell Wechsler note in "Overview and Summary: School Health Policies and Programs Study 2006" (*Journal of School Health*, vol. 77, no. 8, October 2007) that in 2006 the nation's public schools made strides in terms of nutrition and fitness: a full 30% had banned junk food, compared with just 4% in 2000, and the percentage of school districts mandating elementary schools to offer physical education rose from 83% in 2000 to 93% in 2006. Figure 8.1 shows that the percentage of states that prohibit offering junk food in schools grew between 2000 and 2006.

Jeffrey Levi et al. find in *F as in Fat: How Obesity Policies Are Failing in America, 2009* (July 2009, http:// healthyamericans.org/reports/obesity2009/Obesity2009 Report.pdf) that in 2009, 19 states had nutritional standards for school meals and snacks that were stricter than USDA requirements. Just five years prior, only four states had stricter standards. In 2009, 27 states had nutritional standards for competitive foods sold a la carte, in school vending machines, school stores, and school bake sales. By contrast, in 2004 only six states had nutritional standards for competitive foods. Levi et al. define competitive foods "as any foods and beverages—regardless of their nutritional value—that are sold at school, but outside of the USDA school meals program."

During 2009 President Obama and the U.S. Secretary of Agriculture Tom Vilsack (1950–) expressed their desire to see schools offer healthier food choices. Inspired by their support, U.S. Representative Lynn C. Woolsey (1937–; D-CA) introduced in March 2009 a bill that would serve to completely eliminate junk food from schools. H.R. 1324 would amend the Child Nutrition Act

FIGURE 8.1

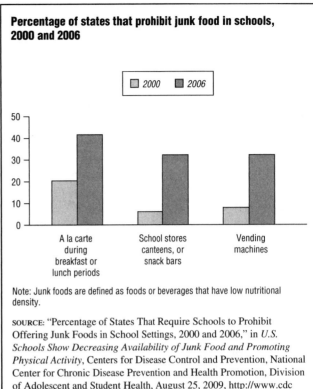

Percentage of states that prohibit junk food in schools, 2000 and 2006

Note: Junk foods are defined as foods or beverages that have low nutritional density.

SOURCE: "Percentage of States That Require Schools to Prohibit Offering Junk Foods in School Settings, 2000 and 2006," in *U.S. Schools Show Decreasing Availability of Junk Food and Promoting Physical Activity*, Centers for Disease Control and Prevention, National Center for Chronic Disease Prevention and Health Promotion, Division of Adolescent and Student Health, August 25, 2009, http://www.cdc .gov/DataStatistics/2007/shpps/ (accessed November 9, 2009)

of 1966 by requiring school food services to serve meals that meet science-based nutrition standards established by Congress and the secretary of agriculture to receive federal funds. Furthermore, the nutrition standards would apply to all foods sold on the school campus at any time of day, as opposed to simply banning the sale of foods of minimal nutritional value during mealtimes or the school day. As of January 2010, the bill had been referred to the Subcommittee on Healthy Families and Communities. It is important to remember that the majority of bills and resolutions do not make it out of committee.

OVERWEIGHT, OBESITY, AND THE LAW

Health care coverage and the availability of services to prevent or treat obesity vary widely. The economic recession that began in late 2007 further compromised access to health care services. The many people who had been laid off lost their health insurance because they could not afford to continue paying for it, and the growing ranks of the uninsured were straining the already strapped Medicaid and other safety net programs. Levi et al. report that in 2008 even people with Medicaid were not guaranteed to receive care to prevent or treat obesity. Ten states did not address nutritional assessment and counseling reimbursement for overweight and obese children, which means these services were probably not reimbursed. Only 11 states reimbursed for nutritional and behavioral therapy for overweight and obese children.

Twenty-six states covered nutritional assessment and consultation for obese adults and 20 explicitly did not cover these services. Even though just 10 states covered drug treatment, 45 states covered weight-loss surgery.

Levi et al. suggest that "health reform should ensure every American has access to coverage for preventive medical services" and describe this care as encompassing "nutrition and obesity counseling and screening for obesity-related diseases, such as type 2 diabetes, heart disease, and some forms of cancer." The researchers assert, "Every American should have access to the most effective practices for preventing, controlling, and treating obesity and obesity-related conditions. Policies also should be put in place to encourage the development and incorporation of emerging and innovative new practices as they become available."

Derrick Z. Jackson notes in "Soda Tax: It's the Real Thing" (*Boston Globe*, September 19, 2009) that President Obama suggested in 2009 that taxes on soda and other foods and beverages with minimal nutritional value should be considered. Health policy researchers at the University of California, Los Angeles, called for taxes on sugary drinks after the results of a study linked soda and obesity to $21 billion in health care costs in California. According to Jackson, Kelly Brownell of Yale University's Rudd Center for Food Policy and Obesity suggests that taxes on foods and beverages with minimal nutritional value, such as those levied on tobacco, could serve as a "key tool in efforts to improve health." Several states have considered taxing these foods and beverages and using the revenues to finance school facilities or childhood obesity prevention initiatives; however, as of January 2010, no legislation to this effect had been enacted.

According to the article "States to Receive Federal Funds to Curb Obesity, Secretary of Health Says" (Fox, Reuters, July 28, 2009), Kathleen Sebelius (1948–), the U.S. secretary of health and human services, said the funding for obesity prevention and control efforts will be increased by the federal government. Speaking at the 2009 Weight of the Nation conference, Sebelius stated that most of the $1 billion appropriated by Congress for disease prevention as part of the economic stimulus package would support Centers for Disease Control and Prevention programs aiming to reduce obesity, heart disease, and other chronic conditions. Sebelius promised that "a significant amount of the money will go to help states and communities attack obesity and other public health challenges." She said health care reform can serve as an opportunity to promote healthy eating and noted "that legislation could support programs that ensure school lunches provide more fruits and vegetables and that encourage grocery stores in poor communities to sell more fresh produce." Sebelius also suggested that phys-

ical education and investment in community projects that support walking and biking should receive more focus.

Legislators Target School Programs

Amy Winterfeld, Douglas Shinkle, and Larry Morandi indicate in *Promoting Healthy Communities and Reducing Childhood Obesity: Legislative Options* (March 2009, http://www.leadershipforhealthycommunities.org/images/stories/NCSL_Legislation_Report_2009.pdf) that in 2007 and 2008 state legislatures were actively considering policy options to address the obesity epidemic. Wanting to start early to prevent the onset of chronic conditions, legislators proposed a variety of policy approaches to create opportunities for a healthier diet and more exercise beginning in childhood. Thirty-seven state legislatures considered or enacted legislation aimed at improving the physical education and activity in schools.

Winterfeld, Shinkle, and Morandi note that in 2007 and 2008 "at least 32 states considered some type of school nutrition legislation, and at least 13 enacted new or additional policies or studies designed to help ensure that students have access to healthier food and beverage options at school." During this same period, 15 states had proposed or enacted some type of student reporting or fitness screening for body mass index (BMI; body weight in kilograms divided by height in meters squared). Every state except Colorado required physical education in schools, but the nature and extent of the requirement varied. Furthermore, legislation aimed at initiating or increasing nutrition education requirements were proposed or enacted in 19 states.

Lawsuits Attack Food Service Industry

A number of individuals and advocacy groups have brought lawsuits against the food service industry. Some claim they deserve compensation for the damage that fattening foods have done to their health. Others focus on advertising and marketing that they feel is deceptive and misleads people into eating unhealthy products. Many attorneys and public health professionals believe such lawsuits can serve as vehicles that reverse the obesity epidemic, in part because the media attention generated by such lawsuits motivates food companies to produce healthier products and to reconsider marketing and advertising practices.

The first class-action suit was the widely publicized case of Caesar Barber, a 56-year-old New Yorker weighing 270 pounds (122 kg), who claimed that four fast-food restaurants (McDonald's, Burger King, Wendy's, and KFC) jeopardized his health by promoting high-calorie, high-fat, and salty menu items. In "Whopper of a Lawsuit: Fast-Food Chains Blamed for Obesity, Illnesses" (ABCNews.com, July 26, 2002), Geraldine Sealey reports that Barber filed the lawsuit in the New York

State Supreme Court "on behalf of an unspecified number of other obese and ill New Yorkers who also feast on fast food." According to Sealey, Barber's suit alleged that the fast-food restaurants, where he ate "four or five times a week even after suffering a heart attack, did not properly disclose the ingredients of their food and the risks of eating too much." Even though Barber's suit was dismissed by two judges and he was barred from filing a third time, legal scholars asserted that more cases like Barber's would be heard by the courts.

The legal community did not have long to wait. In January 2005 an appeals court ordered McDonald's to defend a 2004 lawsuit by the New York teenagers Ashley Pelman and Jazlyn Bradley, who claimed the company hid the health risks of foods that made them obese. Samuel Hirsch, the lawyer who represented Barber, represented the teenagers. The suit was the first complaint accusing a fast-food chain of hiding health risks of its food to be considered by a judge. The teenagers said they ate at McDonald's restaurants three to five times a week over a 15-year period. Their suit claimed the company hid the health risks of Big Macs, Chicken McNuggets, and other foods high in fat and cholesterol in its 1987 advertisements in the United States and in brochures circulated in Great Britain. McDonald's defended the accuracy of its ads and asserted that there was no evidence that the teenage plaintiffs, one of whom was born in 1988, ever saw the ads. As of January 2010, the case was still active in federal court and was being considered by the U.S. district judge Kimba M. Wood (1944–).

Legislation Protects Food Industry Interests

The food industry and others argue that Americans choose what they eat and should not be able to blame the food industry if their personal choices have unhealthy consequences. State and federal legislators who agree with this viewpoint have enacted or attempted to enact laws that protect the food industry from weight-related lawsuits.

In October 2005 the U.S. House of Representatives passed a bill that would prevent most obesity or weight-related claims against the food industry and make it harder for consumers to sue restaurants and food retailers for serving fattening fare. By a vote of 307 to 119, lawmakers endorsed the Personal Responsibility in Food Consumption Act, which informs consumers that if they gain weight as a result of eating high-fat, high-calorie, and sugar-laden food, they have only themselves to blame. However, the legislation did not receive a vote in the U.S. Senate, so it did not become law.

The restaurant and food-processing industries have also championed state measures such as the Idaho Commonsense Consumption Act, signed into law in April 2004, which bans civil lawsuits for obesity and obesity-related health problems. That same month Arizona (2004, http://azleg.state.az.us/alispdfs/46leg/2R/House/Summary JUD.pdf) enacted legislation affirming that "there is no duty to warn a consumer that a non-defective food product may cause health problems if consumed excessively and provides an affirmative defense."

Levi et al. report that in 2008, 24 states had passed legislation to limit obesity liability to provide some measure of protection or even immunity for food companies threatened by obesity lawsuits. Advocates in favor of this legislation contend that the central issue is "common sense and personal responsibility" and generally subscribe to the opinion that obesity is an individual health issue as opposed to a larger societal and public health problem. Opponents of legislation limiting liability suggest that it is unrealistic to expect consumers to assume personal responsibility when food companies do not disclose relevant information about their products such as the number of calories and fat content.

THE FOOD INDUSTRY RESPONDS TO PUBLIC OUTCRY

Mounting pressure on the food industry to change its marketing practices and offer healthier products has had some success. For example, in 2003 Coca-Cola withdrew from exclusive vending-machine contracts in schools and acquired Odwalla, an organic fruit-juice company, to enable the company to offer healthy beverages. Kraft announced intentions to eliminate in-school marketing to children, introduce smaller portions, and develop more nutritious products. Applebee's International offered Weight Watchers selections on its restaurant menus. McDonald's reduced the use of trans fats for cooking its French fries and introduced a line of salads as well as leaner versions of its Chicken McNuggets.

In March 2004 McDonald's responded to growing attention to the relationship between portion size and obesity by announcing that the corporation would discontinue its supersized products—French fries and soft drinks—in an effort to simplify its menu and appeal to consumers' heightened awareness about obesity. McDonald's also piloted a new "Go Active" meal for adults that included a salad, a pedometer to count steps, and a bottle of water in several test markets throughout the country. Industry observers applauded these moves, citing the corporation's shift from the "value" aspect of fast food—providing more food for less money—to a more health-conscious purveyor of salads and reasonable portion sizes that emphasize nutrition rather than value. They also expressed the hope that other fast-food chains would follow suit and offer more nutritional information and low-calorie fare.

In another effort to counter charges that its food is unhealthy and contributes to obesity, McDonald's began to display nutrition facts on the packaging of its menu items in 2006. Customers of the world's largest restaurant company can learn the amount of calories and fat, among other information, in a McDonald's product by looking at the wrapper instead of having to go to its Web site or ask for nutrition information at the counter.

Despite these positive changes, the Ethical Investment Research Services finds in *Obesity Concerns in the Food and Beverage Industry* (February 2006, http://www.eiris.org/files/research%20publications/seeriskobesityfeb06.pdf) that the efforts of six multinational food companies—Cadbury Schweppes, Coca-Cola, Kraft Foods, McDonald's, PepsiCo Inc., and Unilever—were uneven. McDonald's and Unilever were deemed the slowest to respond to the obesity epidemic, although both companies were lauded for acknowledging their responsibility for addressing the problem of childhood obesity. In terms of responsible advertising to children, the report gives the lowest score to McDonald's and the highest to Cadbury Schweppes.

FOOD INDUSTRY LAUNCHES ANTIOBESITY INITIATIVE

In October 2009 a group of over 40 retailers, nongovernmental organizations, and food and beverage manufacturers launched the Healthy Weight Commitment Foundation (HWCF), a national initiative intended to reduce the rate of obesity, especially among children and adolescents, by 2015. In the press release "Retailers, NGOs, and Food and Beverage Industry Launch National Initiative to Help Reduce Obesity" (2009, http://www.healthyweightcommit.org/news/HWC-help-achieve-energy-balance), the HWCF explains that members of the foundation, which include Campbell Soup Co., General Mills Inc., Kellogg Co., Nestlé USA, Ralston Foods/Post Foods, and PepsiCo Inc., have invested $20 million in the initiative. The initiative targets three key audiences—markets, the workplace, and schools—and will conduct a nationwide public education campaign that focuses on ways to help people reach and maintain a healthy weight by balancing calories consumed with calories expended through physical activity.

WEIGHT-BASED DISCRIMINATION

Nearly everyone who is overweight or obese has suffered some form of bias, from disapproving glances and unsolicited advice about how to lose weight to the seemingly unending stream of "fat jokes" and the unflattering and even humiliating portrayal of overweight people in the media. Despite the pervasive anti-fat bias in American culture, until recently there were anecdotal reports, but little evidence, demonstrating that negative attitudes toward obese individuals resulted in stigmatization and clear instances of discrimination.

In "The Stigma of Obesity: A Review and Update" (*Obesity*, vol. 17, no. 5, May 2009), Rebecca M. Puhl and Chelsea A. Heuer of the Rudd Center for Food Policy and Obesity find that the prevalence of weight discrimination increased by 66% between 1995 and 2006 and describe it as comparable to rates of racial discrimination. The researchers review data revealing that systematic discrimination against obese individuals occurs in at least three areas: education, employment, and health care. They also acknowledge that evidence points to discrimination in adoption proceedings, jury selection, and housing.

Puhl and Heuer observe that obese people suffer discrimination in many aspects of life. For example, in the workplace they may be "the target of derogatory humor and pejorative comments from co-workers and supervisors," and in educational settings obese students often experience teasing, taunts, derogatory comments, and derision from peers. Health care professionals and educators have been found to hold and promote negative stereotypes about people who are obese, and the media, especially television and film, continue to stigmatize overweight and obese characters. Puhl and Heuer assert that overweight people "remain one of the last acceptable targets of humor and ridicule in North American television and film." Even the news media contributes by blaming obese people for contributing to "rising fuel prices, global warming, and causing weight gain in their friends."

Several studies find distinct anti-fat bias in children as young as age three and increasingly negative stereotypic attitudes as children age. Puhl and Heuer observe that an analysis of 25 popular videos and 20 popular books for young children attributed many "desirable traits such as sociability, kindness, happiness, and success" to thin female characters, whereas overweight characters were "commonly depicted as evil, unattractive, unfriendly, and cruel."

Anti-fat bias in children is not a recent phenomenon. In "Bias, Discrimination, and Obesity" (*Obesity Research*, vol. 9, no. 12, December 2001), Rebecca M. Puhl and Kelly Brownell of the Rudd Center for Food Policy and Obesity point to a landmark study conducted during the 1960s in which children were shown pictures of six children with various physical characteristics and disabilities, including use of crutches or wheelchair, amputations, or facial disfigurements, and were asked to rank them in order of who they would be most likely to befriend. Most subjects ranked the picture of the obese child last. When this study was performed again in 2001, children in the fifth and sixth grade displayed the strongest bias against the obese child and expressed even more prejudice than their counterparts had 40 years earlier. Teachers also revealed considerable bias, with nearly 30% in one survey describing becoming obese as "the worst possible thing that can happen to a person."

Puhl and Brownell observe that along with the psychological and social consequences of prejudice and exclusion, obese students suffered lower rates of college acceptance, with obese female applicants (31%) gaining college admission less frequently than obese male applicants (42%). They also find that normal-weight college students received more financial support from their families than overweight students and that overweight women were the least likely to receive financial support.

Overweight and obese job applicants and workers may be subjected to weight-based discrimination in employment. Many studies document discrimination in hiring practices, especially when the positions sought involved public contact, such as sales or direct customer service. Obese workers face inequities in wages, benefits, and promotions, and several studies confirm that the economic penalties are greater for women than for men. Overweight women earn less doing the same work as their normal-weight counterparts and have dimmer prospects for promotion. The courts have considered cases in which workers contended that their job terminations were weight-related. The outcomes of these cases indicate that termination can occur because of employer prejudice and arbitrary weight standards.

According to Dalton Conley and Rebecca Glauber, in "Gender, Body Mass, and Economic Status" (May 2005, http://www.nber.org/papers/w11343), overweight women do not fare as well as their normal-weight peers in terms of income, whereas overweight men are as successful, economically and in terms of job status, as normal-weight men. The researchers show that increased BMI significantly decreased women's family income as well as their occupational prestige, a measure of the social status afforded to different jobs. A 1% increase in a woman's BMI reduced her family income by 0.6% and her occupational prestige by 0.4%. Along with lower pay and less-prestigious jobs, heavier women's poorer socioeconomic outcomes were attributable to three factors:

• Overweight women tend to have lower chances of getting married

• When they do marry their spouses tend to have less earning power

• Overweight women have a higher risk for divorce

Consistent with past research, men experience no negative effects of body mass on economic outcomes. Overweight men are not less likely to marry, nor are they at increased risk for divorce, separation, or widowhood.

Weight Bias among Health Professionals

Anti-fat bias among health care professionals may discourage obese people from seeking medical care and compromise the care they receive. Even though research indicates that obese patients often delay or cancel medical appointments for a variety of reasons, including fear about being weighed or undressing in front of health professionals, speculation exists that presumed or real prejudice on the part of health professionals may also deter them from seeking medical care. According to Puhl and Brownell, when researchers asked more than 400 physicians to name patient characteristics that provoked feelings of discomfort, reluctance, or dislike, one-third of the subjects mentioned obesity, making it the fourth most common condition named after drug addiction, alcoholism, and mental illness. The subjects also linked obesity to negative qualities such as poor hygiene, hostility, dishonesty, and noncompliance with prescribed treatment. Another survey of family physicians found that two-thirds said their obese patients lacked self-control, and nearly 40% characterized their obese patients as lazy. Nurses expressed similar attitudes—nearly half reported that they were uncomfortable caring for obese patients and 31% told surveyors they would prefer not to care for obese patients at all.

Kelly Brownell and Rebecca M. Puhl note in "Stigma and Discrimination in Weight Management and Obesity" (*Permanente Journal*, vol. 7, no. 3, summer 2003) documented evidence that deeply held negative stereotypes adversely affect the clinical judgment of health professionals, including diagnosis and the quality of care delivered to obese patients. A survey of more than 1,200 physicians revealed that most were ambivalent about caring for overweight and obese patients and did not treat them with the same determination they displayed toward normal-weight patients. Just 18% said they would refer an overweight patient to a weight-loss program, and 42% would refer a mildly obese patient to a weight-loss program.

Even health professionals who specialize in the medical treatment of obesity are not immune from anti-fat bias. Marlene B. Schwartz et al. administered a standardized test that measured bias to 389 health professionals (physicians, researchers, dieticians, nurses, psychologists, and others) who attended an international obesity conference in Quebec, Canada, in 2001. The researchers reported the test results in "Weight Bias among Health Professionals Specializing in Obesity" (*Obesity Research*, vol. 11, no. 9, September 2003). Bias was assessed using the Implicit Associations Test (IAT), a timed test that analyzes the automatic associations respondents make about particular attributes. For example, the IAT helps identify whether or not test takers hold negative attitudes and stereotypical views about obese people, such as considering them to be lazy, unmotivated, sluggish, or worthless.

Schwartz et al. find that the health professionals they tested—one-third of whom provided direct clinical care to obese patients—exhibited significant anti-fat bias. They linked the stereotypes lazy, stupid, and worthless with obese people, with younger health professionals displaying more anti-fat bias than older health professionals. Schwartz et al. hypothesize that younger health professionals may be more strongly imprinted with societal pressures to be thin, which have intensified in recent decades. Another explanation may be that older health professionals, who have more maturity and experience, may have overcome some of their negative attitudes about obese patients. Despite the presence of bias, the researchers concede that even though it is intuitively appealing to assume that bias has an influence on treatment, their research does not demonstrate that bias resulted in poorer treatment of obese patients.

According to Mary Margaret Huizinga et al., in "Physician Respect for Patients with Obesity" (*Journal of General Internal Medicine*, vol. 24, no. 11, November 2009), physicians have less respect for patients with higher BMIs. The researchers analyzed data from the initial visits of 40 physicians and 238 patients enrolled in a research study of patient-physician communication. Even though higher patient BMI was significantly and negatively associated with physician respect, Huizinga et al. did not examine whether this diminished respect had an impact on the quality of care the obese patients received.

OBESE AMERICANS RECEIVE FEWER PREVENTIVE HEALTH SERVICES. Ironically, people who are obese and usually receive more medical care for chronic diseases related to obesity may also receive fewer preventive services. Does bias contribute to this disparity in preventive care? In "Associations between Obesity and Receipt of Screening Mammography, Papanicolaou Tests, and Influenza Vaccination: Results from the Health and Retirement Study (HRS) and the Asset and Health Dynamics among the Oldest Old (AHEAD) Study" (*American Journal of Public Health*, vol. 95, no. 9, September 2005), Truls Østbye et al. of the Duke University Medical Center examine the association between BMI and receipt of screening mammography and Papanicolaou tests (screening for cervical cancer) among middle-aged women and the association between BMI and receipt of influenza vaccination among older adults. The researchers analyzed data from the Health and Retirement Study (4,439 women aged 50 to 61 years) and the Asset and Health Dynamics among the Oldest Old Study (4,045 women and 2,154 men aged 70 years and older).

Østbye et al. find significant differences in how often obese women were given mammograms and Pap smears to screen for cancer. They also note that obese men and women were less likely to receive flu shots. Seventy-one percent of the obese women studied reported having mammograms, compared with 78% of those who were

not obese. Similarly, 54% of the obese women reported having Pap smears, compared with 73% of the nonobese women. In addition, 57% of the obese men and women whose records were reviewed reported receiving flu shots, compared with 78% of normal-weight people. Østbye et al. pose several potential explanations for the disparity in preventive services: obese patients' reluctance to undress for cancer screening tests, practitioners' difficulties in performing screening tests on obese women, and obese patients may require so many medical care services for chronic diseases that preventive care may be overlooked.

Nancy Klein Amy et al. examine in "Barriers to Routine Gynecological Cancer Screening for White and African-American Obese Women" (*International Journal of Obesity*, vol. 30, no. 1, January 2006) the reasons obese women, who are at higher risk for gynecological cancers than nonobese women, are less likely to get cancer-screening tests. The researchers find that obese women delay cancer-screening tests and believe that their weight is a barrier to obtaining appropriate health care. The obese women reported disrespectful treatment, embarrassment at being weighed, negative attitudes of providers, unsolicited advice to lose weight, and medical equipment that was too small to be functional as reasons they delayed or avoided screening tests. The percentage of women who reported these barriers to seeking preventive care increased as the women's BMI increased.

Airlines Weigh Their Options

In June 2002 Southwest Airlines became the center of a fiery debate when the airline decided to strengthen its enforcement of a policy established in 1980 of requesting and requiring passengers who, because of excessive girth, must occupy two airplane seats to purchase both seats. The policy allows passengers to be reimbursed for the additional seat if their flight is not full. The National Association to Advance Fat Acceptance, an advocacy group, and other consumer groups called the move discriminatory. Regardless, Southwest Airlines is not the only airline with this policy; Continental, Northwest, and other commercial carriers also require large-sized passengers to pay for two seats.

In 2003 the Federal Aviation Administration (FAA) proposed requiring all passengers on small airlines to be weighed in along with their luggage. The FAA asserted that before takeoff, the pilot must calculate the weight of the aircraft as well as that of its passengers, luggage, and crew to determine which seats passengers should occupy to ensure proper balance. For this reason it is vital to know exact passenger and luggage weights on small planes, where several people with a few extra pounds can tilt the plane away from its center of gravity. Even though operators of smaller commuter airlines acknowledged the safety issue, they were reluctant to support the FAA recommendation because they feared that weighing people would discourage them from using commuter airlines, many of which were already strapped financially.

In May 2003 the FAA ruled that airlines must assume that passengers weigh between 190 and 195 pounds (86 and 89 kg), depending on the season. At the same time, checked bags on domestic flights were adjusted from an estimated 25 pounds (11 kg) to 30 pounds (14 kg). The 30-pound estimate for checked bags on international flights remained unchanged. The requirement followed shortly after the crash of a commuter plane that killed all 21 people aboard. Investigators suspect the propeller plane was slightly above its maximum weight on takeoff, with most of the weight toward the tail. The weight distribution problem was compounded by a maintenance error that made it difficult to lower the nose with the control column. After the 19-seat plane rose above the ground, its nose pointed dangerously skyward; the pilots were unable to level it off, and the plane spun to the ground.

Andrew L. Dannenberg, Deron C. Burton, and Richard J. Jackson estimate in "Economic and Environmental Costs of Obesity: The Impact on Airlines" (*American Journal of Preventive Medicine*, vol. 27, no. 3, October 2004) that the average American gained 10 pounds (4.5 kg) during the 1990s. The extra weight required an additional 350 million gallons (1.3 billion L) of fuel used by airlines in 2000. This extra weight translated into about $275 million in excess costs in 2000 alone. The extra fuel represented 2.4% of the total volume of jet fuel used domestically that year, and along with the monetary cost, there was the environmental impact of burning all that extra jet fuel to transport what Dannenberg, Burton, and Jackson call "this additional adiposity." The article "Gov't Study: Obese Passengers Pushing up Cost of Flights" (Associated Press, November 4, 2004) notes that Jack Evans, the spokesperson for the Air Transport Association of America, which represents major U.S. airlines, agreed that weight is a real issue. He explained that weight considerations and fuel prices have prompted airlines to replace metal forks and spoons with plastic utensils and to forgo bulky magazines: "We're dealing in a world of small numbers—even though it has a very incremental impact. When you consider airlines are flying millions of miles, it adds up over time."

In "Airline Policies Juggle Larger Passengers" (CNN.com, June 26, 2009, http://www.cnn.com/2009/TRAVEL/06/26/obese.passengers.airlines/index.html), Stephanie Chen reports that an increasing number of airlines are forcing bigger passengers to pay more than normal-weight passengers. In April 2009 United Airlines established the policy that "passengers who are unable to safely fit into one seat must pay full price for a second seat. They may receive it free if the plane has vacant seats. Flight attendants on the airlines are responsible for making sure passengers are fitting in their seats and may ask heavier passengers requiring two seats to pay extra." Chen observes that "some larger passengers don't mind paying for the second seat. Other heavier fliers argue while tall passengers pay a fee for legroom, the fees are only a fraction of the price of an entire seat." In a case that became famous via Twitter feeds following a February 13, 2010, incident, film director Kevin Smith (1970–) was asked to disembark from a Southwest flight from Burbank to Oakland, California, because of his size. Smith had originally paid for two seats, but decided to fly standby on an earlier flight that had only one available seat. After seating him, airline attendants then asked him to leave because they believed he was infringing on the passenger next to him and his weight was creating a safety risk. Smith insisted that he was able to put both armrests down, per Southwest's policy, but that Southwest had still asked him to deplane for safety reasons. Southwest later apologized to Smith, but maintained his removal from the flight was for the safety and comfort of other passengers.

Obese Female Shoppers Face Discrimination

Eden B. King et al. report in "The Stigma of Obesity in Customer Service: A Mechanism for Remediation and Bottom-Line Consequences of Interpersonal Discrimination" (*Journal of Applied Psychology*, vol. 91, no. 3, May 2006) the results of a study that revealed widespread rude behavior and discrimination against obese female shoppers. The researchers discover that when women aged 19 to 28 wore prosthetic suits designed to make them appear obese, they were treated more rudely and received less eye contact and fewer smiles from sales clerks at a Houston, Texas, shopping mall than when they shopped without the fat suit. Even though nearly three-quarters of the sales clerks were women, they tended to interact less with the obese female shoppers, ending interactions abruptly and assuming more negative tones of voice with them.

Treatment of the obese shoppers was worse when they were dressed casually than when they wore professional attire, and their treatment improved when they shopped sipping diet soda and volunteered that they were trying to lose weight. A survey of shoppers conducted as part of this study found that survey respondents who were obese reported being subjected to more rude treatment from sales clerks, which prompted them to spend less time and money in the stores where they experienced discrimination. King et al. are optimistic that the financial and ethical implications of this study will provide powerful incentives for retailers to address size discrimination with employees.

San Francisco Bans Weight-Based Discrimination and Hears Landmark Cases

The San Francisco Human Rights Commission reports in *Compliance Guidelines to Prohibit Weight and Height Discrimination* (http://www.sf-hrc.org/Modules/ShowDocument.aspx?documentid=159) that on July 26, 2001, it unanimously approved historic guidelines for implementing a height-weight antidiscrimination law, and the city became the first jurisdiction in the United States to offer guidelines on how to prevent discrimination based on weight or height. Santa Cruz, California; Seattle, Washington; Washington, D.C.; and Michigan have similar laws banning discrimination based on height or weight.

The strength of the ordinance was tested two years later when Jennifer Portnick, a 240-pound (109-kg) aerobics instructor, was refused a job at Jazzercise Inc., an international dance-fitness organization based in Carlsbad, California, and brought her case before the San Francisco Human Rights Commission. She eventually reached an agreement with the company to drop a requirement about the appearance of instructors. It was the first case settled under the San Francisco ordinance, which has become known as the "Fat and Short Law."

Patricia Leigh Brown reports in "240 Pounds, Persistent. and Jazzercise's Equal" (*New York Times*, May 8, 2002) that Portnick's attorney, Sondra Solovay, the author of *Tipping the Scales of Justice: Fighting Weight-Based Discrimination* (2000), said Portnick was "geographically lucky" to have filed her case in one of just four jurisdictions in the country that outlawed weight-based discrimination.

Weight Bias Influences Adoption Decision

Grant Slater reports in "Man Resorts to Surgery to Adopt Child" (Associated Press, August 25, 2007) the case of Gary Stocklaufer, a man weighing 558 pounds (253 kg) who was prevented from adopting a child because of his weight. Stocklaufer and his wife were ordered by a Missouri judge to give the four-month-old boy, a relative of the couple, whom they had raised since he was one week old, to another couple for possible adoption. Because the Stocklaufers served as licensed foster parents and already had one adopted child, they and adoption activists alleged that weight was the deciding factor. In a desperate attempt to regain the child, Stocklaufer dieted to 480 pounds (218 kg) before he underwent bariatric surgery, which eventually reduced his weight to 308 pounds (140 kg). According to the article "Judge Rules in Baby Max Custody Case" (January 7, 2008, http://www.kmbc.com/news/14994541/detail.html), in January 2008 the Stocklaufers were awarded custody of the then eight-month-old baby boy. The presiding judge ruled that "in the child's best interest

[the Stocklaufers will] be permitted to adopt him." Adoption experts consider this a landmark case because it is the first one in which a couple seeking to adopt has resorted to surgery to surmount the increasingly prevalent practice of denying adoptions on the basis of weight.

The Origins of Stigma and Bias

Rebecca M. Puhl and Kelly Brownell observe in "Psychosocial Origins of Obesity Stigma: Toward Changing a Powerful and Pervasive Bias" (*Obesity Reviews*, vol. 4, no. 4, November 2003) that many people intensely dread the possibility of becoming obese. In one survey 24% of women and 17% of men said they would sacrifice three or more years of their life to be thin. There are reports of women who choose not to become pregnant because they fear gaining weight and becoming fat. Others smoke cigarettes in an effort to remain thin or reject the advice that they quit smoking because they fear they will gain weight should they quit. This powerful fear of fat, coupled with widespread perceptions that overweight people lack competence, self-control, ambition, intelligence, and attractiveness, create a culture in which it is socially acceptable to hold negative stereotypes about obese individuals and to discriminate against them.

One explanation of the origin of weight stigma is that traditionally Americans believe in self-determination and individualism—people get what they deserve and are responsible for their circumstances. In this context, when overweight is viewed as resulting from controllable behaviors, it is easy to understand that if an individual believes overweight people are to blame for their weight, then they should be stigmatized. Other research findings—that many Americans view life as predictable, with effort and ability inevitably producing the desired outcomes, and that attractive people are deemed good and believed to embody many positive qualities—support this theory. Interestingly, researchers find that in other countries the best predictors of anti-fat attitudes were cultural values that held both negative views about fatness and the belief that people are responsible for their life outcome.

Several other theories about the origins of weight stigma have been proposed. Conflict theory suggests that prejudice arises from conflicts of interest between groups and struggles to acquire or retain resources or power. Social identity theory posits that groups develop their social identities by comparing themselves to other groups and designating other groups as inferior. Integrated threat theory proposes that stigmatized groups are perceived as a threat. Proponents of this theory suggest that overweight and obese people threaten deeply held cultural values of self-discipline, self-control, moderation, and thinness. Another theory, evolved dispositions theory, proposes that members of a group will be stigmatized if they threaten or undermine group functioning. This evolutionary adaptation may predispose people to shun obese individuals because they are at increased health risk and may not be able to make sufficient contributions to the group's welfare because of weight-related illness or disability.

Reducing Weight Bias and Stigma

In "Demonstrations of Implicit Anti-fat Bias: The Impact of Providing Causal Information and Evoking Empathy" (*Health Psychology*, vol. 22, no. 1, January 2003), Bethany A. Teachman et al. wondered if anti-fat bias would be reduced when people were told that an individual's obesity resulted largely from genetic factors rather than from overeating and lack of exercise. The researchers assigned study participants to one of three groups. The first group received no information about the cause of obesity; the second group was given an article asserting that the principal cause of obesity was genetic; and the third group was given an article that attributed most obesity to overeating and lack of physical activity. As the researchers anticipated, the group told that obesity was controllable—resulting from overeating and inactivity—revealed the greatest amount of bias. However, to their surprise, Teachman et al. find that the group informed that obesity was primarily genetic in origin did not have significantly lower levels of bias than either the control group that had received no prior information or the group informed that obesity was caused by overeating and inactivity.

Teachman et al. also wanted to find out whether eliciting empathy for obese people would significantly reduce negative attitudes. The researchers hypothesized that by sharing written stories about weight-based discrimination with study participants they would feel empathy with the subjects in the stories, which they would then generalize to the entire population of obese people. Even though some study participants in the group that read the stories displayed lower bias, the majority did not have lower bias than the control group that had not read the stories of discrimination. The researchers speculate that the stories describing negative evaluations of an obese person might actually have served to reinforce rather than diminish bias.

Puhl and Brownell note in "Psychosocial Origins of Obesity Stigma" that the increasing prevalence of obesity has not acted to reduce weight bias. They also refute the notion that stigma is necessary to motivate overweight and obese people to lose weight. They reiterate that dieting is not associated with long-term weight loss, regardless of the individual's motivation. Furthermore, they indicate that stigma can lead to discrimination and exert a harmful influence on health and quality of life. Puhl and Brownell assert that unless stigma is reduced, obese people will continue to contend with prejudice and discrimination.

Even though few studies have evaluated the effectiveness of strategies to reduce weight stigma, a variety of initiatives have produced varying degrees of attitudinal change. These approaches include:

- Educating participants about external uncontrollable causes such as the biological and genetic factors that contribute to obesity

- Teaching and encouraging young children to practice size acceptance

- Improving attitudes by combining efforts to elicit empathy with education about the uncontrollable causes of obesity

- Encouraging direct personal contact with overweight and obese individuals to dispel negative stereotypes

- Changing individuals' beliefs by exposing them to opposing attitudes and values held by a group that they consider important. This approach, which is called social consensus theory, relies on the observation that after learning that a group does not share the individuals' beliefs, they are more likely to modify their beliefs to be similar to those expressed by the group they respect or wish to join.

In "Psychosocial Origins of Obesity Stigma," Puhl and Brownell describe the results of their experiments using social consensus theory to modify attitudes toward obese people. They conducted experiments with university students in which participants reported their attitudes toward obese people before and after the researchers offered them varying consensus opinions of other students. In one experiment, participants who were told that other students held more favorable attitudes about obese people reported significantly fewer negative attitudes and more positive attitudes about obese people than they had before they learned about the opinions of other students. Furthermore, they also changed their ideas about the causes of obesity, favoring the uncontrollable causes after they were told the other students believed obesity was attributable to these causes.

A second experiment confirmed that the power to alter the participants' beliefs depended on whether the source of the opposing beliefs was an in-group or out-group. Not surprisingly, participants' attitudes toward obese people were more likely to change when the information they were given came from a source they valued—an in-group. In a third experiment the researchers compared attitudinal change produced by social consensus with other methods to reduce stigma, including one in which participants were given written material about the controllable or uncontrollable causes of obesity. Puhl and Brownell find that social consensus was as effective as or more effective than any of the other methods they applied. They state that social consensus theory also offers an explanation about why obese individuals themselves express negative stereotypes—they want to belong to the valued social group and choose to accept negative stereotypes to align themselves with current culture. Furthermore, by accepting prevailing cultural values and beliefs, they not only resemble the in-group more closely but also distance themselves from the out-group, where identity and membership are defined by being overweight or obese.

Even though Puhl and Brownell consider social consensus a promising approach to reducing weight bias and stigma, they caution that there are many unanswered questions about its widespread utility and effectiveness. They conclude that "an ideal and comprehensive theory of obesity stigma would identify the origins of weight bias, explain why stigma is elicited by obese body types, account for the association between certain negative traits and obesity, and suggest methods for reducing bias. Existing theories do not yet meet all these criteria."

Advocacy Groups Promote Size and Weight Acceptance

Our vision [is] a society in which people of every size are accepted with dignity and equality in all aspects of life. Our mission [is] to eliminate discrimination based on body size and provide fat people with the tools for self-empowerment though public education, advocacy, and support.

—The National Association to Advance Fat Acceptance (2009)

There is a growing social movement that advocates size and weight acceptance with the overarching goal of assisting people to have a positive body image at any weight and to achieve health at any size. Nearly all the organizations that champion size acceptance characterize the preoccupation with dieting and weight loss as unhealthy and unproductive, citing statistics about diet failures, the dangers of weight cycling (the repeated loss and regain of body weight), and low self-esteem. The size acceptance movement proposes that it is possible to be fit and fat and that health and beauty are attainable at all weights. It also works to reduce "fat phobia," anti-fat bias, and weight-based discrimination.

The International Size Acceptance Association (ISAA) promotes size acceptance and aims to end size discrimination throughout the world by means of advocacy and visible, lawful actions. In "Healthy Body Esteem: Love Your Body It's the Only One You Have"

(2003, http://www.size-acceptance.org/downloads/Healthy _Body_Esteem.pdf), the ISAA discusses its Respect Fitness Health Initiative and Healthy Body Esteem campaigns, which provide an alternative to the "diet-of-the-day" pressures and doom-and-gloom predictions about size and weight that assault people every day. The ISAA asserts that people of all sizes can become more fit and is committed to helping people of all sizes strive for higher levels of fitness and improvement in their overall quality of life. Similarly, the ISAA observes that everyone can benefit from healthier food choices and is committed to helping inform the public about healthy nutrition.

The Council on Size and Weight Discrimination, a nonprofit advocacy organization working to end "sizism," bigotry, and discrimination against people who are heavier than average, focuses its advocacy efforts on affecting changes in medical treatment, job discrimination, and media images. The council's basic principles were derived from "Tenets of the Nondiet Approach" (Karin Kratina, Dayle Hayes, and Nancy King, *Moving away from Diets: Healing Eating Problems and Exercise Resistance*, 2003) and focus on:

- Total health enhancement and well-being, rather than on weight loss or achieving a specific "ideal weight"

- Self-acceptance and respect for the diversity of bodies that come in a wide variety of shapes and sizes, rather than on the pursuit of an idealized weight at all costs

- The pleasure of eating well, based on internal cues of hunger and satiety (the feeling of fullness or satisfaction after eating), rather than on external food plans or diets

- The joy of movement, encouraging all physical activities, rather than on prescribing a specific routine of regimented exercise

The National Association to Advance Fat Acceptance (NAAFA; 2009, http://www.naafaonline.com/dev2/about/ index.html) is a nonprofit human rights organization dedicated to eliminating discrimination based on body size and providing people with the "tools for self-empowerment through advocacy, public education, and support." The NAAFA has assumed a proactive role in protesting social prejudice, bias, and discrimination and in working with the Federal Trade Commission to stop diet fraud. The organization also seeks to improve legal protection for people who are overweight and obese by educating lawmakers and serving as a national legal clearinghouse for attorneys challenging size discrimination.

CHAPTER 9

DIET AND WEIGHT-LOSS LORE, MYTHS, AND CONTROVERSIES

One of the challenges facing public health professionals as they seek to combat obesity among Americans is helping consumers to distinguish myths, lore, legends, and outright fraud from accurate, usable information about nutrition, diet, exercise, and weight loss. Some of these inaccuracies are so long-standing and deeply rooted in American culture that even the most educated consumers unquestioningly accept them as facts. Others began with a kernel of truth but have been so wildly distorted or misinterpreted that they are confusing, misleading, or entirely erroneous. The rapid influx and dissemination of information about the origins of overweight and obesity and the conflicting accounts of how best to treat these problems compound the challenge. With media reports and advertisements trumpeting different diets nearly every week, it is no wonder that Americans are confused about diet and weight loss.

The fiction that people who are overweight or obese are lazy and weak-willed is among the most harmful myths because it serves to promote stigma, bias, and discrimination. Another common misconception is that it is equally easy or difficult for all people to lose weight. There are biological and behavioral factors that affect an individual's body weight, and people vary in terms of genetic propensity to become overweight, basal metabolic rate (BMR), and the number of fat cells. BMR, often referred to simply as the metabolic rate, is the number of calories an individual expends at rest to maintain normal body functions. BMR changes with age, weight, height, diet, and exercise habits (and varies based on gender) and has been found to vary by as much as 1,000 calories per day. Differences in metabolic rate explain, in part, why not all people who adhere to the same diet achieve the same results in terms of pounds lost or rate of weight loss. Another factor that produces variation in weight loss is the number of fat cells in the dieter's body. Even though fat cells do not determine body weight, they are affected by weight gain and act to limit weight loss because their

number cannot be decreased. For example, a normal-weight person has about 40 billion fat cells, whereas an individual who weighs 250 pounds (113 kg) with a body mass index (BMI; body weight in kilograms divided by height in meters squared) of 40 may have as many as 100 billion fat cells. Weight loss causes fat cells to shrink in size but does not decrease their number. As a result, individuals with twice as many fat cells as normal-weight people may be able to shrink their fat cells to a normal size but even when they have attained a healthy weight they will still have twice as many fat cells.

DIET AND WEIGHT-LOSS MYTHS

It is impossible to recount all the fantastic and improbable claims that have been made in recent years. This section considers some of the most persistent myths about diet, exercise, and weight loss.

Low-Carbohydrate Diets

MYTH. A low-carbohydrate diet is the fastest, healthiest, and best way to lose weight.

FACT. Low-carbohydrate diets may initially produce more rapid weight loss than other diets; however, most of the loss is water weight rather than fat. The water loss occurs as the kidneys flush out the excess waste products resulting from the digestion of protein and fat. Many low-carbohydrate diets encourage the consumption of high-fat foods, such as butter, heavy cream, bacon, and cheese. Long-term, high-fat diets may raise blood cholesterol levels. In addition low-carbohydrate, high-protein diets produce a state of ketosis (the accumulation of ketones from partly digested fats as a result of inadequate carbohydrate intake), which may increase the risk of gout (a severe arthritis attack that occurs in one joint—typically the big toe, ankle, or knee—and is caused by defects in uric acid metabolism) and kidney stones. Furthermore, most nutritionists and researchers concur that even though some weight-loss diets are nutritionally inadequate and others are even dangerously insufficient, nearly all diets can affect weight loss, and currently no compelling evidence exists to proclaim that one diet is vastly superior to another. A key factor in the success of any weight-loss diet is adherence (whether dieters can remain faithful to the regimen they have chosen), and as of January 2010, low-carbohydrate diets had not demonstrated superiority in terms of adherence. Boredom and frustration with a low-carbohydrate regimen may occur when dieters crave the carbohydrates that they are forbidden or can eat only in small amounts.

Still, there is one unanswered question about diet and weigh loss: Why do some dieters successfully lose weight using a low-carbohydrate or low-fat diet, whereas others on the same diet are unsuccessful? Cara B. Ebbeling et al. of the Children's Hospital Boston in Boston, Massachusetts, assert in "Effects of a Low-Glycemic Load vs Low-Fat Diet in Obese Young Adults" (*Journal of the American Medical Association*, vol. 297, no. 19, May 16, 2007) that which diet will be the most effective for each individual depends in part on the dieter's hormonal profile—specifically on differences in insulin secretion as measured by the serum insulin concentration. The researchers compared 73 subjects following a low-glycemic load diet or a low-fat diet and measured their body weight, body fat, and insulin concentration before and after six months of dieting and during a 12-month follow-up period. During the six months of dieting, high insulin secretors lost more weight (2.2 pounds [0.9 kg] per month) on the low-glycemic load diet, than on the low-fat diet (0.9 pound [0.4 kg] per month). After 18 months the high insulin secretors had lost a total of 12.8 pounds (5.8 kg) on the low-glycemic load diet, compared with just 2.6 pounds (1.2 kg) on the low-fat diet. The low-glycemic load dieters also lost more body fat than the low-fat dieters and were more successful at maintaining their weight loss. In contrast, dieters who were considered low insulin secretors fared equally well on both diets. Ebbeling et al. also observe that independent of insulin secretion status, the low-glycemic load diet had beneficial effects: high-density lipoprotein increased and triglycerides decreased. Subjects on the low-fat diet did not realize these benefits, but they did experience reductions in low-density lipoprotein.

Calorie Reduction

MYTH. The dieter needs to cut calories drastically to lose weight.

FACT. Weight loss may be accomplished with modest reductions in calorie consumption. Low-calorie diets often result in metabolic adaptations, such as a significant reduction in the resting metabolic rate, which may produce weight maintenance or even weight gain rather than the desired weight loss. Many nutritionists and diet plans advise simultaneously reducing total caloric-intake and

modifying the balance of macronutrients (nutrients that the body uses in relatively large amounts: carbohydrates, fats, and proteins)—some weight-loss diets reduce fat intake, others reduce carbohydrates.

Negative-Calorie Foods

MYTH. It takes more calories to eat and digest some foods such as celery or cabbage than these foods contain, so eating them causes or speeds weight loss.

FACT. There are no foods, including celery and cabbage, that when eaten cause weight loss. However, foods containing caffeine may temporarily boost metabolism but they do not cause weight loss. In addition, some evidence suggests that eating grapefruit or drinking grapefruit juice may help people who are obese to lose weight. Ken Fujioka et al. of the Scripps Clinic in San Diego, California, compare weight loss over a 12-week period among 91 obese individuals. One-third of the subjects ate half a grapefruit before each meal three times per day and another third drank a glass of grapefruit juice before every meal. The third group did not include grapefruit in their meals. In "The Effects of Grapefruit on Weight and Insulin Resistance: Relationship to the Metabolic Syndrome" (*Journal of Medicinal Food*, vol. 9, no. 1, spring 2006), Fujioka et al. report that after 12 weeks subjects who ate grapefruit lost an average of 3.6 pounds (1.6 kg), and those who drank grapefruit juice lost an average of 3.3 pounds (1.5 kg), whereas those in the control group who consumed no grapefruit lost an average of 0.6 of a pound (0.3 kg). Fujioka et al. attribute the weight loss, not to the direct eating of grapefruit, but to lowered levels of insulin, which were confirmed by measurements of blood glucose and insulin levels. They posit that the more efficiently sugar is metabolized, the less likely it is to be stored as fat. Furthermore, lowering insulin levels reduces feelings of hunger—elevated insulin levels stimulate the brain's hypothalamus, producing feelings of hunger.

Similarly, a review of 11 studies about the effects of green tea on weight loss and weight maintenance finds some evidence that green tea may help regulate body weight. In "The Effects of Green Tea on Weight Loss and Weight Maintenance: A Meta-analysis" (*International Journal of Obesity*, vol. 33, no. 9, September 2009), Rick Hursel, Wolfgang Viechtbauer, and Margriet S. Westerterp-Plantenga of Maastricht University report that "catechins [phytochemical compounds] or an epigallocatechin gallate (EGCG [the most abundant catechin in tea])-caffeine mixture have a small positive effect on weight loss and weight management."

Eating at Night

MYTH. Eating after 8:00 p.m. causes weight gain.

FACT. Weight gain or loss does not depend on the time of day food is consumed—excess calories will be stored as fat whether they are consumed midmorning or just before bedtime. In general, weight is governed by the amount of food consumed (measured in total calorie count) and the amount of physical activity expended during the day.

However, there is evidence that eating early in the day and eating breakfast are habits associated with maintaining a healthy weight. In "Make It an Early Bird" (*New York Times*, November 21, 2007), Jennifer Ackerman indicates that research reveals that people who eat breakfast tend to consume fewer calories throughout the day, compared with those who make dinner their biggest meal. This may be because the system in the brain that signals satiety (the feeling of fullness or satisfaction after eating) is more effective early in the day—at night an individual may be more prone to succumb to overeating.

Natural Weight-Loss Products

MYTH. Organic, natural, or herbal weight-loss products are safer than synthetic (produced in the laboratory) over-the-counter (nonprescription) or prescription drugs.

FACT. Simply because products are organic or naturally occurring does not necessarily mean they are effective, risk-free, or safe. The Mayo Clinic states in "Over-the-Counter Weight-Loss Pills: Do They Work?" (February 15, 2008, http://www.mayoclinic.com/health/weight-loss/HQ01160) that several types of herbal or dietary supplement "weight-loss pills are available at your local drugstore, supermarket or health food store. Even more options are available online. Most haven't been proved safe and effective, and some are downright dangerous." For example, Katherine Zeratsky of the Mayo Clinic explains in "Is Bitter Orange Safe and Effective for Weight Loss?" (November 25, 2009, http://mayoclinic.com/health/bitter-orange/AN01218) that bitter orange (*Citrus aurantium*) may help promote weight loss, but it can also cause side effects comparable to those of ephedra, such as rapid heart rate, increased blood pressure, and increased risk of fainting and developing migraines. It may even increase the risk for heart attack or stroke, especially when consumed in conjunction with other stimulants such as caffeine. Furthermore, bitter orange may interfere with the absorption and action of prescription medications, which in turn can cause or exacerbate a health problem.

Low-Fat and Low-Carbohydrate Foods

MYTH. Low fat, nonfat, and low-carbohydrate mean few or no calories.

FACT. A low-fat or nonfat food is usually lower in calories than the same sized portion (as measured by weight) of the full-fat food; however, a food product can contain zero grams of fat and still have a high calorie content. Many fat-free foods replace the fat with sugar and contain just as many or more calories as full-fat

versions. Even though most fruits and vegetables are naturally low in fat and calories, processed low-fat or nonfat foods may be high in calories because extra sugar, flour, or starch thickeners have been added to enhance the low-fat foods' taste or texture.

Similarly, low-carbohydrate foods are often higher in calories than their "regular" counterparts because their fat content is higher. Many foods that are naturally low in carbohydrates such as meat, butter, and cheese are also calorie-dense. Many nutritionists suggest limiting the consumption of low-carbohydrate versions of foods, such as low-carbohydrate frozen desserts, because they not only contain as many or more calories per serving than regular frozen desserts but also are often sweetened with artificial sweeteners that lack any nutrients.

Eliminating Starchy Foods

MYTH. Pasta, potatoes, and bread are fattening foods and should be eliminated or sharply limited when trying to lose weight.

FACT. Potatoes, rice, pasta, bread, beans, and some starchy vegetables such as squash, yams, sweet potatoes, turnips, beets, and carrots are not innately fattening. (They are often fattening only due to the "extras" put on them, such as butter, sour cream, margarine, or cheese.) They are rich in complex carbohydrates, which are important sources of energy. Furthermore, foods that are high in complex carbohydrates are often low in fat and calories because carbohydrates contain only 4 calories per gram, compared with the 9 calories per gram contained by fats. In "A Randomized Trial of a Low-Carbohydrate Diet vs Orlistat Plus a Low-Fat Diet for Weight Loss" (*Archives of Internal Medicine*, vol. 170, no. 2, January 25, 2010), William S. Yancy et al. report the results of a study in which dieters on a low-carbohydrate diet lost the same amount of weight as dieters on a low-fat, high-carbohydrate diet. The 146 overweight or obese subjects were randomly assigned to one of the two diets and the diet drug orlistat, and after 48 weeks both diets helped subjects lose about 10% of their initial, pre-diet weight. The diets were comparable in terms of adherence, and both groups decreased their calorie consumption by about 29% from the baseline.

Genetic Destiny

MYTH. People from families where many members are overweight or obese are destined to become overweight.

FACT. It is true that studies of families find similarities in body weight and that immediate relatives of obese people are at an increased risk for overweight and obesity, compared with people with normal-weight family members. Even though it is generally accepted that genetic susceptibility or predisposition to overweight or obesity is a factor, researchers believe environmental and behavioral factors make equally strong, if not stronger, contributions to the development of obesity. As a result, people from overweight or obese families may have to make concerted efforts to maintain healthy body weight and prevent weight gain, but they are not destined to become overweight or obese simply by virtue of the genes they inherited.

Exercise Alone

MYTH. Exercise is a better way to lose weight than dieting.

FACT. Even though there are many health benefits from exercise, weight loss is not generally considered a direct benefit. Research consistently demonstrates that for weight loss, diet trumps exercise because it is simpler to reduce caloric intake significantly through diet than to increase caloric expenditure significantly through exercise. For example, if a 155-pound (70-kg) person wants to reduce his or her consumption by 400 calories per day, it might be achieved by simply eliminating dessert and reducing portion sizes. In contrast, expending 400 calories requires considerable effort. To burn 400 calories, a 155-pound person has to spend an hour bicycling 10 miles per hour (16 km/hr); ice skating at 9 miles per hour (14.5 km/hr); or water skiing or walking uphill at about 3.5 miles per hour (5.6 km/hr). However, many studies demonstrate that exercise is an important way to prevent overweight and maintain weight loss.

D. Enette Larson-Meyer et al. combined calorie restriction with exercise and reported their findings in "Caloric Restriction with or without Exercise: The Fitness vs. Fatness Debate" (*Medicine and Science in Sports and Exercise*, vol. 42, no. 1, January 2010). The researchers randomly assigned 36 otherwise healthy overweight adults to a 25% caloric restricted diet alone or to a 25% energy deficit regime produced equally by calorie restriction and exercise—12.5% by decreasing food intake and 12.5% by increasing energy expended through regular aerobic exercise.

Subjects in both groups lost about the same amount of weight and visceral fat; however, the calorie restriction and exercise group had improved insulin sensitivity, low-density lipoprotein and cholesterol levels, and diastolic blood pressure. Larson-Meyer et al. conclude that "results of the current study suggest that beyond changes in fatness, combining caloric restriction with exercise is important for increasing aerobic fitness and optimizing improvements in risk factors for diabetes and cardiovascular disease."

Eating Disorders

MYTH. Eating disorders occur exclusively among middle- and upper-class white females.

FACT. Like many myths about diet, weight, and nutrition, this one is based on fact: an estimated 90% of people with anorexia nervosa or bulimia nervosa are female. However, according to Susan Z. Yanovski of the National Institutes of Health, in "Eating Disorders, Race, and Mythology" (*Archives of Family Medicine*, vol. 9, no. 1, January 2000), binge-eating disorder occurs in both genders and across all socioeconomic classes. Yanovski attributes the myth that eating disorders are limited to middle- and upper-class white women to the fact that many studies were conducted on college campuses where few minority students were enrolled, and other research looked at people seeking treatment, often at referral centers. Yanovski observes that "studies done on such populations, which may be more likely to be white and of higher socioeconomic status, have limited generalizability." She also cites research that finds that minorities are substantially affected by eating disorders—one study found that African-American women were as likely as white women to report binge eating. Another revealed that the prevalence of binge eating was comparable among Hispanic, non-Hispanic white, and African-American women, but that binge-eating symptoms were more severe among the Hispanic group. Yanovski concludes that the "recognition that eating disorders are color-blind can ensure that appropriate recognition and treatment are available to all patients at risk."

According to Anna Keski-Rahkonen et al., in "Epidemiology and Course of Anorexia Nervosa in the Community" (*American Journal of Psychiatry*, vol. 164, no. 8, August 2007), there is a substantially higher lifetime prevalence of anorexia nervosa than reported in previous studies—as high as 270 cases per 100,000 among women between the ages of 15 to 19. Keski-Rahkonen et al. also offer a hopeful finding: most young women recovered within five years and usually progressed to full recovery.

Katie Gentile et al. of the John Jay College of Criminal Justice refute the notion that eating disorders only afflict white middle-class women in "It Doesn't Happen Here: Eating Disorders in an Ethnically Diverse Sample of Economically Disadvantaged, Urban College Students" (*Eating Disorders*, vol. 15, no. 5, October–December 2007). The researchers surveyed 884 incoming college freshmen and found that 10% had an eating disorder—12.2% of the women and 7.3% of the men. Gentile et al. observe that even though women were more likely than men to have an eating disorder, neither male nor female students were "protected from eating disorder diagnoses by their ethnicity, class or gender." Interestingly, the majority of students found to have eating disorders were

Hispanic men and women or "other," with white women receiving the fewest diagnoses.

WHY DIETS FAIL

Historically, diets have been considered to have "failed" when lost weight is regained. Many nutritionists and obesity researchers believe diets fail because most are not sustainable. The more restrictive the diet, the less likely an individual will be to remain faithful to it because, in general, people cannot endure extended periods of hunger and deprivation. Diets may also fail because they neglect to teach dieters new eating habits to assist them to maintain their weight loss. Most overweight people gained their excess weight by consuming more calories per day than they needed. Dieting creates a temporary deficit of calories or specific macronutrients such as carbohydrates or fat. Because the weight-loss diet is viewed as a temporary measure with a beginning and an end, at its conclusion most dieters return to their previous eating habits and often regain the lost weight or even more weight. Many nutritionists and dieticians who work with people who are overweight or obese assert that diets do not fail; instead, dieters fail to learn how to eat properly to prevent weight regain.

Consumers are not the only ones who believe that diets are doomed to failure. Many health professionals and researchers cite the statistic that 95% of diets fail. This oft-cited statistic has been attributed to Albert James Stunkard (1922–) of the University of Pennsylvania and the director emeritus of the American Obesity Association. Stunkard put forth the 95% failure rate based on research he performed in 1959, which involved advising 100 overweight patients to diet, with no follow-up or support to increase their adherence to the diet. In "Whether Obesity Should Be Treated?" (*Health Psychology*, vol. 12, no. 5, September 1993), Kelly D. Brownell observes that this statistic has been widely applied even though it is quite dated, was not confirmed by subsequent studies, and involved only subjects in university-based research programs.

The article "New Diet Winners: We Rate the Diet Books and Plans" (*Consumer Reports*, June 2007) observes that only recently have successful dieters been studied to learn from their successes and incorporate them into more effective, and ideally sustainable, weight-loss plans. It cites as an example the new emphasis on achieving satiety without consuming too many calories by consuming low-density foods. This article may help dispel the myth that dieters are doomed to failure.

Improving Long-Term Weight Loss

More recent research demonstrates that dieters find it challenging to maintain weight loss; however, it refutes the 95% failure rate. In "One-Year Weight Maintenance after Significant Weight Loss in Healthy Overweight and Obese Subjects: Does Diet Composition Matter?" (*American Journal of Clinical Nutrition*, vol. 90, no. 5, November 2009), Elizabeth A. Delbridge et al. observe that "for many people, maintenance of weight loss is elusive." The researchers also find that the protein or carbohydrate composition of the diet used for weight loss had no effect on successful weight maintenance.

Kelly S. Dale et al. compare in "Determining Optimal Approaches for Weight Maintenance: A Randomized Controlled Trial" (*Canadian Medical Association Journal*, vol. 180, no. 10, May 12, 2009) the effectiveness of two support programs—one providing intensive support from nutrition and activity specialists and the other consisting of weigh-ins and encouragement from a relatively inexperienced nurse—and two diets—a high-fat diet and a high-carbohydrate diet—intended to promote long-term weight maintenance. The study subjects were 200 women aged 25 to 70 who had intentionally lost at least 5% of their initial body weight in the previous six months and had a BMI of 27 or greater.

The researchers find that over the course of two years subjects assigned to either of the diets had reduced weight, BMI, waist circumference, and blood pressure, with no significant differences between the two diets. Similarly, subjects who received intensive and relatively costly support from highly trained health professionals fared no better than those who received less intensive support from a less experienced nurse. Dale et al. conclude, "We have shown that women who are sufficiently motivated to join a 2-year study can maintain their weight and, in many instances, further reduce their weight, waist circumference and body fat mass with a simple, inexpensive nurse-support program."

Nutrigenetics (using genetic information to custom-tailor a weight-loss diet) may help improve the success of weight-loss and weight-maintenance efforts. In "Improved Weight Management Using Genetic Information to Personalize a Calorie Controlled Diet" (*Nutrition Journal*, vol. 6, October 18, 2007), Ioannis Arkadianos et al. indicate that they offered nutrigenetic testing and developed individual diets for people who historically had failed to lose weight. They compare the results these dieters achieved to a control group that did not receive nutrigenetic screening or a personalized diet and find that subjects in the nutrigenetic group fared better in terms of adherence to their diet, weight loss and maintenance, and improvements in blood glucose levels.

Approaches to enhance motivation focus on two areas: improved social supports and tangible financial incentives. Strategies to improve social supports emphasize including spouses or significant others in the weight-loss process to teach them to provide social support for their partner's weight-loss efforts. Such strategies demonstrate modest success as do contracts in which groups agree to aim for individual or group weight loss.

According to Eric A. Finkelstein et al., in "A Pilot Study Testing the Effect of Different Levels of Financial Incentives on Weight Loss among Overweight Employees" (*Journal of Occupational and Environmental Medicine*, vol. 49, no. 9, September 2007), financial incentives may be effective inducements to lose weight. The researchers followed 200 overweight workers in North Carolina, who were randomly assigned to one of three groups. One group received no incentives, whereas the other two groups received either $7 or $14 for each percentage point of weight lost. For example, a 200-pound (91-kg) subject in the group received $7 for each percentage point of weight lost. The subject lost 10 pounds (4.5 kg), or 5% of his or her weight, and received $35. Finkelstein et al. find that workers who received the most money and other incentives such as time off lost the most weight. At three months, subjects with no financial incentive lost 2 pounds (0.9 kg), those in the $7 group lost approximately 3 pounds (1.4 kg), and those in the $14 group lost 4.7 pounds (2.1 kg).

Teaching patients skills that are useful for weight maintenance as opposed to weight loss emphasizes that there are two distinctly different sets of strategies: one set focuses on weight loss and the other set focuses on maintaining a stable energy balance around a lower weight. The most commonly used model for teaching maintenance-specific skills is relapse prevention, which involves teaching people to identify situations in which lapses in behavioral adherence are likely to occur, to plan strategies in advance to prevent lapses, and to get back on track should they occur. Relapse prevention is based on the idea that breaking the so-called rules in terms of remaining faithful to diet and exercise programs may often lead to negative psychological reactions that in turn prompt reversion to pre-weight-loss behaviors. As of January 2010, only one study—Bas Verplanken and Wendy Wood's "Interventions to Break and Create Consumer Habits" (*Journal of Public Policy and Marketing*, vol. 25, no. 1, spring 2006)—had examined the effectiveness of this approach. The researchers hypothesize that learning and practicing a well-defined, positive response to relapses might help people sustain weight loss. However, their findings do not support this hypothesis.

WEIGHT-LOSS SCHEMES DEFRAUD CONSUMERS

There is a long history of marketing so-called fat-burning pills, potions, and products to Americans seeking effortless weight loss. Peter N. Stearns, in *Fat History: Bodies and Beauty in the Modern West* (1997), and Laura Fraser, in *Losing It: False Hopes and Fat Profits in the Diet Industry* (1998), offer detailed histories of magical cures and weight-loss fads. At the beginning of the 20th century products such as obesity belts and chairs that delivered electrical stimulation, as well as corsets, tonics, and mineral waters, claimed to cause weight loss.

Diet pills appeared in 1910 with the introduction of weight-loss tablets that contained arsenic (a poisonous metallic element), strychnine (a plant toxin formerly used as a stimulant), caffeine, and pokeberries (formerly used as a laxative). In the 1920s cigarette makers promoted their product as a diet aid, urging Americans to smoke rather than eat. During the 1930s diet pills containing dinitrophenol, a chemical used to manufacture explosives, dyes, and insecticides, enjoyed brief popularity after it was observed that factory workers making munitions lost weight. Their popularity was short lived, as cases of temporary blindness and death were attributed to their use.

The second half of the 20th century saw the proliferation of questionable, and often entirely worthless, weight-loss devices and gimmicks, including inflatable suits to "sweat off pounds," diet drinks and cookies, and slimming creams, patches, shoe inserts, and wraps to reduce fat thighs and abdomens. Even though the claims made for many of these products sounded too good to be true, unsuspecting Americans spent billions of dollars in the hope of achieving quick, easy, and permanent weight loss.

The promotion of dubious and potentially dangerous weight-loss products continued in the first decade of the 21st century. For example, in April 2009 the U.S. Food and Drug Administration (FDA; http://www.accessdata.fda.gov/scripts/cdrh/cfdocs/psn/transcript.cfm?show=85) issued a warning about a dietary supplement marketed for weight loss called "Venom Hyperdrive 3.0" because it was found to contain sibutramine, a prescription appetite-suppressant drug that should only be used under medical supervision. Besides the potential for abuse or addiction, sibutramine may elevate blood pressure and the heart rate, which in turn may jeopardize the health of people with a history of cardiovascular disease. In November 2009 a manufacturer voluntarily recalled one of its weight-loss supplements after an FDA analysis (http://www.fda.gov/Safety/Recalls/ucm190403.htm) revealed that it contained sibutramine and phenolphthalein, a solution used in chemical experiments and a suspected cancer-causing agent that is not approved for marketing in the United States.

Weighing the Claims

In May 2000 the Partnership for Healthy Weight Management, a coalition of scientific, academic, health care, government, commercial, and public interest representatives, initiated consumer and media education programs that not only aimed to increase public awareness of the obesity epidemic in the United States but also to promote responsible marketing of weight-loss products and programs. The partnership also published the consumer guide *Finding a Weight Loss Plan That Works for You* (2005, http://www.ftc.gov/bcp/edu/pubs/consumer/health/hea05.pdf), which was designed to help overweight and obese consumers find weight-loss solutions to meet their needs. The guide contains a checklist that enables consumers to compare weight-loss plans based on a variety of criteria. (See Table 9.1.) It also advises consumers about how to select weight-loss programs and services based on specific information from potential providers. According to the article "Web Watch" (*Obesity Management*, vol. 1, no. 4, September 2005), the coalition also launched the Ad Nauseam campaign to encourage the media to demand proof before accepting advertising copy that contains unbelievable, dubious, or extravagant promises of weight-loss success.

In November 2002 the Federal Trade Commission (FTC) convened a workshop attended by researchers, scholars, media experts, and medical professionals from the government, academia, and private industry that aimed to evaluate claims and develop new and more effective ways to combat false and deceitful weight-loss advertising claims. The FTC summarized the workshop proceedings, including attendees' assessments of eight broad categories of advertising claims, in *Deception in Weight-Loss Advertising Workshop: Seizing Opportunities and Building Partnerships to Stop Weight-Loss Fraud* (December 2003, http://www.ftc.gov/os/2003/12/031209weightlossrpt.pdf). The following section considers the advertising claims and summarizes the attendees' assessments of these claims. It also draws on an analysis of the FTC report by Stephen Barrett in "Impossible Weight-Loss Claims: Summary of an FTC Report" (December 16, 2003, http://www.quackwatch.org/01QuackeryRelatedTopics/PhonyAds/weightlossfraud.html).

No Diet or Exercise Required

CLAIM. The advertised product causes substantial weight loss without exercise or diet.

EXAMPLES. "U.S. patent reveals weight loss of as much as 28 pounds in 4 weeks.... Eat all your favorite foods and still lose weight. The pill does all the work," and "Lose up to 2 pounds daily without diet or exercise." Table 9.2 contains other examples of comparable claims.

ASSESSMENT. The consensus was that products purporting to cause weight loss without diet or exercise would either need to cause malabsorption (impair the absorption) of calories or to increase metabolism. Because the number of calories that can be malabsorbed is limited to 1,200 to 1,300 calories per week, or about 0.3 of a pound (0.1 kg) per week, malabsorption alone is unlikely to lead to substantial weight loss.

Similarly, there is no thermogenic (heat producing) agent, such as ephedrine combined with caffeine, able to boost metabolism enough to produce weight loss without diet or exercise. In fact, the mechanism by which ephedrine products appear to assist weight loss is by suppressing appetite rather than by speeding metabolism. Furthermore, even though green tea extract was found to increase metabolism, it was by a scant 4%.

No Restrictions on Eating

CLAIM. Users can lose weight while still enjoying unlimited amounts of high-calorie foods.

EXAMPLE. "Eat All the Foods You Love and Still Lose Weight (Pill Does All the Work)."

ASSESSMENT. This claim was viewed as a variation of the assertion that dieters can lose weight without reducing caloric intake or increasing exercise, because this claim states that users not only can lose weight without reducing caloric intake but also may increase caloric intake and still lose weight. The assembled experts concurred that if this claim was true, it would defy the laws of physics.

Permanent Weight Loss

CLAIM. The advertised product causes permanent weight loss.

EXAMPLES. "Take it off and keep it off. You won't gain the weight back afterwards because your weight will have reached an equilibrium," and "People who use this product say that even when they stop using the product, their weight does not jump up again."

ASSESSMENT. Even if a product caused weight loss through a reduction of calories, appetite suppression, or malabsorption, weight would be regained once use of the product stopped and calorie consumption returned to previous levels. Researchers and health professionals have repeatedly observed that dieters tend to regain weight lost over time once the diet, intervention, or other treatment ends. According to the National Academy of Science, Food, and Nutrition Board, "Many programs and services exist to help individuals achieve weight control. But the limited studies paint a grim picture: those who complete weight-loss programs lose approximately 10 percent of their body weight only to regain two-thirds of it back within 1 year and almost all of it back within 5 years." Furthermore, there are no published scientific studies supporting the claim that a nonprescription drug, dietary supplement, cream, wrap, device, or patch can cause permanent weight loss.

TABLE 9.1

Checklist for evaluating weight loss products and services

Use this checklist to gather and compare information from all weight loss programs you're considering.

Make several copies of the blank form so you can fill out one for each program. A provider's willingness to give you this information is an important factor in choosing a program. If you need help to evaluate the information you gather, talk with your primary health care provider or a registered dietitian.

Program name _____

Address _____

Phone number _____

In this program, my daily caloric intake will be: _____

My daily caloric intake is determined by: _____

I will   will not be evaluated initially by program staff.

The evaluation will be made by (check all that apply):
Physician   Nurse   Registered dietitian   Other company-trained employee

My progress is supervised by (check all that apply):
Physician   Nurse   Licensed psychologist
Registered dietitian   Company-trained employee

I will   will not be evaluated by a physician during the course of my treatment.

During the first month, my progress will be monitored:
Weekly   Biweekly   Monthly   Other _____

After the first month, my progress will be monitored:
Weekly   Biweekly   Monthly   Other _____

My weight loss plan includes (check all that apply):
Nutrition information about healthy eating   At least 1,200 calories/day for women or 1,400 calories/day for men
Suggested menus and recipes   Keeping food diaries or other monitoring activities
Portion control   Liquid meal replacements
Prepackaged meals   Dietary supplements (vitamins, minerals, botanicals, herbals)
Prescription weight loss drugs   Help with weight maintenance and lifestyle changes
Surgery

My plan includes regular physical activity that is (check both if both apply):
Supervised (at the program site)   _____ times per week, _____ minutes per session.
Unsupervised (on my own time)   _____ times per week, _____ minutes per session.

The physical activity includes (check all that apply):
Walking   Swimming   Stationary cycling
Strength training   Aerobic dancing   Other _____

The weight loss plan includes (check all that apply):
Family counseling   Group support   Lifestyle modification advice
Weight maintenance advice   Weight maintenance counseling
The staff explained the risks associated with this weight loss progam. They are:

_____

The staff explained the costs of this program. (Check all that apply and fill in the blanks.)
I will be charged a one-time entry fee of $ ___.
I will be charged $ ___ per visit.
Food replacements will cost about $ ___ per month.
Prescription weight loss drugs will cost about $ ___ per month.
Vitamins and other dietary supplements will cost about $ ___ per month.
Diagnostic tests are required and will cost about $ ___ .
Other costs include _____ at $ ___ .

Total cost for this program $____

The program gave me information about:
The health risks of being overweight.   The difficulty many people have maintaining weight loss.
The health benefits of weight loss.   How to improve my chances at maintaining my weight.

Other information to ask for:
Participants in this program have lost an average of ___ lbs. over ___ months/years.
Participants in this program have kept off ___ % of their weight loss for ___ years.

This information is based on the following (check one):
All participants.
Participants who completed the program.
Other _____

Notes: _____

SOURCE: "Checklist for Evaluating Weight Loss Products and Services," in *Finding a Weight Loss Program That Works for You*, Federal Trade Commission, The Partnership for Healthy Weight Management, 2005, http://www.ftc.gov/bcp/edu/pubs/consumer/health/hea05.pdf (accessed November 18, 2009)

TABLE 9.2

Examples of claims that promise weight loss without diet or exercise

"Awesome attack on bulging fatty deposits... has virtually eliminated the need to diet." (Konjac root pill)

"They said it was impossible, but tests prove [that] my astounding diet-free discovery melts away. . . 5, 6, even 7 pounds of fat a day." (ingredients not disclosed)

"The most powerful diet pill ever discovered! No diet or workout required. The secret weight-loss pill behind Fitness models, Show Biz and Entertainment professionals! No prescription required to order." (ingredients not disclosed)

"Lose up to 30 lbs . . . No impossible exercise! No missed meals! No boring foods or small portions!" (plant extract fucus vesiculosus)

"Lose up to 8 to 10 pounds per week... [n]o dieting, no strenuous exercise." (elixir purportedly containing 16 plant extracts)

"My 52 lbs of unwanted fat relaxed away without dieting or grueling exercise." (hypnosis seminar)

"No exercise... [a]nd eat as much as you want—the more you eat, the more you lose, we'll show you how." (meal replacement)

SOURCE: Richard L. Cleland et al., "Table 5. Lose Weight without Diet or Exercise Claims," in *Weight-Loss Advertising: An Analysis of Current Trends*, Federal Trade Commission, September 2002, http://www.ftc.gov/bcp/reports/weightloss.pdf (accessed November 18, 2009)

Fat Blockers

CLAIM. The advertised product causes substantial weight loss through the blockage or absorption of fat or calories.

EXAMPLES. "[The named ingredient] can ingest up to 900 times its own weight in fat, that's why it's a fantastic fat blocker," and "The Super Fat Fighting Formula inhibits fats, sugars and starches from being absorbed in the intestines and turning into excess weight, so that you can lose pounds and inches easily."

ASSESSMENT. Science does not support the possibility that sufficient malabsorption of fat or calories can occur to cause substantial weight loss. To lose even 1 pound (0.5 kg) per week requires malabsorption of about 500 calories per day or about 55 grams of fat. To lose 2 pounds (0.9 kg) per day, as promised in some advertisements, would require the malabsorption of 7,000 calories per day, which is impossible given that it is several times the total calories that most people consume daily, let alone the number of calories consumed from fat. The FTC has challenged deceptive fat-blocker claims for some of the most popular diet products on the market. The evidence supports the position that consumers cannot lose substantial weight through the blockage of absorption of fat. It is not scientifically feasible for a nonprescription drug, dietary supplement, cream, wrap, device, or patch to cause substantial weight loss through the blockage of absorption of fat or calories.

Quick Weight Loss

CLAIM. The user of the advertised product can safely lose more than 3 pounds (1.4 kg) a week for time periods

TABLE 9.3

Examples of claims that promise fast results

"This combination of plant extracts constitutes a weight-loss plan that facilitates what is probably the fastest weight loss ever observed from an entirely natural treatment." (elixir purportedly containing 16 plant extracts)

"Just fast and easy, effective weight loss!" (fucus vesiculosus)

"Lose 10 lbs. in 8 Days!" (apple cider vinegar)

"Rapid weight loss in 28 days!" (ephedra)

"Knock off your unwanted weight and fat deposits at warp speeds! You can lose 18 pounds in one week!" (ingredients not disclosed)

"Clinically proven to cause rapid loss of excess body fat." (phosphosterine)

"Two clinically proven fat burning formulations that are guaranteed to get you there fast or it costs you absolutely nothing." (ingredients not disclosed)

SOURCE: Richard L. Cleland et al., "Table 4. Representative Claims That Promise Fast Results," in *Weight Loss Advertising: An Analysis of Current Trends*, Federal Trade Commission, September 2002, http://www.ftc.gov/bcp/reports/weightloss.pdf (accessed November 18, 2009)

exceeding four weeks. Table 9.3 shows claims that promise unbelievably rapid results.

EXAMPLE. "Lose three pounds per week, naturally and without side effects."

ASSESSMENT. Significant health risks are associated with medically unsupervised, rapid weight loss over extended periods of time. Basically, "the more restrictive the diet, the greater are the risks of adverse effects associated with weight loss." One documented risk is the increased incidence of gallstones. The claim that consumers using products such as these can safely lose more than 3 pounds per week for a period of more than four weeks is not scientifically feasible.

Weight-Loss Creams and Patches

CLAIM. The advertised product that is worn on the body or rubbed into the skin causes substantial weight loss.

EXAMPLES. "Lose two to four pounds daily with the Diet Patch," and "Thigh Cream drops pounds and inches from your thighs."

ASSESSMENT. Diet patches and creams that are worn or applied to the skin have not been proven to be safe or effective. Furthermore, their alleged mechanisms of action are not scientifically credible.

Guaranteed Success

CLAIM. The advertised product causes substantial weight loss for all users.

EXAMPLE. "Lose excess body fat. No willpower required. Works for everyone no matter how many times you've tried and failed before."

ASSESSMENT. This claim assumes that overweight and obesity arise from a single cause or are amenable to a single solution. Because the causes of overweight and obesity are thought to be genetic factors and environmental conditions, and contributing factors such as diet, metabolic rate, level of physical activity, and adherence to weight-loss treatment vary, it is unlikely that one product will be effective for all users. Even FDA-approved prescription drugs for weight loss have a high level of nonresponders, and surgical treatment for obesity is not successful 100% of the time. The claim that a nonprescription drug, dietary supplement, cream, wrap, device, or patch will cause substantial weight loss for all users is not scientifically feasible.

Targeted Weight-Loss Products

CLAIM. Users of the advertised product can lose weight from only those parts of the body where they wish to lose weight.

EXAMPLE. "And it has taken off quite some inches from my butt (5 inches) and thighs (4 inches), my hips now measure 35 inches. I still wear the same bra size though. The fat has disappeared from exactly the right places."

ASSESSMENT. Small published studies of aminophylline cream indicate that its use may cause the redistribution of fat from the thighs to other fat stores; however, it has not been shown to cause fat loss. Even if some products were capable of causing more weight loss from certain areas of the body, no part would be spared completely—fat is lost from all fat stores throughout the body.

Red Flag Campaign and Big Fat Lie Initiative Target Phony Weight-Loss Claims

Another outcome of the November 2002 workshop was the design of an education initiative to assist the media to voluntarily screen weight-loss product ads containing claims that are "too good to be true." The media were targeted for intensive education not only because broad-based public education has proven largely inadequate to protect consumers from persuasive messages trumpeting easy weight loss but also to acknowledge the media's powerful ability to reduce weight-loss fraud by sharply reducing the dissemination of obviously false weight-loss advertising. In December 2003 the FTC launched its Red Flag campaign to assist the media to reduce deceptive weight-loss advertising and promote positive, reliable advertising messages about weight loss. The FTC (June 19, 2009, http://www.ftc.gov/bcp/edu/microsites/redflag/falseclaims.html) defines red flag claims as those that promise to:

- Cause weight loss of two pounds or more a week for a month or more without dieting or exercise

- Cause substantial weight loss no matter what or how much the consumer eats

- Cause permanent weight loss (even when the consumer stops using product)

- Block the absorption of fat or calories to enable consumers to lose substantial weight

- Safely enable consumers to lose more than three pounds per week for more than four weeks

- Cause substantial weight loss for all users

- Cause substantial weight loss by wearing it on the body or rubbing it into the skin

In April 2004 the FTC filed claims against seven companies for making false weight-loss claims, and in November 2004 the FTC announced six new cases against advertisers using bogus weight-loss claims. In each of these cases, the FTC sought to stop the bogus ads and to secure reparation for consumers. The FTC also launched in November 2004 Operation Big Fat Lie, a nationwide law enforcement action against the six companies making false weight-loss claims in national advertisements. Operation Big Fat Lie aims to stop deceptive advertising and provide refunds to consumers harmed by unscrupulous weight-loss advertisers; to encourage the media not to carry advertisements containing bogus weight-loss claims; and to educate consumers to be wary of companies promising miraculous weight loss without diet or exercise. The FTC also launched a Web site (http://wemarket4u.net/fatfoe/) to help consumers identify false weight-loss claims.

In *2004 Weight-Loss Advertising Survey* (April 2005, http://www.ftc.gov/os/2005/04/050411weightlosssurvey04.pdf), the FTC reports that compared with the 2001 survey, there had been a significant decline in the frequency of red flag claims in the media (television, radio, and print advertisements) included in the 2004 survey. The 2004 survey found that 15% of advertisements made red flag claims, compared with 46% in the 2001 survey. (See Table 9.4.) Table 9.5 shows the frequency of the types of red flag claims made by various types of weight-loss products and services in 2004. Even though a reduction

TABLE 9.4

Frequency of weight-loss ads, 2001 and 2004

Comparison	2004	2001
# of distinct weight-loss ads	34	13
# of distinct ads containing red flag claims	5	6
% of distinct ads containing red flag claims	15%	46%

SOURCE: "Table 3. Ad Frequency Comparison," in *2004 Weight-Loss Advertising Survey*, Federal Trade Commission, April 2005, http://www.ftc.gov/os/2005/04/050411weightlosssurvey04.pdf (accessed November 18, 2009)

TABLE 9.5

Frequency of "red flag" claims in weight-loss ads, 2004

Red flag claim	Number of ads in 2004 sample containing claim	Percentage of ads in 2004 sample containing claim
RF#1 Consumers who use the advertised product can lose two pounds or more a week (over four or more weeks) without reducing caloric intake and/or increasing their physical activity	16	5%
RF#2 Consumers who use the advertised product can lose substantial weight while still enjoying unlimited amounts of high calorie foods.	11	4%
RF#3 The advertised product will cause permanent weight loss (even when the user stops using the product).	13	4%
RF#4 The advertised product will cause substantial weight loss through the blockage of absorption of fat or calories.	9	3%
RF#5 Consumers who use the advertised product (without medical supervision) can safely lose more than three pounds per week for a period of more than four weeks.	10	3%
RF#6 Users can lose substantial weight through the use of the advertised product that is worn on the body or rubbed into the skin.	11	4%
RF#7 The advertised product will cause substantial weight loss for all users.*	13	4%

Notes: The total number of "red flag" claims is 67, while there are only 45 ads with at least one "red flag" claim. Thus, there are about 1.5 "red flag" claims per advertisement for the subset of advertisements with at least one "red flag" claim (67/45).
*A related survey question addressed whether the advertisement claimed that the product would work—even if consumers had tried other products and gotten no results. Eight percent of the advertisements (22 advertisements) communicated that the product works, no matter how many times the user has tried and failed to lose weight before.

SOURCE: "Table 2. Frequency of Red Flag Claims," in *2004 Weight-Loss Advertising Survey*, Federal Trade Commission, April 2005, http://www.ftc.gov/os/2005/04/050411weightlosssurvey04.pdf (accessed November 18, 2009)

in red flag claims occurred after the FTC's 2003 initiative, it is unclear how much the initiative contributed to the observed reduction in questionable and false claims.

DO VERY LOW-CALORIE DIETS INCREASE LONGEVITY?

Even though many Americans are overweight, some people are experimenting with very low-calorie diets in the hope that by remaining extremely thin they will stave off disease and live longer. Advocates of extreme caloric restriction (CR) contend that sharply reducing caloric intake creates biochemical changes that slow the aging process, which theoretically should increase life expectancy.

Most people would find it impossible to adhere to semi-starvation diets, but there is sound scientific evidence—such as Luigi Fontana and Samuel Klein's "Aging, Adiposity, and Calorie Restriction" (*Journal of the American Medical Association*, vol. 297, no. 9, March 7, 2007) and Arthur V.

Everitt and David G. Le Couteur's "Life Extension by Calorie Restriction in Humans" (*Annals of the New York Academy of Sciences*, vol. 1114, October 2007)—that subsistence diets increase the life span of fruit flies, worms, spiders, guppies, mice, and hamsters by between 10% and 40%. In theory, semistarvation prolongs life by reducing metabolism (how quickly glucose is used for energy) in an evolutionary adaptation to conserve calories during periods of famine. Dieters are familiar with this process—they know from experience that as they eat less, their metabolic rate drops, which makes losing weight increasingly more difficult. CR adherents experience comparable drops in metabolic rate—one study found that their body temperature dropped by a full degree. Proponents of CR assert that even though metabolism is vital for life, it is also destructive because it produces unstable molecules known as free radicals that can damage cells through a process called oxidation.

Animal studies find that CR inhibits the growth of cancerous tumors, possibly because at lower body temperatures the body may be better able to repair damaged deoxyribonucleic acid (DNA), which provides the genetic information necessary for the organization and functioning of most living cells and controls the inheritance of traits and characteristics. Animals on CR diets have reduced levels of blood sugar and insulin and greater insulin sensitivity, all of which reduces their risk for diabetes and cardiovascular disease. There is even evidence that CR boosts brain function. Mice with the tendency to develop neurological conditions such as Alzheimer's or Parkinson's disease developed these conditions later and more slowly when they were placed on CR diets, and rodents on CR diets displayed better memory and learning than those on normal diets. There is also evidence that CR influences patterns of gene expression. As animals age, certain genes tend to turn off and become inactive, whereas others are activated. Gene expression profiling can be used to evaluate the biological age of a tissue, because in animals on a CR regime, these profiles correlate with biological as opposed to chronological age. In "A Low Dose of Dietary Resveratrol Partially Mimics Caloric Restriction and Retards Aging Parameters in Mice" (*PLoS One*, vol. 3, no. 6, June 4, 2008), Jamie L. Barger et al. indicate that CR inhibits gene expression profiles associated with heart and skeletal muscle aging and prevents age-related heart problems.

In 2004 the National Institutes of Health began the seven-year Comprehensive Assessment of Long-Term Effects of Reducing Intake of Energy (Calerie) study (http://calerie.dcri.duke.edu/) to explore the effects of CR on human metabolism. The study explores the benefits and risks associated with CR in an effort to determine whether calorie restriction enables people to age in better health using an approach that no existing drug or technology comes close to approximating. The study also aims to find out whether calorie restriction affects aging in a way that promotes longevity.

CR adherents report immediate health benefits including increased mental acuity, reduced need for sleep, sharply reduced cholesterol and fasting blood sugar levels, weight loss, and reduced blood pressure. The regimen is clearly not easy, and even its staunchest advocates, such as members of the Caloric Restriction Society, concede that many people who practice CR experience constant hunger, obsessions with food, mood disorders such as irritability and depression, and lowered libido (sex drive). CR can also cause people to feel cold, and even with adequate vitamin and mineral supplementation it can cause some people to suffer from osteoporosis (decreased bone mass) and hair loss. In "The Calorie-Restriction Experiment" (*New York Times*, October 7, 2009), Jon Gertner reports that the majority of subjects in the Calerie study have achieved their weight loss goals and are maintaining their weight loss by sticking to their diet, but notes that it is a challenging undertaking and one that most Americans would forgo. Gertner opines that "living a life of less in a culture of more—is extremely difficult to achieve and even more difficult to maintain. Americans' seemingly inexorable slide toward obesity tends to indicate as much: for the majority of us, the desire to eat can easily overwhelm personal willpower and (so far) any messages from public-health campaigns."

In "Why Dietary Restriction Substantially Increases Longevity in Animal Models but Won't in Humans" (*Ageing Research Reviews*, vol. 4, no. 3, August 2005), John P. Phelan and Michael R. Rose challenge the notion that CR will increase longevity. The researchers conclude that severely restricting calories over decades may add a few years to a human life span, but will not enable humans to live to 125 years or more. Phelan and Rose developed a mathematical model based on the known effects of calorie intake and life span that shows that people who consume the most calories have a shorter life span. It also shows that if people severely restrict their calories over their lifetime, their life span increases by between 3% and 7%—far less than the 20-plus years some hoped could be achieved by drastic CR. The researchers suggest that "longevity is not a trait that exists in isolation; it evolves as part of a complex life history, with a wide range of underpinning physiological mechanisms involving, among other things, chronic disease processes." They advise Americans to "try to maintain a healthy body weight, but don't deprive yourself of all pleasure. Moderation appears to be a more sensible solution."

Everitt and Le Couteur confirm that even though short-term CR does improve specific markers associated with longevity such as deep body temperature and plasma insulin levels, CR is unlikely to offer markedly increased longevity. The researchers cite as evidence the Okinawans, the longest-lived people on Earth, who consume 40% fewer calories than the average American and live just four years longer. Everitt and Le Couteur surmise that "the effects of CR on human life extension are probably much smaller than those achieved by medical and public health interventions, which have extended life by about 30 years in developed countries in the 20th century, by greatly reducing deaths from infections, accidents, and cardiovascular disease."

The long-term effects of CR are not yet known. Nicholas Wade reports in "Quest for a Long Life Gains Scientific Respect" (*New York Times*, September 29, 2009) that in September 2009 CR adherents attended a conference on aging held at Harvard Medical School. Wade notes that at least one researcher, Cynthia Kenyon of the University of California, San Francisco, was inspired to modify her diet based on her laboratory findings that food with a scant 2% sugar decreased the life span of laboratory roundworms. Kenyon said she started a low-carbohydrate diet in 2002 and that "I try to steer clear of desserts and starches, though I do eat chocolate."

CHAPTER 10
PREVENTING OVERWEIGHT AND OBESITY

As I finish up my tenure as Acting SG I have the strong conviction that curbing the obesity crisis and improving the health of Americans is doable. A healthy future based on prevention is within our grasp. Many of you in the room are national leaders, trend setters, key implementers of the changes in this country that will be needed to reduce obesity. As a nation we stand to make and sustain progress because of commitments from people like you, who came to listen, to learn and to share ideas on how to help. I also hope each of you, full of inspiration at the end of this conference—will make a commitment to working even more furiously toward change in the conditions that have brought this country an obesity epidemic that we simply must turn around.

—Steven Galson, acting U.S. Surgeon General, "Opening Remarks: The Weight of the Nation" (July 27, 2009)

Many obesity researchers and health professionals believe the most effective way to win the war on obesity is to intensify efforts to prevent overweight and obesity among children, adolescents, and adults. They assert that over time prevention is far more cost effective than the expenditures associated with weight-loss efforts and medical treatment of obesity-related diseases. They also observe that prevention is a preferable strategy because there is no universally effective long-term treatment that consistently produces and maintains weight loss.

The landmark report *Surgeon General's Call to Action to Prevent and Decrease Overweight and Obesity, 2001* (2001, http://www.surgeongeneral.gov/topics/obesity/call toaction/CalltoAction.pdf) calls for the design and implementation of interventions to prevent and decrease overweight and obesity, both individually and collectively. It asserts that effective actions must occur at many levels and acknowledges that—even though individual behavioral change is at the core of all strategies to reduce overweight and obesity—to be optimally effective, efforts must not be limited to individual behavioral change.

The report recommends actions to modify group influences by initiating prevention programs that target families, communities, employers and workers, the health care delivery system, and the media, as well as changes in public policy. Furthermore, the report calls for concerted efforts and predicts that actions to prevent and reduce overweight and obesity will fail unless changes are made at every level of American society. Characterizing these problems as societal rather than as individual, the report observes that individual behavioral change is possible only in "a supportive environment with accessible and affordable healthy food choices and opportunities for regular physical activity." The report also warns that actions aimed exclusively at individual behavioral change that do not consider social, cultural, economic, and environmental influences will be counterproductive, serving only to reinforce negative stereotypes, bias, and stigmatization of people who are overweight or obese.

The report promises to abide by five overarching principles to guide its recommendations about how to prevent and decrease overweight and obesity:

- Promote the recognition of overweight and obesity as major public health problems.

- Assist Americans in balancing healthful eating with regular physical activity to achieve and maintain a healthy or healthier body weight.

- Identify effective and culturally appropriate interventions to prevent and treat overweight and obesity.

- Encourage environmental changes that help prevent overweight and obesity.

- Develop and enhance public-private partnerships to help implement this vision.

Many public health professionals believe environmental and policy interventions are the most promising strategies for generating and maintaining healthy nutrition and physical activity behaviors in Americans. Environmental interventions are those actions that modify availability of, access to, pricing of, or education about foods at the places where they are purchased. Policy interventions legislate, regulate, or, through formal or informal rules, serve to guide individual and collective behavior. Examples of environmental and policy initiatives that have met with success include:

- Increasing the availability of fruits and vegetables at school and workplace cafeterias and adding fresh fruit to refrigerated vending machines

- Replacing soft drinks in school vending machines with fruit juices and water

- Instituting daily physical education requirements for students

- Providing point-of-purchase nutrition information at restaurants and grocery stores to encourage healthy food choices

- Allowing workers adequate break time and a location where nursing mothers can express milk so their babies can continue to accrue the health benefits of breastfeeding even after their mothers return to work

PREVENTION EFFORTS TARGET FAMILIES, COMMUNITIES, AND SCHOOLS

Public health education, communication, and other programs aimed at families and communities are identified as the cornerstone of prevention efforts. The *Call to Action* report puts forth communication strategies and corresponding actions to promote awareness about the effects of overweight on health and to support healthy eating and physical activity. For example, the communication strategy of educating expectant parents and other community members about the protective effect of breastfeeding against the development of obesity was translated into the action of creating community environments that promote and support breastfeeding. (The Centers for Disease Control and Prevention [CDC] notes in *Does Breastfeeding Reduce the Risk of Pediatric Overweight?* [July 2007, http://www.cdc.gov/nccdphp/dnpa/nutrition/pdf/breastfeeding_r2p.pdf] that children who are breastfed for nine months are 30% less likely to become overweight.) Similarly, the communication strategy to heighten consumer awareness about reasonable food and beverage portion sizes was coupled with action to encourage the food industry to provide sensible food and beverage portion sizes.

Prevention efforts were not only directed to families and communities but also to policy makers, whose actions to establish environmental and social policy could support families and communities to be more physically active and consume a healthier diet. Policy makers were exhorted to create more community-based obesity prevention and

treatment programs for children and adults and to provide demonstration grants to improve access to, and availability of, healthy affordable foods in inner cities. They were also advised to enact public policy to create and maintain safe and accessible sidewalks, walking and bicycle paths, and stairs.

In the community, schools offer ideal settings and multiple opportunities for preventing overweight and obesity by educating children about, and engaging them in, healthy eating and physical activity. To reinforce their messages concerning the importance of school physical activity and nutrition programs, schools can ensure that breakfast and lunch programs meet nutrition standards and provide food options that are low in fat, calories, and added sugars. Other ways to enact this communication strategy include offering healthy snacks in vending machines and school stores and providing all students with quality daily physical education to cultivate the knowledge, attitudes, skills, behaviors, and confidence needed to be physically active for life.

Community Strategies to Prevent Obesity

In "Recommended Community Strategies and Measurements to Prevent Obesity in the United States" (*Morbidity and Mortality Weekly Report*, vol. 58, no. RR07, July 24, 2009), Laura Kettel Khan et al. review studies of population-based interventions targeting communities and identify 24 environmental- and policy-level strategies that communities and local governments can use to plan and monitor changes to help prevent obesity.

Table 10.1 enumerates the 24 recommended strategies and the suggested measurements to monitor their effectiveness. The strategies fall into six broad categories and aim to:

1. Promote the availability of affordable healthy food and beverages

2. Support healthy food and beverage choices

3. Encourage breastfeeding

4. Encourage physical activity or limit sedentary activity among children and youth

5. Create safe communities that support physical activity

6. Encourage communities to organize for change

Federally Funded National Nutrition Education

Together, the U.S. Department of Health and Human Services (HHS) and the U.S. Department of Agriculture (USDA) update *Nutrition and Your Health: Dietary Guidelines for Americans* every five years. First published in 1980, the guidelines serve as the basis for federal food and nutrition education programs. Historically, some public health professionals believed that the USDA food pyramid was flawed because its composition

TABLE 10.1

Community strategies and measurements to prevent obesity, 2009

Strategies to promote the availability of affordable healthy food and beverages

Strategy 1	Communities should increase availability of healthier food and beverage choices in public service venues.
Suggested measurement	A policy exists to apply nutrition standards that are consistent with the dietary guidelines for Americans (US Department of Health and Human Services, US Department of Agriculture. Dietary guidelines for Americans. 6th ed. Washington, DC: U.S. Government Printing Office; 2005.) to all food sold (e.g., meal menus and vending machines) within local government facilities in a local jurisdiction or on public school campuses during the school day within the largest school district in a local jurisdiction.
Strategy 2	Communities should improve availability of affordable healthier food and beverage choices in public service venues.
Suggested measurement	A policy exists to affect the cost of healthier foods and beverages (as defined by the Institute of Medicine [IOM] [Institute of Medicine. Preventing childhood obesity: health in the balance. Washington, DC: The National Academies Press; 2005]) relative to the cost of less healthy foods and beverages sold within local government facilities in a local jurisdiction or on public school campuses during the school day within the largest school district in a local jurisdiction.
Strategy 3	Communities should improve geographic availability of supermarkets in underserved areas.
Suggested measurement	The number of full-service grocery stores and supermarkets per 10,000 residents located within the three largest underserved census tracts within a local jurisdiction.
Strategy 4	Communities should provide incentives to food retailers to locate in and/or offer healthier food and beverage choices in underserved areas.
Suggested measurement	Local government offers at least one incentive to new and/or existing food retailers to offer healthier food and beverage choices in underserved areas.
Strategy 5	Communities should improve availability of mechanisms for purchasing foods from farms.
Suggested measurement	The total annual number of farmer-days at farmers' markets per 10,000 residents within a local jurisdiction.
Strategy 6	Communities should provide incentives for the production, distribution, and procurement of foods from local farms.
Suggested measurement	Local government has a policy that encourages the production, distribution, or procurement of food from local farms in the local jurisdiction.

Strategies to support healthy food and beverage choices

Strategy 7	Communities should restrict availability of less healthy foods and beverages in public service venues.
Suggested measurement	A policy exists that prohibits the sale of less healthy foods and beverages (as defined by IOM [Institute of Medicine. Preventing childhood obesity: health in the balance. Washington, DC: The National Academies Press; 2005]) within local government facilities in a local jurisdiction or on public school campuses during the school day within the largest school district in a local jurisdiction.
Strategy 8	Communities should institute smaller portion size options in public service venues.
Suggested measurement	Local government has a policy to limit the portion size of any entree (including sandwiches and entree salads) by either reducing the standard portion size of entrees or offering smaller portion sizes in addition to standard portion sizes within local government facilities within a local jurisdiction.
Strategy 9	Communities should limit advertisements of less healthy foods and beverages.
Suggested measurement	A policy exists that limits advertising and promotion of less healthy foods and beverages within local government facilities in a local jurisdiction or on public school campuses during the school day within the largest school district in a local jurisdiction.
Strategy 10	Communities should discourage consumption of sugar-sweetened beverages.
Suggested measurement	Licensed child care facilities within the local jurisdiction are required to ban sugar-sweetened beverages, including flavored/sweetened milk and limit the portion size of 100% juice.

Strategy to encourage breastfeeding

Strategy 11	Communities should increase support for breastfeeding.
Suggested measurement	Local government has a policy requiring local government facilities to provide breastfeeding accommodations for employees that include both time and private space for breastfeeding during working hours.

Strategies to encourage physical activity or limit sedentary activity among children and youth

Strategy 12	Communities should require physical education in schools.
Suggested measurement	The largest school district located within the local jurisdiction has a policy that requires a minimum of 150 minutes perweek of PE in public elementary schools and a minimum of 225 minutes per week of PE in public middle schools and high schools throughout the school year (as recommended by the National Association of Sports and Physical Education).
Strategy 13	Communities should increase the amount of physical activity in PE programs in schools.
Suggested measurement	The largest school district located within the local jurisdiction has a policy that requires K–12 students to be physically active for at least 50% of time spent in PE classes in public schools.
Strategy 14	Communities should increase opportunities for extracurricular physical activity.
Suggested measurement	The percentage of public schools within the largest school district in a local jurisdiction that allow the use of their athletic facilities by the public during non-school hours on a regular basis.
Strategy 15	Communities should reduce screen time in public service venues.
Suggested measurement	Licensed child care facilities within the local jurisdiction are required to limit screen viewing time to no more than 2 hours per day for children aged ≥2 years.

was unduly influenced by pressure from the food industry, whose members knew that even subtle changes to the guidelines affected a food manufacturer's sales. Furthermore, these public health professionals asserted that the guidelines should not be expected to represent objective scientific evidence because they were developed by the U.S. government agency responsible for agriculture, rather than for health.

TABLE 10.1

Community strategies and measurements to prevent obesity, 2009 [CONTINUED]

Strategies to create safe communities that support physical activity

Strategy 16	Communities should improve access to outdoor recreational facilities.
Suggested measurement	The percentage of residential parcels within a local jurisdiction that are located within a half-mile network distance of at least one outdoor public recreational facility.
Strategy 17	Communities should enhance infrastructure supporting bicycling.
Suggested measurement	Total miles of designated shared-use paths and bike lanes relative to the total street miles (excluding limited access highways) that are maintained by a local jurisdiction.
Strategy 18	Communities should enhance infrastructure supporting walking.
Suggested measurement	Total miles of paved sidewalks relative to the total street miles (excluding limited access highways) that are maintained by a local jurisdiction.
Strategy 19	Communities should support locating schools within easy walking distance of residential areas.
Suggested measurement	The largest school district in the local jurisdiction has a policy that supports locating new schools, and/or repairing or expanding existing schools, within easy walking or biking distance of residential areas.
Strategy 20	Communities should improve access to public transportation.
Suggested measurement	The percentage of residential and commercial parcels in a local jurisdiction that are located either within a quarter-mile network distance of at least one bus stop or within a half-mile network distance of at least one train stop (including commuter and passenger trains, light rail, subways, and street cars).
Strategy 21	Communities should zone for mixed use development.
Suggested measurement	Percentage of zoned land area (in acres) within a local jurisdiction that is zoned for mixed use that specifically combines residential land use with one or more commercial, institutional, or other public land uses.
Strategy 22	Communities should enhance personal safety in areas where persons are or could be physically active.
Suggested measurement	The number of vacant or abandoned buildings (residential and commercial) relative to the total number of buildings located within a local jurisdiction.
Strategy 23	Communities should enhance traffic safety in areas where persons are or could be physically active.
Suggested measurement	Local government has a policy for designing and operating streets with safe access for all users which includes at least one element suggested by the national complete streets coalition (http://www.completestreets.org)

Strategy to encourage communities to organize for change

Strategy 24	Communities should participate in community coalitions or partnerships to address obesity.
Suggested measurement	Local government is an active member of at least one coalition or partnership that aims to promote environmental and policy change to promote active living and/or healthy eating (excluding personal health programs such as health fairs).

SOURCE: Laura Kettel Khan et al., "Table. Summary of Recommended Community Strategies and Measurements to Prevent Obesity in the United States," in "Recommended Community Strategies and Measurements to Prevent Obesity in the United States," in *MMWR Recommendations and Reports*, vol. 58, no. RR07, July 24, 2009, http://www.cdc.gov/mmwr/preview/mmwrhtml/rr5807a1.htm#box1 (accessed November 18, 2009)

In January 2004 members of the Dietary Guidelines Advisory Committee met to discuss the sixth version of the dietary guidelines, *Dietary Guidelines for Americans, 2005* (January 2005, http://www.health.gov/dietaryguide lines/dga2005/document/pdf/DGA2005.pdf). Among the issues the committee considered were a reassessment of the food pyramid, the components of a healthy American diet, and energy balance. In preparation for the meeting, the 13 committee members reviewed recent scientific research, including the Institute of Medicine's *Dietary Reference Intakes for Energy, Carbohydrate, Fiber, Fat, Fatty Acids, Cholesterol, Protein, and Amino Acids* (2002) and the World Health Organization's (WHO) *Diet, Nutrition, and the Prevention of Chronic Diseases* (2003, http://whqlibdoc.who.int/trs/WHO_TRS_916.pdf).

The Institute of Medicine report asserts that to meet daily energy and nutritional needs while minimizing the risk for chronic disease, adults should get 45% to 65% of their calories from carbohydrates, 20% to 35% from fat, and 10% to 35% from protein. The guidelines for children are similar to those for adults, except that infants and younger children are advised a slightly higher

proportion of fat—25% to 40% of their caloric intake. The report also emphasizes balancing diet with physical activity and recommends total daily calorie consumption for individuals based on height, weight, gender, and four different levels of physical activity. Its recommendation of an hour per day of physical activity was derived from studies of average daily energy expended by people who maintain a healthy weight.

The WHO report calls on a team of global experts to identify new recommendations for governments on diet and exercise to combat obesity and related chronic diseases. The report advises changing daily nutritional intake and increasing energy expenditure by:

- Reducing consumption of foods high in saturated fat and sugar

- Sharply reducing the amount of salt in the diet

- Increasing the amount of fresh fruit and vegetables in the diet

- Engaging in moderate-intensity physical activity for at least one hour per day

The WHO report specifically recommends limiting fat to between 15% and 30% of total daily intake and saturated fats to less than 10% of this total. It suggests that between 55% and 75% of daily intake should be carbohydrates but that added sugars (refined or simple sugars as opposed to those naturally occurring in fruit and complex carbohydrates) should be limited to 10% or less. Protein should make up 10% to 15% of calorie intake and salt should be restricted to less than 5 grams per day (about 1 teaspoon).

New Food Pyramids Debuted in 2005

The new dietary guidelines offered a number of recommendations that made the food pyramid outdated. For example, the guidelines emphasized choosing complex carbohydrates over simple ones, such as by choosing bread and pasta made from whole-grain flour instead of white flour. They also stipulated that Americans should keep saturated fat below 10% of their total calorie intake. Furthermore, they advised sharply limiting added sugars and choosing and preparing foods with little salt (sodium chloride) so that daily intake totaled less than 2,300 milligrams (approximately 1 teaspoon of salt) of sodium. Table 10.2 shows the sodium content for selected foods. It is interesting to note that processed foods that do not necessarily taste salty, such as tomato soup, nevertheless contain significant amounts of added sodium.

In April 2005 the government replaced the single, one-size-fits-all triangular pyramid with 12 individually tailored food pyramids and a new guide, called MyPyramid (http://www.mypyramid.gov/), to help Americans improve their eating habits. Each food pyramid is intended to meet the varying nutritional needs of people based on their age and level of physical activity. Table 10.3 displays the

TABLE 10.2

Range of sodium content for selected foods

Food group	Serving size	Range (mg)
Breads, all types	1 oz	95–210
Frozen pizza, plain, cheese	4 oz	450–1200
Frozen vegetables, all types	1/2 c	2–160
Salad dressing, regular fat, all types	2 Tbsp	110–505
Salsa	2 Tbsp	150–240
Soup (tomato), reconstituted	8 oz	700–1260
Tomato juice	8 oz (~1 c)	340–1040
Potato chips*	1 oz (28.4 g)	120–180
Tortilla chips*	1 oz (28.4 g)	105–160
Pretzels*	1 oz (28.4 g)	290–560

*All snack foods are regular flavor, salted.
Note: None of the examples provided were labeled low-sodium products. Serving sizes were standardized to be comparable among brands within a food. Pizza and bread slices vary in size and weight across brands.

SOURCE: "Table 15. Range of Sodium Content for Selected Foods," in *Dietary Guidelines for Americans, 2005*, 6th ed., U.S. Department of Health and Human Services and U.S. Department of Agriculture, January 2005, http://www.health.gov/dietaryguidelines/dga2005/document/pdf/Chapter8.pdf (accessed November 20, 2009)

TABLE 10.3

Estimated calorie requirements for each gender and age group at three levels of physical activity

[Estimates are rounded to the nearest 200 calories]

Gender	Age (years)	Activity level[a, b, c]		
		Sedentary[a]	Moderately active[b]	Active[c]
Child	2–3	1,000	1,000–1,400[d]	1,000–1,400[d]
Female	4–8	1,200	1,400–1,600	1,400–1,800
	9–13	1,600	1,600–2,000	1,800–2,200
	14–18	1,800	2,000	2,400
	19–30	2,000	2,000–2,200	2,400
	31–50	1,800	2,000	2,200
	51+	1,600	1,800	2,000–2,200
Male	4–8	1,400	1,400–1,600	1,600–2,000
	9–13	1,800	1,800–2,200	2,000–2,600
	14–18	2,200	2,400–2,800	2,800–3,200
	19–30	2,400	2,600–2,800	3,000
	31–50	2,200	2,400–2,600	2,800–3,000
	51+	2,000	2,200–2,400	2,400–2,800

Note: These levels are based on estimated energy requirements (EER) from the Institute of Medicine Dietary Reference Intakes Macronutrients Report, 2002, calculated by gender, age, and activity level for reference-sized individuals. "Reference size," as determined by the Institute of Medicine, is based on median height and weight for ages up to age 18 years of age and median height and weight for that height to give a body mass index (BMI) of 21.5 for adult females and 22.5 for adult males.
[a]Sedentary means a lifestyle that includes only the light physical activity associated with typical day-to-day life.
[b]Moderately active means a lifestyle that includes physical activity equivalent to walking about 1.5 to 3 miles per day at 3 to 4 miles per hour, in addition to the light physical activity associated with typical day-to-day life.
[c]Active means a lifestyle that includes physical activity equivalent to walking more than 3 miles per day at 3 to 4 miles per hour, in addition to the light physical activity associated with typical day-to-day life.
[d]The calorie ranges shown are to accommodate needs of different ages within the group. For children and adolescents, more calories are needed at older ages. For adults, fewer calories are needed at older ages.

SOURCE: "Table 3. Estimated Calorie Requirements (in Kilocalories) for Each Gender and Age Group at Three Levels of Physical Activity," in *Dietary Guidelines for Americans, 2005*, 6th ed, U.S. Department of Health and Human Services and U.S. Department of Agriculture, January 2005, http://www.health.gov/dietaryguidelines/dga2005/document/pdf/Chapter2.pdf (accessed November 20, 2009)

calorie requirements based on age, gender, and physical activity level calculated by the Institute of Medicine and included in the new dietary guidelines.

In contrast to the older food pyramid from 1992, which featured horizontal bands representing food groups, the new food pyramids contain rainbow-colored bands that run vertically from the tip of the pyramid to the base. The new pyramids also have staircases climbing up one side, exhorting sedentary Americans to become more active. Figure 10.1 shows the cornerstones of the new pyramid food guidance system: physical activity, moderation, personalization, proportionality, variety, and gradual improvement. Furthermore, unlike the old food pyramid, the new food pyramids aim to help people control their portion sizes. The old food pyramid used serving sizes, whereas the new ones offer standardized measures such as cups and ounces.

The pyramid food guidance system delivers basic messages about healthy eating and physical activity that are nearly universally applicable. Americans should:

FIGURE 10.1

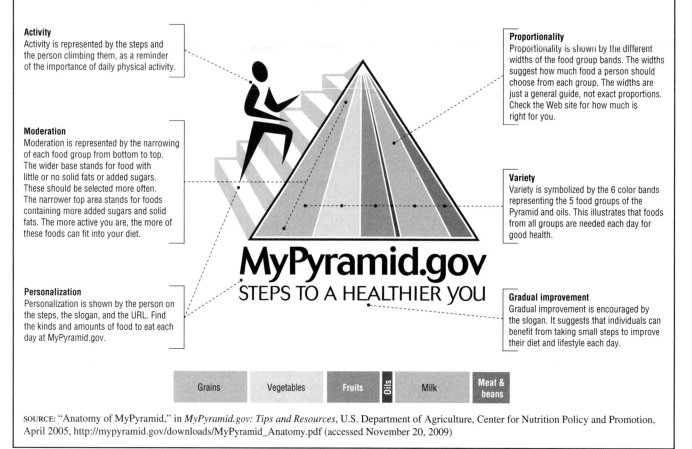

Anatomy of MyPyramid

One size doesn't fit all
USDA's new MyPyramid symbolizes a personalized approach to healthy eating and physical activity. The symbol has been designed to be simple. It has been developed to remind consumers to make healthy food choices and to be active every day. The different parts of the symbol are described below.

Activity
Activity is represented by the steps and the person climbing them, as a reminder of the importance of daily physical activity.

Moderation
Moderation is represented by the narrowing of each food group from bottom to top. The wider base stands for food with little or no solid fats or added sugars. These should be selected more often. The narrower top area stands for foods containing more added sugars and solid fats. The more active you are, the more of these foods can fit into your diet.

Personalization
Personalization is shown by the person on the steps, the slogan, and the URL. Find the kinds and amounts of food to eat each day at MyPyramid.gov.

Proportionality
Proportionality is shown by the different widths of the food group bands. The widths suggest how much food a person should choose from each group. The widths are just a general guide, not exact proportions. Check the Web site for how much is right for you.

Variety
Variety is symbolized by the 6 color bands representing the 5 food groups of the Pyramid and oils. This illustrates that foods from all groups are needed each day for good health.

Gradual improvement
Gradual improvement is encouraged by the slogan. It suggests that individuals can benefit from taking small steps to improve their diet and lifestyle each day.

MyPyramid.gov
STEPS TO A HEALTHIER YOU

Grains | Vegetables | Fruits | Oils | Milk | Meat & beans

SOURCE: "Anatomy of MyPyramid," in *MyPyramid.gov: Tips and Resources*, U.S. Department of Agriculture, Center for Nutrition Policy and Promotion, April 2005, http://mypyramid.gov/downloads/MyPyramid_Anatomy.pdf (accessed November 20, 2009)

- Eat at least 3 ounces (8.5 g) of whole-grain cereals, rice, or pasta every day

- Choose low-fat or fat-free milk, yogurt, and other dairy products

- Choose food and beverages low in added sugars

Mypyramid.gov offers consumers the opportunity to receive customized food plans based on their age, gender, and activity level. Consumers may then print personalized posters, worksheets, and other information to help them start on their healthy eating plan. The revised pyramid food guidance system offers a wealth of detailed information about food intake including the number of calories people of various ages and activity levels should consume, the amounts of food to consume from different food groups, and portion size information for 12 different calorie levels, ranging from 1,000 calories to 3,200 calories per day. (See Table 10.4 and Table 10.5.)

The 2005 pyramid education plan includes sample menus such as the 2,000-calorie food plans shown in Table 10.6 and Table 10.7. It also provides a food tracking chart that helps consumers monitor their intake and assess the quality of their food choices in terms of meeting their nutritional needs within the allotted calorie level.

Fans of the revised dietary guidelines and pyramids assert that even if the new pyramids and online educational resources fail to motivate Americans to change their diet and increase their activity level, the guidelines will still have a salutary effect in terms of their influence on the food industry. For example, they suggest food manufacturers will be prompted to eliminate trans fats from their products and add whole-grain products in response to the guidelines.

Other groups have customized the new pyramid food guidance system to meet the varying needs of different populations. For example, Alice H. Lichtenstein et al. of the Jean Mayer USDA Human Nutrition Research Center on Aging at Tufts University explain in "Modified MyPyramid for Older Adults" (*Journal of Nutrition*, vol. 138, no. 1, January 2008) that they developed a

TABLE 10.4

MyPyramid food intake pattern calorie levels

	Males				Females		
Activity level	Sedentary*	Mod. active*	Active*	Activity level	Sedentary*	Mod. active*	Active*
Age				Age			
2	1,000	1,000	1,000	2	1,000	1,000	1,000
3	1,000	1,400	1,400	3	1,000	1,200	1,400
4	1,200	1,400	1,600	4	1,200	1,400	1,400
5	1,200	1,400	1,600	5	1,200	1,400	1,600
6	1,400	1,600	1,800	6	1,200	1,400	1,600
7	1,400	1,600	1,800	7	1,200	1,600	1,800
8	1,400	1,600	2,000	8	1,400	1,600	1,800
9	1,600	1,800	2,000	9	1,400	1,600	1,800
10	1,600	1,800	2,200	10	1,400	1,800	2,000
11	1,800	2,000	2,200	11	1,600	1,800	2,000
12	1,800	2,200	2,400	12	1,600	2,000	2,200
13	2,000	2,200	2,600	13	1,600	2,000	2,200
14	2,000	2,400	2,800	14	1,800	2,000	2,400
15	2,200	2,600	3,000	15	1,800	2,000	2,400
16	2,400	2,800	3,200	16	1,800	2,000	2,400
17	2,400	2,800	3,200	17	1,800	2,000	2,400
18	2,400	2,800	3,200	18	1,800	2,000	2,400
19–20	2,600	2,800	3,000	19–20	2,000	2,200	2,400
21–25	2,400	2,800	3,000	21–25	2,000	2,200	2,400
26–30	2,400	2,600	3,000	26–30	1,800	2,000	2,400
31–35	2,400	2,600	3,000	31–35	1,800	2,000	2,200
36–40	2,400	2,600	2,800	36–40	1,800	2,000	2,200
41–45	2,200	2,600	2,800	41–45	1,800	2,000	2,200
46–50	2,200	2,400	2,800	46–50	1,800	2,000	2,200
51–55	2,200	2,400	2,800	51–55	1,600	1,800	2,200
56–60	2,200	2,400	2,600	56–60	1,600	1,800	2,200
61–65	2,000	2,400	2,600	61–65	1,600	1,800	2,000
66–70	2,000	2,200	2,600	66–70	1,600	1,800	2,000
71–75	2,000	2,200	2,600	71–75	1,600	1,800	2,000
76 and up	2,000	2,200	2,400	76 and up	1,600	1,800	2,000

Note: Calorie levels are provided for each year of childhood, from 2–18 years, and for adults in 5-year increments.
*Calorie levels are based on the estimated energy requirements (EER) and activity levels from the Institute of Medicine Dietary Reference Intakes Macronutrients Report, 2002.
Sedentary=less than 30 minutes a day of moderate physical activity in addition to daily activities.
Mod. active=at least 30 minutes up to 60 minutes a day of moderate physical activity in addition to daily activities.
Active=60 or more minutes a day of moderate physical activity in addition to daily activities.

SOURCE: "MyPyramid Food Intake Pattern Calorie Levels," in *MyPyramid.gov: Tips and Resources*, U.S. Department of Agriculture, Center for Nutrition Policy and Promotion, April 2005, http://mypyramid.gov/downloads/MyPyramid_Calorie_Levels.pdf (accessed November 20, 2009)

modified food guide pyramid for older adults (aged 70 and older) so that it focuses on nutrient-rich foods and ensures adequate water consumption. The modified pyramid suggests food choices that are easier to prepare and have a longer shelf life such as frozen pre-cut vegetables in resealable bags and single-servings of canned fruits and dry fruits. The modified pyramid also has physical activity—walking, swimming, and yard work—at its base to help older adults remain active and manage their weight.

A New Pyramid for Children

In September 2005 the USDA released MyPyramid for Kids (http://www.mypyramid.gov/kids/index.html), a new pyramid food guidance system for children aged six to 11 years that replaced the 1999 version. Like the adult pyramids, the children's pyramid displays each of the six major food groups using familiar images such as apples for fruits and bread for grains to encourage children to choose healthy foods rather than burgers and fries. The children's version of the pyramid features a girl running up the steps to the top and kids playing soccer, baseball, and basketball, walking a dog, riding a bike, stretching, picnicking, and doing yoga. (See Figure 10.2.)

Children are encouraged to play hard and be more physically active to meet the government's recommended 60 minutes of exercise per day. The USDA suggests that children set up home gyms, substituting items such as soup cans and stairs for weights and stair machines. Just as it does for adults, the USDA Web site provides a worksheet that allows kids to record and track their food consumption and physical activity.

To attract, inform, and entertain children, the USDA Web site features an interactive computer spaceship game. Players who balance food and exercise properly can blast off in a spaceship to Planet Power. Choosing too many foods high in fat and sugar will cause the ship to sputter on the launch pad and release black smoke.

The MyPyramid for Kids program also employs an array of teaching materials for parents, childcare providers, and educators, including tip sheets and posters,

TABLE 10.5

MyPyramid food intake patterns

Calorie level[a]	1,000	1,200	1,400	1,600	1,800	2,000	2,200	2,400	2,600	2,800	3,000	3,200
Daily amount of food from each group												
Fruits[b]	1 cup	1 cup	1.5 cups	1.5 cups	1.5 cups	2 cups	2 cups	2 cups	2 cups	2.5 cups	2.5 cups	2.5 cups
Vegetables[c]	1 cup	1.5 cups	1.5 cups	2 cups	2.5 cups	2.5 cups	3 cups	3 cups	3.5 cups	3.5 cups	4 cups	4 cups
Grains[d]	3 oz-eq	4 oz-eq	5 oz-eq	5 oz-eq	6 oz-eq	6 oz-eq	7 oz-eq	8 oz-eq	9 oz-eq	10 oz-eq	10 oz-eq	10 oz-eq
Meat and beans[e]	2 oz-eq	3 oz-eq	4 oz-eq	5 oz-eq	5 oz-eq	5.5 oz-eq	6 oz-eq	6.5 oz-eq	6.5 oz-eq	7 oz-eq	7 oz-eq	7 oz-eq
Milk[f]	2 cups	2 cups	2 cups	3 cups	3 cups	3 cups	3 cups	3 cups	3 cups	3 cups	3 cups	3 cups
Oils[g]	3 tsp	4 tsp	4 tsp	5 tsp	5 tsp	6 tsp	6 tsp	7 tsp	8 tsp	8 tsp	10 tsp	11 tsp
Discretionary calorie allowance[h]	165	171	171	132	195	267	290	362	410	426	512	648
Vegetable subgroup amounts are per week												
Dark green vegetables	1 c/wk	1.5 c/wk	1.5 c/wk	2 c/wk	3 c/wk	3 c/wk	3 c/wk	3 c/wk	3 c/wk	3 c/wk	3 c/wk	3 c/wk
Orange vegetables	.5 c/wk	1 c/wk	1 c/wk	1.5 c/wk	2 c/wk	2 c/wk	2 c/wk	2 c/wk	2.5 c/wk	2.5 c/wk	2.5 c/wk	2.5 c/wk
Legumes	.5 c/wk	1 c/wk	1 c/wk	2.5 c/wk	3 c/wk	3 c/wk	3 c/wk	3 c/wk	3.5 c/wk	3.5 c/wk	3.5 c/wk	3.5 c/wk
Starchy vegetables	1.5 c/wk	2.5 c/wk	2.5 c/wk	2.5 c/wk	3 c/wk	3 c/wk	6 c/wk	6 c/wk	7 c/wk	7 c/wk	9 c/wk	9 c/wk
Other vegetables	3.5 c/wk	4.5 c/wk	4.5 c/wk	5.5 c/wk	6.5 c/wk	6.5 c/wk	7 c/wk	7 c/wk	8.5 c/wk	8.5 c/wk	10 c/wk	10 c/wk

Notes: The suggested amounts of food to consume from the basic food groups, subgroups, and oils to meet recommended nutrient intakes at 12 different calorie levels. Nutrient and energy contributions from each group are calculated according to the nutrient-dense forms of foods in each group (e.g., lean meats and fat-free milk). The table also shows the discretionary calorie allowance that can be accommodated within each calorie level, in addition to the suggested amounts of nutrient-dense forms of foods in each group.

Estimated daily calorie needs To determine which food intake pattern to use for an individual, the following chart gives an estimate of individual calorie needs. The calorie range for each age/sex group is based on physical activity level, from sedentary to active.

	Calorie range					Calorie range		
Children	**Sedentary[i]**	→	**Active[j]**	**Children**	**Sedentary[i]**	→	**Active[j]**
2–3 years	1,000	→	1,400	2–3 years	1,000	→	1,400
Females				**Males**			
4–8 years	1,200	→	1,800	4–8 years	1,400	→	2,000
9–13	1,600	→	2,200	9–13	1,800	→	2,600
14–18	1,800	→	2,400	14–18	2,200	→	3,200
19–30	2,000	→	2,400	19–30	2,400	→	3,000
31–50	1,800	→	2,200	31–50	2,200	→	3,000
51+	1,600	→	2,200	51+	2,000	→	2,800

[a]Calorie levels are set across a wide range to accommodate the needs of different individuals. The calorie range chart can be used to help assign individuals to the food intake pattern at a particular calorie level.
[b]Fruit group includes all fresh, frozen, canned, and dried fruits and fruit juices. In general, 1 cup of fruit or 100% fruit juice, or 1/2 cup of dried fruit can be considered as 1 cup from the fruit group.
[c]Vegetable group includes all fresh, frozen, canned, and dried vegetables and vegetable juices. In general, 1 cup of raw or cooked vegetables or vegetable juice, or 2 cups of raw leafy greens can be considered as 1 cup from the vegetable group.
[d]Grains group includes all foods made from wheat, rice, oats, cornmeal, barley, such as bread, pasta, oatmeal, breakfast cereals, tortillas, and grits. In general, 1 slice of bread, 1 cup of ready-to-eat cereal, or 1/2 cup of cooked rice, pasta, or cooked cereal can be considered as 1 ounce equivalent from the grains group. At least half of all grains consumed should be whole grains.
[e]Meat & beans group in general, 1 ounce of lean meat, poultry, or fish, 1 egg, 1 Tbsp. peanut butter, 1/4 cup cooked dry beans, or 1/2 ounce of nuts or seeds can be considered as 1 ounce equivalent from the meat and beans group.
[f]Milk group includes all fluid milk products and foods made from milk that retain their calcium content, such as yogurt and cheese. Foods made from milk that have little to no calcium, such as cream cheese, cream, and butter, are not part of the group. Most milk group choices should be fat-free or low-fat. In general, 1 cup of milk or yogurt, 1 1/2 ounces of natural cheese, or 2 ounces of processed cheese can be considered as 1 cup from the milk group.
[g]Oils include fats, from many different plants and from fish, that are liquid at room temperature, such as canola, corn, olive, soybean, and sunflower oil. Some foods are naturally high in oils, like nuts, olives, some fish, and avocados. Foods that are mainly oil include mayonnaise, certain salad dressings, and soft margarine.
[h]Discretionary calorie allowance is the remaining amount of calories in a food intake pattern after accounting for the calories needed for all food groups—using forms of foods that are fat-free or low-fat and with no added sugars.
[i]Sedentary means a lifestyle that includes only the light physical activity associated with typical day-to-day life.
[j]Active means a lifestyle that includes physical activity equivalent to walking more than 3 miles per day at 3 to 4 miles per hour, in addition to the light physical activity associated with typical day-to-day life.

SOURCE: "MyPyramid Food Intake Patterns," in *MyPyramid.gov: Tips and Resources*, U.S. Department of Agriculture, Center for Nutrition Policy and Promotion, April 2005, http://mypyramid.gov/downloads/MyPyramid_Food_Intake_Patterns.pdf (accessed November 20, 2009)

lesson plans, CDs, Go Fish game cards, coloring books, and songs. The USDA Web site "Team Nutrition" (http://www.fns.usda.gov/tn/) offers school success stories and provides initiatives ranging from planting a school garden and organizing a school health fair to nutrition education programs, cooking classes, and poster contests.

Like its adult counterpart, MyPyramid for Kids garnered praise and criticism. According to the press release "'MyPyramid for Kids' a Kid-Friendly Flop, Says CSPI" (September 28, 2005, http://www.cspinet.org/new/2005 09281.html), the Center for Science in the Public Interest (CSPI) states that if the government "wanted to reduce the toll of diet-related disease, it could start by aggressively promoting increased consumption of fruits, vegetables, and whole grains; removing soda and junk foods from schools; getting junk-food ads off children's television; and supporting legislation that would put calorie counts on fast-food menu boards." Other consumer groups said they believed federal funds would be better

TABLE 10.6

Sample menus for a 2000-calorie food plan

Day 1	Day 2	Day 3	Day 4	Day 5
Breakfast	**Breakfast**	**Breakfast**	**Breakfast**	**Breakfast**
Breakfast burrito	Hot cereal	Cold cereal	1 whole wheat English muffin	Cold cereal
1 flour tortilla (7" diameter)	1/2 cup cooked oatmeal	1 cup bran flakes	2 tsp soft margarine	1 cup puffed wheat cereal
1 scrambled egg (in 1 tsp soft margarine)	2 tbsp raisins	1 cup fat-free milk	1 tbsp jam or preserves	1 tbsp raisins
1/3 cup black beans*	1 tsp soft margarine	1 small banana	1 medium grapefruit	1 cup fat-free milk
2 tbsp salsa	1/2 cup fat-free milk	1 slice whole wheat toast	1 hard-cooked egg	1 small banana
1 cup orange juice	1 cup orange juice	1 tsp soft margarine	1 unsweetened beverage	1 slice whole wheat toast
1 cup fat-free milk		1 cup prune juice		1 tsp soft margarine
	Lunch		**Lunch**	1 tsp jelly
Lunch	Taco salad	**Lunch**	White bean–vegetable soup	
Roast beef sandwich	2 ounces tortilla chips	Tuna fish sandwich	1 1/4 cup chunky vegetable soup	**Lunch**
1 whole grain sandwich bun	2 ounces ground turkey, sauteed in 2 tsp sunflower oil	2 slices rye bread	1/2 cup white beans	Smoked turkey sandwich
3 ounces lean roast beef	1/2 cup black beans*	3 ounces tuna (packed in water, drained)	2 ounce breadstick	2 ounces whole wheat pita bread
2 slices tomato	1/2 cup iceberg lettuce	2 tsp mayonnaise	8 baby carrots	1/4 cup romaine lettuce
1/4 cup shredded romaine lettuce	2 slices tomato	1 tbsp diced celery	1 cup fat-free milk	2 slices tomato
1/8 cup sauteed mushrooms (in 1 tsp oil)	1 ounce low-fat cheddar cheese	1/4 cup shredded romaine lettuce		3 ounces sliced smoked turkey breast*
1 1/2 ounce part-skim mozzarella cheese	2 tbsp salsa	2 slices tomato	**Dinner**	1 tbsp mayo-type salad dressing
1 tsp yellow mustard	1/2 cup avocado	1 medium pear	Rigatoni with meat sauce	1 tsp yellow mustard
3/4 cup baked potato wedges*	1 tsp lime juice	1 cup fat-free milk	1 cup rigatoni pasta (2 ounces dry)	1/2 cup apple slices
1 tbsp ketchup	1 unsweetened beverage		1/2 cup tomato sauce tomato bits*	1 cup tomato juice*
1 unsweetened beverage		**Dinner**	2 ounces extra lean cooked ground beef (sauteed in 2 tsp vegetable oil)	
	Dinner	Roasted chicken breast	3 tbsp grated Parmesan cheese	**Dinner**
Dinner	Spinach lasagna	3 ounces boneless skinless chicken breast*		Grilled top loin steak
Stuffed broiled salmon	1 cup lasagna noodles, cooked (2 oz dry)	1 large baked sweet potato	Spinach salad	5 ounces grilled top loin steak
5 ounce salmon filet	2/3 cup cooked spinach	1/2 cup peas and onions	1 cup baby spinach leaves	3/4 cup mashed potatoes
1 ounce bread stuffing mix	1/2 cup ricotta cheese	1 tsp soft margarine	1/2 cup tangerine slices	2 tsp soft margarine
1 tbsp chopped onions	1/2 cup tomato sauce tomato bits*	1 ounce whole wheat dinner roll	1/2 ounce chopped walnuts	1/2 cup steamed carrots
1 tbsp diced celery	1 ounce part-skim mozzarella cheese	1 tsp soft margarine	3 tsp sunflower oil and vinegar dressing	1 tbsp honey
2 tsp canola oil	1 ounce whole wheat dinner roll	1 cup leafy greens salad	1 cup fat-free milk	2 ounces whole wheat dinner roll
1/2 cup saffron (white) rice	1 cup fat-free milk	3 tsp sunflower oil and vinegar dressing		1 tsp soft margarine
1 ounce slivered almonds			**Snacks**	1 cup fat-free milk
1/2 cup steamed broccoli	**Snacks**	**Snacks**	1 cup low-fat fruited yogurt	
1 tsp soft margarine	1/2 ounce dry-roasted almonds*	1/4 cup dried apricots		**Snacks**
1 cup fat-free milk	1/4 cup pineapple	1 cup low-fat fruited yogurt		1 cup low-fat fruited yogurt
	2 tbsp raisins			
Snacks				
1 cup cantaloupe				

TABLE 10.6

Sample menus for a 2000-calorie food plan (CONTINUED)

Day 6	Day 7
Breakfast	**Breakfast**
French toast	Pancakes
2 slices whole wheat French toast	3 buckwheat pancakes
2 tsp soft margarine	2 tsp soft margarine
2 tbsp maple syrup	3 tbsp maple syrup
1/2 medium grape fruit	1/2 cup strawberries
1 cup fat-free milk	3/4 cup honeydew melon
	1/2 cup fat-free milk
Lunch	**Lunch**
Vegetarian chili on baked potato	Manhattan clam chowder
1 cup kidney beans*	3 ounces canned clams (drained)
1/2 cup tomato sauce w/tomato tidbits*	3/4 cup mixed vegetables
3 tbsp chopped onions	1 cup canned tomatoes*
1 ounce low fat cheddar cheese	10 whole wheat crackers*
1 tsp vegetable oil	1 medium orange
1 medium baked potato	1 cup fat-free milk
1/2 cup cantaloupe	
3/4 cup lemonade	
Dinner	**Dinner**
Hawaiian pizza	Vegetable stir-fry
2 slices cheese pizza	4 ounces tofu (firm)
1 ounce canadian bacon	1/4 cup green and red bell peppers
1/4 cup pineapple	1/2 cup bok choy
2 tbsp mushrooms	2 tbsp vegetable oil
2 tbsp chopped onions	1 cup brown rice
Green salad	1 cup lemon-flavored iced tea
1 cup leafy greens	
3 tsp sunflower oil and vinegar dressing	
1 cup fat-free milk	
Snacks	**Snacks**
5 whole wheat crackers*	1 ounce sunflower seeds*
1/8 cup hummus	1 large banana
1/2 cup fruit cocktail (in water or juice)	1 cup low-fat fruited yogurt

Food group		Daily average over one week
Grains	Total grains (oz eq)	6.0
	Whole grains	3.4
	Refined grains	2.6
Vegetables*	Total vegetables (cups)	2.6
Fruits	Fruits (cups)	2.1
Milk	Milk (cups)	3.1
Meat & beans	Meat/beans (oz eq)	5.6
Oils	Oils (tsp/grams)	7.2 tsp/32.4 g
*Vegetable subgroups	(Weekly totals)	
	Dark-green vegetables (cups)	3.3
	Orange vegetables (cups)	2.3
	Beans/peas (cups)	3.0
	Starchy vegetables (cups)	3.4
	Other vegetables (cups)	6.6

Nutrient	Daily average over one week
Calories	1,994
Protein, g	98
Protein, % kcal	20
Carbohydrate, g	264
Carbohydrate % kcal	53
Total fat, g	67
Total fat, % kcal	30
Saturated fat, g	16
Saturated fat, % kcal	7
Monounsaturated fat, g	23
Polyunsaturated fat, g	23
Linoleic acid, g	21
Alpha-linolenic acid, mg	1.1
Cholesterol, mg	207
Total dietary fiber, g	31
Potassium, mg	4,715
Sodium, mg*	1,948
Calcium, mg	1,389
Magnesium, mg	432
Copper, mg	1.9
Iron, mg	2.5
Phosphorus, mg	1,830
Zinc, mg	14
Thiamin, mg	1.9
Riboflavin, mg	21
Niacin equivalents, mg	24
Vitamin in B6, mg	2.9
Vitamin in B12, mcg	18.4
Vitamin in C, mg	190
Vitamin in E, mg (AT)	18.9
Vitamin in A, mcg (RAE)	1,430
Dietary folate equivalents, mcg	558

*Starred items are foods that are labelled as no-salt-added, low-sodium, or low-salt versions of the foods. They can also be prepared from scratch with little or no added salt. All other foods are regular commercial products which contain variable levels of sodium. Average sodium level of the 7 day menu assumes no-salt-added in cooking or at the table.

Notes: Averaged over a week, this seven day menu provides all of the recommended amounts of nutrients and food from each food group.

SOURCE: "Sample Menus for a 2000 Calorie Food Plan," in *MyPyramid.gov: Tips and Resources*, U.S. Department of Agriculture, Center for Nutrition Policy and Promotion, April 2005, http://www.mypyramid.gov/downloads/sample_menu.pdf (accessed November 20, 2009)

TABLE 10.7

MyPyramid food choices based on 2,000 calories per day

[Based on the information you provided, this is your daily recommended amount from each food group.]

Grains 6 ounces	Vegetables 2 1/2 cups	Fruits 2 cups	Milk 3 cups	Meat & beans 5 1/2 ounces

Make half your grains whole
Aim for at least 3 ounces
    of whole grains a day
	Vary your veggies
	Aim for these amounts each week:
	Dark green veggies=3 cups
	Orange veggies=2 cups
	Dry beans & peas=3 cups
	Starchy veggies=3 cups
	Other veggies=6 1/2 cups
		Focus on fruits
		Eat a variety of fruit
		Go easy on fruit juices
			Get your calcium-rich foods
			Go low-fat or fat-free when you
			    choose milk, yogurt, or cheese
				Go lean with protein
				Choose low-fat or lean meats and
				    poultry
				Vary your protein routine-choose more
				    fish, beans, peas, nuts, and seeds

Find your balance between food and physical activity.
Be physically active for at least 30 minutes most days of the week.
Know your limits on fats, sugars, and sodium.
Your allowance for oils is 6 teaspoons a day.
Limit extras—solid fats and sugars—to 265 calories a day.

Your results are based on a 2,000 calorie pattern.   Name:_____

Note: This calorie level is only an estimate of your needs. Monitor your body weight to see if you need to adjust your calorie intake.

SOURCE: "MyPyramid Steps to a Healthier You," in *MyPyramid.gov: Tips and Resources*, U.S. Department of Agriculture, Center for Nutrition Policy and Promotion, April 2005, http://mypyramid.gov/downloads/results/results_2000_18.pdf (accessed November 20, 2009)

spent on a mass media campaign to promote eating fruits and vegetables.

In "Childhood Obesity Study: A Pilot Study of the Effect of the Nutrition Education Program Color My Pyramid" (*Journal of School Nursing*, vol. 25, no. 3, June 2009), Jean Burley Moore et al. report the results of a pilot study looking at the effects of the nutrition education program Color My Pyramid, which consisted of six classes taught over a three-month period. The program incorporated the principles of My Pyramid for Kids and focused on nutrition knowledge and the health status of elementary school children. The 126 fourth- and fifth-grade students who took part in the program were assessed before and after the program and their knowledge, activity level, nutrition status, and blood pressure were compared with students who did not participate in the program. The program increased both the children's nutrition knowledge and activity levels, but there were no significant differences observed in the body mass index (BMI; body weight in kilograms divided by height in meters squared) between the children who had completed the program and those who had not.

5 a Day for Better Health Program

The 5 a Day for Better Health program is the nation's largest public-private nutrition education initiative. The program originated in the California Department of Health Services in 1988 and is jointly sponsored by the National Cancer Institute and the Produce for Better Health Foundation (PBH), a non-profit consumer-education foundation representing the fruit and vegetable industry. In 2001 the national 5 a Day partnership expanded to include other voluntary health organizations and produce associations. Besides the National Cancer Institute and the PBH, the partnership now includes representatives from the USDA, the CDC, the American Cancer Society, the Produce Marketing Association, the United Fresh Fruit and Vegetable Association, the National Alliance for Nutrition and Activity, and the Association of State and Territorial Directors of Health Promotion and Public Health Education.

The 5 a Day for Better Health program (January 2009, http://www.keepkidshealthy.com/nutrition/5_a_day.html) aims to increase fruit and vegetable consumption. Its objectives are "to increase public awareness of the importance of eating five or more servings of fruits and vegetables every day for better health; and to provide consumers with specific information about how to include more servings of fruits and vegetables into daily eating patterns." Studies indicate that the majority of American adults and adolescents are not eating the recommended two or more servings of fruit and three or more servings of vegetables per day. For example, in "Correlates of Fruit and Vegetable Intakes in US Children" (*Journal of the American Dietetic Association*, vol. 109, no. 3, March 2009), Barbara A. Lorson, Hugo R. Melgar-Quinonez, and Christopher A. Taylor find that fruit and vegetable consumption among children and teens varies by age, race, sex, ethnicity, and household income. The study of 6,513 children and adolescents aged 2 to 18 years finds that:

- 2- to 5-year-olds consumed significantly more fruit and juice than 6- to 11- and 12- to 18-year-olds.

- Total vegetable consumption was significantly higher among 12- to 18-year-olds than among younger children.

FIGURE 10.2

MyPyramid for kids

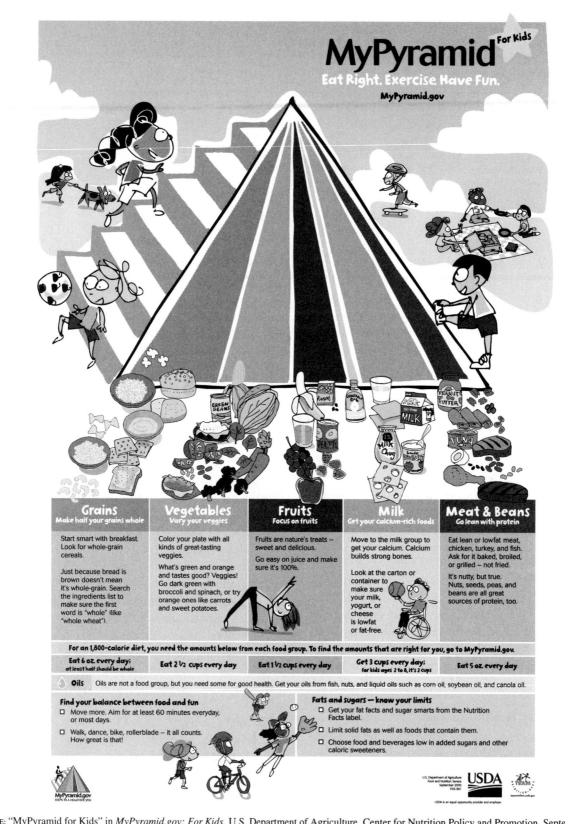

SOURCE: "MyPyramid for Kids" in *MyPyramid.gov: For Kids*, U.S. Department of Agriculture, Center for Nutrition Policy and Promotion, September 2005, http://teamnutrition.usda.gov/Resources/mpk_poster2.pdf (accessed February 2, 2010)

- A scant 8% of vegetables consumed by children of all groups were dark green or orange; fried potatoes accounted for nearly half (46%) of total vegetable consumption.

- Mexican-Americans consumed significantly more fruit than non-Hispanic white children and adolescents.

- African-American children and adolescents consumed significantly more dark-green vegetables and fewer deep-yellow vegetables than Mexican-American and non-Hispanic white children and adolescents.

- Children and teens who failed to meet the recommendations tended to be male, older, and living in households making between 130% and 350% of the federal poverty level.

- Male children and adolescents living in households below 350% of the poverty level were more likely to consume energy-dense fruits and vegetables, such as fruit juice and french fries, and were at greater risk for overweight.

Nutrition research reveals that active men should consume more than the five servings of fruit and vegetables the program has promoted since its inception. In 2000 the 5 a Day for Better Health program launched the Men Shoot for 9 program to encourage active men to eat nine servings of fruits and vegetables every day. Along with reducing the risk for heart disease, high blood pressure, stroke, many cancers, and diabetes, diets rich in fruits and vegetables can help prevent overweight and obesity. Fruits and vegetables are naturally low in calories and fat, and their high water and fiber content produce feelings of satiety (the feeling of fullness or satisfaction after eating). Combined with an active lifestyle and a low-fat diet, eating greater amounts of fruits and vegetables and fewer high-calorie foods at meals can help control weight. The Men Shoot for 9 program teaches active men that they can feel full and consume fewer calories when they substitute vegetables for foods that contain more fat and calories.

In "How Many Fruits & Vegetables Do You Need?" (2010, http://www.fruitsandveggiesmatter.gov/), the CDC offers information about the benefits of eating fruits and vegetables, recipes, interactive tools, and information about how to use fruits and vegetables to help consumers manage their weight. For example, Table 10.8 shows fruit and vegetable choices that total 100 calories or less. The CDC advocates in *How to Use Fruits and Vegetables to Help Manage Your Weight* (June 5, 2009, http://www.cdc.gov/nccdphp/dnpa/nutrition/pdf/CDC_5-A-Day.pdf) lightening the calorie load of meals by substituting vegetables for some meat or cheese in meals and substituting a serving of fruits or vegetables for high-calorie snacks such as corn chips.

TABLE 10.8

Servings of fruit and vegetables with 100 calories or less

- a medium-size apple (72 calories)
- a medium-size banana (105 calories)
- 1 cup steamed green beans (44 calories)
- 1 cup blueberries (83 calories)
- 1 cup grapes (100 calories)
- 1 cup carrots (45 calories), broccoli (30 calories), or bell peppers (30 calories) with 2 tbsp. hummus (46 calories)

SOURCE: "About 100 Calories or Less," in *How to Use Fruits and Vegetables to Help Manage Your Weight*, Centers for Disease Control and Prevention, June 5, 2009, http://www.cdc.gov/nccdphp/dnpa/nutrition/pdf/CDC_5-A-Day.pdf (accessed November 21, 2009)

State Funding for Prevention Efforts

The CDC Division of Nutrition, Physical Activity, and Obesity aims to help states prevent obesity and other chronic diseases by focusing on poor nutrition and inadequate physical activity. The division assists states in developing and implementing nutrition and physical activity interventions, and sponsoring initiatives to help populations balance caloric intake and expenditure, increase physical activity, improve nutrition by increasing consumption of fruits and vegetables, reduce television time, and increase breastfeeding.

In 2009, 25 states received funding for capacity building, in which state health departments gather data, build partnerships, and create statewide health plans. Essentially, capacity building lays the necessary groundwork on which to institute nutrition and physical activity interventions. In addition, the states received funding for basic implementation. Figure 10.3 shows the states that received funding by the Division of Nutrition, Physical Activity, and Obesity in 2009. The funding was used to support the creation of initiatives. For example, the CDC (August 19, 2009, http://www.cdc.gov/obesity/state programs/fundedstates/arkansas.html) indicates that Arkansas, which has received funding since 2004, created the Arkansas Healthy Employee Lifestyle Program, "an incentive-based worksite wellness initiative that encourages participants to engage in and track their healthy behaviors." The program includes private businesses, community organizations, and all state agencies. The CDC notes, "In 2007, the state legislature passed an act allowing state employees to earn time off for participating in and tracking healthy activities."

IS NUTRITION EDUCATION WORKING TO IMPROVE AMERICANS' DIETS?

The Healthy Eating Index (HEI) is a measure developed in 1990 by the USDA to assess the overall health value of Americans' diets. It captures the type and quantity of foods people eat and the degree to which diets comply with specific recommendations in the USDA

FIGURE 10.3

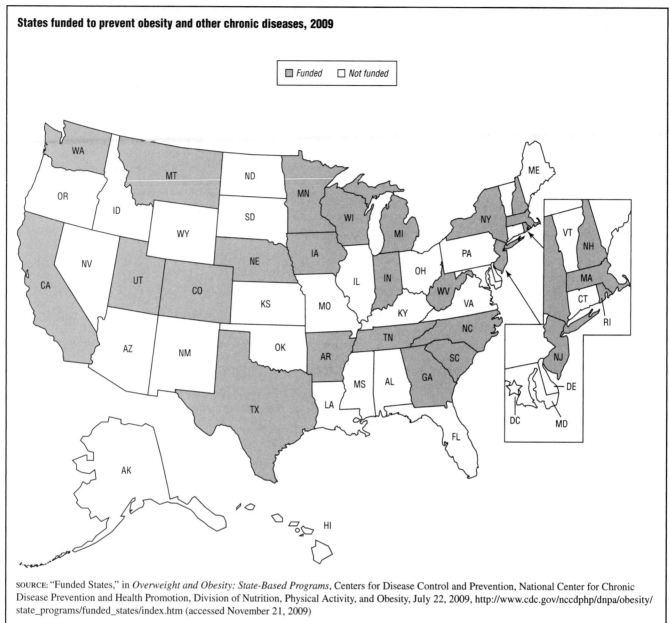

States funded to prevent obesity and other chronic diseases, 2009

☐ Funded   ☐ Not funded

SOURCE: "Funded States," in *Overweight and Obesity: State-Based Programs*, Centers for Disease Control and Prevention, National Center for Chronic Disease Prevention and Health Promotion, Division of Nutrition, Physical Activity, and Obesity, July 22, 2009, http://www.cdc.gov/nccdphp/dnpa/obesity/state_programs/funded_states/index.htm (accessed November 21, 2009)

dietary guidelines and the food pyramids. The HEI assigns points for eating consistently within USDA guidelines. It assesses 10 dietary components—grains, vegetables, fruits, milk, meat, total fat, total saturated fat, cholesterol, sodium, and a varied diet—on a scale of 0 to 10. Individuals who eat grains, vegetables, fruits, milk, meat (including chicken and fish), as well as a variety of foods at or above the USDA recommended levels receive a maximum score of 10. A score of 0 is assigned when the recommended amount of those components is not eaten. For fat, saturated fat, cholesterol, and sodium, a score of 10 is awarded for eating the recommended amount or less. The highest possible score is 100; a score of 80 or above is considered a healthy diet, scores between 51 and 80 show a need for dietary improvement, and scores below 50 indicate poor diets.

Table 10.9 shows the components and standards for scoring used in the 2005 HEI.

The market research firm NPD Group reports in *24th Annual Eating Patterns in America* (2009) that Americans have changed some, but not all, of their food purchasing and eating habits. Adults surveyed in 2009 said they were:

- Eating fewer restaurant meals—the annual number of meals purchased at restaurants declined from a high of 211 in 2001 to 202 in 2009

- Eating home-cooked meals at about the same rate from previous years—49% of all main dishes served at home were fresh or homemade—this rate has not varied considerably since 2000, but it is sharply lower than the 63% reported in 1984

TABLE 10.9

Healthy Eating Index, 2005

Component	Maximum points	Standard for maximum score	Standard for minimum score of zero
Total fruit (includes 100% juice)	5	≥0.8 cup equiv. per 1,000 kcal	No fruit
Whole fruit (not juice)	5	≥0.4 cup equiv. per 1,000 kcal	No whole fruit
Total vegetables	5	≥1.1 cup equiv. per 1,000 kcal	No vegetables
Dark green and orange vegetables and legumes[a]	5	≥0.4 cup equiv. per 1,000 kcal	No dark green or orange vegetables or legumes
Total grains	5	≥3.0 oz equiv. per 1,000 kcal	No grains
Whole grains	5	≥1.5 oz equiv. per 1,000 kcal	No whole grains
Milk[b]	10	≥1.3 cup equiv. per 1,000 kcal	No milk
Meat and beans	10	≥2.5 oz equiv. per 1,000 kcal	No meat or beans
Oils[c]	10	≥12 grams per 1,000 kcal	No oil
Saturated fat	10	≤7% of energy[d]	≥15% of energy
Sodium	10	≤0.7 gram pr 1,000 kcal[d]	≥2.0 grams per 1,000 kcal
Calories from solid fat, alcohol, and added sugar (SoFAAS)	20	≤20% of energy	≥50% of energy

Note: Intakes between the minimum and maximum levels are scored proportionately, except for saturated fat and sodium (see footnote d).
[a]Legumes counted as vegetables only after meat and beans standard is met.
[b]Includes all milk products, such as fluid milk, yogurt, and cheese.
[c]Includes nonhydrogenated vegetable oils and oils in fish, nuts, and seeds.
[d]Saturated fat and sodium get a score of 8 for the intake levels that reflect the 2005 Dietary Guidelines, <10% of calories from saturated fat and 1.1 grams of sodium/1,000 kcal, respectively.

SOURCE: Patricia M. Guenther et al., "Healthy Eating Index—2005 Components and Standards for Scoring," in *Healthy Eating Index—2005*, USDA, Center for Nutrition Policy and Promotion, December 2006, http://www.cnpp.usda.gov/Publications/HEI/healthyeatingindex2005factsheet.pdf (accessed November 12, 2007)

- Using microwaves more often—the percent of main meals prepared in microwave ovens rose from 11% in 1985 to 23% in 2009

- Continuing to favor easy meal preparation methods when eating at home

- Doing less meal preparation on the stovetop, from 52% in 1985 to 33% in 2009

- Purchasing more store and private-label brands since 2002

- Purchasing fewer breakfasts at restaurants—probably in response to the economic downturn that began in 2007

The NPD Group report indicates that healthy eating was a casualty of the economic downturn as consumers reduced their consumption of organic foods and healthier choices. The report also observes that more food purchases were made at supermarkets—not because there is more cooking at home—but because supermarket prices were lower in 2009 than 2008 while restaurant prices actually increased during the same period.

According to the report, Harry Balzer, the vice president of the NPD Group, names convenience as the driving force behind many of the consumers' food choices and observes that "many of the eating pattern shifts blamed on the economy began happening years or even decades ago. It was just more topical to blame them on the recession." Balzer opines, "What's important to consider is that the changes caused by the current state of the economy are short-term, but those changes that have been occurring for a greater length of time will resonate for years to come."

In the press release "NPD Finds Moms' Eating Habits and Nutritional Knowledge Influences What Their Kids Eat" (October 19, 2009, http://www.npd.com/press/releases/press_091019.html), the NPD Group finds that mothers' eating habits and knowledge of nutrition have a powerful impact on their children's diet. Its research reveals that when the adult female in a household with children has a good HEI score, then the children are also eating well. The NPD Group indicates that 67% of mothers consider themselves "extremely or very knowledgeable about nutrition and eating." However, it finds that even though mothers may have adequate knowledge and good intentions, they are less likely to purchase healthy foods: three-quarters of new mothers and about two-thirds of experienced mothers claim "they actively seek out foods with nutrition benefits." The majority (81%) of mothers feel that they are the primary source of nutrition education for their children. Yet when these same mothers were asked to assess their children's level of nutritional knowledge, few considered their children extremely or very knowledgeable—only about half of children aged six to 17 were considered somewhat knowledgeable and a quarter described their six- to 12-year-old children as not very knowledgeable.

Americans' Snack Food Choices

In 2004 the NPD Group released its first-ever study about Americans' snack food choices: *Snacking in America*. The report finds that salty snacks such as pretzels, potato chips, and tortilla chips accounted for about a quarter of the convenience foods Americans choose for snacks.

Even though children and teens snack on sugary treats such as candy, gum, chewy fruit snacks, and breath mints, which accounted for an additional 14% of snack food choices, some of the fastest-growing snack foods among children and adolescents aged two to 18 were healthier choices. Yogurt was the fastest-growing snack food in terms of consumption frequency among children under the age of 13. On average, children under the age of 13 ate yogurt 11 times more in 2003 than they did in 1999. Children aged two to seven ate yogurt as a snack nearly 14 times more often in 2003 than they did in 1999, and children aged eight to 12 snacked on yogurt 8.5 times more in 2003 than in 1999. Children may be making some healthier choices when it comes to snacks, but they are also snacking more frequently—in 2003 children and teens consumed about 22 more snacks per person per year than reported in 1999.

In June 2005 the NPD Group's SnackTrack reported that fruit was the number-one snack food consumed by children aged two to 12. Among boys aged two to seven, fresh fruit was consumed more often than any other snack food, followed by yogurt, potato chips, chocolate candy, and cookies. Girls the same age ranked fresh fruit first, followed by yogurt, gum, potato chips, and chocolate candy. Boys aged eight to 12 named fresh fruit, potato chips, gum, ice cream, and chocolate candy as their top-five picks, and girls the same age said fresh fruit, gum, potato chips, ice cream, and chocolate candy were their favorite snack foods.

Chewing gum was the number-one snack food named by adults aged 18 to 54 in 2005. The NPD Group's Snack-Track found that age was a factor in the gum-chewing habits of Americans. Even though gum was a popular snack among children under the age of 13, it did not rank as number one until the teenage years. After gum, the top-ranking snack foods among men in 2005 were chocolate candy, fresh fruit, potato chips, breath/candy mints, ice cream, nuts, cookies, tortilla chips, and candy bars. Women said chocolate candy, fresh fruit, potato chips, breath/candy mints, ice cream, cookies, nuts, yogurt, and crackers were their choices.

The NPD Group predicts in the press release "NPD Looks into the Future of Eating and Finds a Whole Lot of Snacking Going On" (August 31, 2009, http://www.npd.com/press/releases/press_090831.html) that snacking at home will outpace population growth in the second decade of the 21st century. Between 2008 and 2018 snacking at home is projected to increase 19%. Snacking at home in the morning is projected to increase by 23%, afternoon snacking is expected to rise by 20%, and evening snacking is forecasted to increase by 15%. Besides predicting increasing reliance on convenience foods, the NPD Group believes that the use of frozen foods, canned ingredients, and completely home-cooked dinners will decline.

Interventions to Promote Healthy Weight

In "Guide to Community Preventive Services: Obesity Prevention—Interventions in Community Settings" (September 23, 2009, http://www.thecommunityguide.org/obesity/communitysettings.html), the CDC's Task Force on Community Preventive Services reviews the effectiveness of interventions that prevent obesity and promote healthy eating and physical activity. The task force considers the effectiveness of population-based interventions that promote healthy growth and development of children and adolescents and that support healthy weights among adults. It also focuses on school-based strategies, work-site programs, health care system interventions, and community-wide initiatives.

The task force recommends interventions that reduce the time children and teens spend watching television, playing video or computer games, and surfing the Internet. It endorses work-site programs that combine nutrition and physical activity as effective strategies to reduce and control overweight and obesity. It also indicates that more research is needed to determine the extent to which school-based programs help control overweight and obesity.

PREVENTION PROGRAMS AT THE WORK SITE

Along with school-based nutrition programs and education initiatives aimed at the public at large, several notable obesity prevention efforts involve developing and implementing strategies to integrate physical activity and healthy food choices into routine work-site activities. Examples of such activities include incorporating planned activity breaks with music into long meetings; offering healthy food choices during meetings and breaks and in employee cafeterias: and hosting walking meetings.

Because more than 100 million Americans (over one out of every three people in the United States, as of the end of 2009) spend a large number of their waking hours at work, the work site presents another opportunity for prevention programs. In "Guide to Community Preventive Services," the CDC advises moving beyond traditional workplace health education programs. It recommends more intensive and comprehensive efforts such as modifying physical and social environments, instituting policies consistent with the objective of preventing overweight and obesity, and extending work-site prevention efforts not only to employees but also to the families of employees and their communities.

Examples of work-site obesity prevention and weight-control strategies include:

- Educating workers using lectures, written materials provided in print or online, and educational software

- Ensuring that healthy food options are available in cafeterias and vending machines

- Establishing work-site exercise facilities or creating incentives for employees to join local fitness centers

- Developing incentives, rewards, and reinforcements for workers to achieve and maintain a healthy body weight

- Encouraging employers to require weight management and physical activity counseling as covered benefits in health insurance contracts

- Providing individual or group behavioral counseling

Research suggests that obesity may begin at the office. W. Kerry Mummery et al. examine in "Occupational Sitting Time and Overweight and Obesity in Australian Workers" (*American Journal of Preventive Medicine*, vol. 29, no. 2, August 2005) the role of the workplace in the problem of overweight and obesity by studying the association between occupational sitting time and overweight and obesity in a sample of adults employed full time. The researchers find that the more time workers sat at their desk, the more likely they were to be overweight. Higher total daily sitting time was associated with a 68% increased risk of being overweight or obese.

Overall, men sat an average of 209 minutes while at work, 20 minutes more than the average for women. Mummery et al. suggest that the extra 20 minutes might make a difference because they find a significant association between sitting time and overweight and obesity in male workers, but not in female workers.

Mummery et al. assert that encouraging workers to exercise may favorably influence a company's bottom line. They conclude, "Time and productivity lost due to chronic diseases associated with overweight and obesity may make it financially worthwhile for employers to be more proactive in the health of their employees by promoting physical activity at work."

Offices of the Future May Improve, Rather Than Imperil, Health and Fitness

Steve Karnowski notes in "Researcher Sees Future Where People Walk at Work" (Associated Press, June 7, 2005) that James A. Levine, a Mayo Clinic obesity researcher who studies nonexercise activity thermogenesis (NEAT; the calories people burn during everyday activities such as standing, walking, or even fidgeting), redesigned his office in 2005 to encourage physical activity to burn calories. Levine explains that because it is metabolically more effective and probably easier for most people to put more NEAT into their lives to achieve and maintain a healthy body weight than to seek organized exercise, the physically active office would be a natural outgrowth of NEAT research.

Levine's office of the future holds meetings while walking laps on a track rather than sitting around a conference table eating donuts. Workers at computers walk on a treadmill rather than sit, and presentations are made standing at magnetic marker boards rather than sitting at desks or conference tables.

Levine's retrofitted office even appeals to his colleagues who already exercise regularly because they assert that standing and moving keeps them alert and focused throughout the day. Levine admits that there is pressure in his office to work while standing and to keep moving throughout the day, but he contends that this positive peer pressure is preferable to the pressure to bring unhealthy snack foods to the work site.

In *Move a Little, Lose a Lot: New NEAT Science Reveals How to Be Thinner, Happier, and Smarter* (2009), James A. Levine and Selene Yeager explain that Americans' reliance on electronics and especially the Internet has deprived them of the opportunity to be physically active and burn calories. They assert that changing office workers' routines to include more standing, turning, and bending throughout the course of the workday can burn 2,100 calories per week, boost metabolism, reduce blood pressure, and increase mental clarity.

INTENSIFYING THE PREVENTION AGENDA IN THE HEALTH CARE SYSTEM

Interactions with health care professionals are important opportunities to deliver powerful prevention messages. Physicians' and other health professionals' prescriptions and recurring advice to prevent weight gain to prevent disease or reduce symptoms of existing disease are often powerful inducements for behavioral change. Most Americans have at least annual contact with a health care professional, and if this contact includes information about the importance of weight management, then it may reinforce prevention messages received in other settings such as schools and work sites. Furthermore, health care professionals are instrumental in shaping public policy and can leverage their expertise and credibility to present accurate messages in the media and catalyze sweeping changes in the community at large.

Examples of strategies to expand on prevention efforts in the health care delivery system include:

- Training health care providers and health profession students to use effective techniques to prevent and treat overweight and obesity

- Cultivating partnerships between health care providers, schools, faith-based groups, and other community organizations to target social and environmental causes of overweight and obesity

- Classifying obesity as a disease to enable reimbursement for prevention efforts

- Partially or fully covering weight-management services including nutrition education and physical activity programs as health plan benefits

In November 2009 the U.S. House of Representatives approved a historic bill to overhaul and reform the U.S. health care system—a 10-year, $1.1 trillion bill to provide near-universal health care coverage. The bill would establish a government-run health-insurance plan option to compete with private insurers and would eliminate insurers' ability to deny or cancel coverage because of preexisting medical conditions. The bill would also emphasize community prevention as an important strategy for improving the nation's health and curbing the huge costs associated with untreated chronic disease.

By January 2010 the bill, and the far-reaching health care reform it promised, seemed unlikely to move forward. In "Democrats Put Lower Priority on Health Bill" (*New York Times*, January 26, 2010), David M. Herszenhorn and Robert Pear report that Democrats no longer felt the same urgency or optimism about enacting sweeping health care reform. Herszenhorn and Pear observe, "Some lawmakers said they expected that Congress would try to adopt a vastly pared-down bill once they returned to the issue."

In "American Public Supports Investment in Prevention as Part of Health Care Reform: Solid Majorities Favor Prevention Proposals" (November 10, 2009, http://healthy americans.org/assets/files/TFAH-RWJFPreventionSurveyII .pdf), Greenberg Quinlan Rosner Research indicates that Americans support devoting resources to focus on prevention. Based on a poll that it conducted in November 2009, it finds that 71% of Americans supported "increasing the level of funding for prevention." Even the cost— an estimated $34 billion—of intensifying prevention programs did not seem to faze Americans. They not only felt that prevention is worth the cost but also that it will ultimately save money.

USING THE MEDIA TO COMMUNICATE THE PREVENTION MESSAGE

The media plays a pivotal role in prevention efforts. It can communicate and educate the public about healthy behaviors and health risks associated with overweight and obesity. It can introduce and reinforce prevention messages from health care professionals. It can also assist to alter attitudes and perceptions by celebrating healthy eating and physical activity.

The International Food Information Council (IFIC) has tracked media coverage of diet, nutrition, and food safety since 1995. In its first report, *Food for Thought* (1995), the IFIC noted that the leading nutrition and food issues receiving newspaper, television, and other media coverage during the previous 12 months were reducing fat intake; the impact of diet on disease risks; and discussions of foodborne illnesses, vitamin and mineral intake, disease causation, caloric intake, antioxidants, cholesterol intake, sugar intake, and fiber intake. As obesity became a more prominent issue in the late 1990s, the IFIC reports in "Executive Summary" (*Food for Thought VI* [December 2005, http://internal.ific.org/ research/fftres.cfm]) that the number of stories about diet, weight loss, nutrition, and obesity increased from 1,270 in 1995 to 2,412 in 2005. This increase reflected both a rising volume of coverage and an escalation in the number of media outlets reporting about diet, overweight, and obesity. In *Food for Thought VI*, the IFIC reports that obesity was the leading topic in food and nutrition media stories during 2004, followed by disease prevention, physical activity, weight management, disease causation, vitamin and mineral intake, fat intake, functional foods, mad cow disease, calorie intake, and biotechnology.

In 2007 some observers expressed dismay with Small Steps (http://www.smallstep.gov/), a media campaign targeting obesity that was created by the Ad Council and the HHS. The government-funded campaign, which costs over $1.5 million per year, features television spots intended to encourage people to make changes—such as eating healthy snacks and taking stairs instead of elevators—to improve their health.

According to the article "U.S. Obesity Ads Called 'Namby-Pamby'" (Associated Press, October 22, 2007), critics describe the ads—one of which features people finding blobs of fat on the floor and observing that it must be fat lost by someone choosing healthy snacks—as lacking the dramatic impact of the antismoking campaigns and as too tame to be effective. They also question whether it is appropriate to tackle the urgent health consequences of an obesity epidemic with a campaign that emphasizes such small lifestyle changes. Describing the campaign, Michael F. Jacobson of the CSPI suggests, "It's so namby-pamby I think people will shrug it off," and Kelly D. Brownell, the director of Yale University's Center for Eating and Weight Disorders, opines, "I think 'Small Steps' is a euphemism for small vision." Jacobson also contends that the campaign fails to acknowledge one of the root causes of the obesity epidemic—ready access to inexpensive high-fat and high-calorie food—that the government should address. According to Jacobson, "The U.S. government doesn't have the guts to go after junk food producers."

Claire Prentice reports in "Anti-obesity Ad Shocks New Yorkers" (BBC News, October 7, 2009) that in 2009 the New York City Department of Health launched the antiobesity advertising campaign "Pouring on the Pounds" to educate consumers about the consequences of drinking sugary soft drinks. New York City health officials indicate the images used in the new campaign are intended to be disturbing enough to prompt consumers to think about their behavior and beverage choices. Critics of the campaign feel the shocking, ugly images of yellow human fat being poured into a glass from a soda bottle may turn viewers off so quickly that they will not take in the ad's message. In contrast, the multimedia advertising campaign "Did You Play Today?" by the HHS that also debuted in 2009 is comparatively mild. Using characters from Maurice Sendak's (1928–) classic children's story *Where the Wild Things Are*, the campaign exhorts children to lead healthy lifestyles. Critics of this campaign believe its message is too mild and describe it as "too little, too late" in terms of its potential impact on children's behaviors.

TARGETING CHILDHOOD OBESITY AND WOMEN

In 2005 the American Heart Association (AHA) launched a new initiative aimed at combating childhood obesity. The initiative provides recommendations specifically directed at the promotion of physical activity in schools. The AHA is also acting to enhance existing programs such as Choose to Move, an Internet-based program that helps women add activity to their daily life and provides nutrition education. The AHA notes in "Nine of 10 Women Attempt Exercise Goals after Initial Failure, Survey Shows" (October 16, 2007, http://www.choosetomove.org/pdf/CTM%20Exercise%20Survey%202007%20FINAL.pdf) that it added a new feature, the Choose to Move Countdown, a downloadable desktop tool that offers daily exercise tips, motivation, and nutrition information for 12 weeks to help women jumpstart healthy lifestyle changes.

In *A Nation at Risk: Obesity in the United States Statistical Sourcebook* (May 2005, http://www.americanheart.org/downloadable/heart/1114880987205NationAtRisk.pdf), the AHA provides solid science about nutrition, physical activity, and weight to the public, health care professionals, and policy makers.

The AHA notes in the abstract "Increased Obesity Hindering Success at Reducing Heart Disease Risk" (November 17, 2009, http://americanheart.mediaroom.com/index.php?s=43&item=860) that Kami Banks et al. gave a presentation at the 2009 AHA's Scientific Sessions, which were held in Orlando, Florida, in November 2009. The researchers revealed that there has been no progress in reducing Americans' risk factors for developing cardiovascular disease. Between 1988 and 2006 the average BMI rose from 26.5 to 28.2, and there were commensurate increases in blood pressure and fasting blood glucose. Banks et al. averred, "Despite focused public health efforts, there is no net improvement in the overall cardiovascular risk factor profile over the past two decades in the U.S. population," and they called on the medical community to intensify prevention efforts to combat obesity.

Carole Bartoo reports in "American Heart Association Lauds Pediatric Obesity Research" (*Reporter* [Nashville, TN], October, 9, 2009) that in October 2009 Sabina Gesell was given the AHA Clinical Research Award "for promising early career investigators." A pediatric obesity researcher, Gesell is conducting research that attempts to disrupt the pattern of mother-to-child obesity that starts in pregnancy. Because a mother who is obese increases the risk for obesity in her child, Gesell's research seeks to prevent excessive weight gain during pregnancy and the retention of weight gain after birth. The award provided Gesell with a $150,000 grant to help further her research. This award underscores the AHA's focus on preventing obesity as a key strategy for reducing the incidence of heart disease in future generations.

ECONOMIC INCENTIVES FOR PREVENTION AND TREATMENT

Richard Hyer indicates in "Government-Funded Weight-Loss Programs Recommended for Low-Income Population" (*Medscape Medical News*, October 8, 2007) that many clinicians and obesity researchers believe participation in weight-loss programs in low-income communities would increase if the federal and state governments provided funding for the programs.

According to Kevin G. Volpp et al., in "Financial Incentive-Based Approaches for Weight Loss: A Randomized Trial" (*Journal of the American Medical Association*, vol. 300, no. 22, December 10, 2008), subjects that were given a financial incentive to lose weight lost more weight than those that were not given this incentive. The researchers observe that this approach was successful in keeping participants engaged and that significant weight loss was achieved without coupling the incentive program with an intensive, expensive weight-loss program. However, because study subjects regained weight between the end of the weight-loss phase and the follow-up at three months, Volpp et al. conclude that "incentive approaches based on behavioral economic concepts appear to be highly effective in inducing initial weight loss [but that] further work is needed to test the effectiveness and cost-effectiveness of these approaches in achieving sustained weight loss."

CHAPTER 11

PUBLIC OPINION AND ACTION ABOUT DIET, WEIGHT, NUTRITION, AND PHYSICAL ACTIVITY

The average American is now 23 pounds overweight and collectively we are 4.6 billion pounds overweight.

—Thomas Frieden, director of the Centers for Disease Control and Prevention, at the Weight of the Nation conference (July 27, 2009)

Americans are growing heavier each year. Lydia Saad of the Gallup Organization notes in *Americans' Weight Issues Not Going Away* (November 26, 2008, http://www.gallup.com/poll/112426/Americans-Weight-Issues-Going-Away.aspx) that a November 2008 Gallup poll found that men's and women's weight had increased steadily between 2002 and 2008. Women gained nearly 1 pound (0.5 kg) per year and reported an average weight of 160 pounds (73 kg) in 2008, up from 153 pounds (69 kg) in 2001. (See Figure 11.1.) Men said they weighed an average of 194 pounds (88 kg) in 2008, up from 189 pounds (86 kg) in 2001. Interestingly, men and women have increased the weight they deem "ideal." Saad observes that from 2001 to 2007 women felt their ideal body weight was between 134 to 138 pounds (61 to 63 kg); in 2008 their ideal weight had risen to 140 pounds (64 kg). For men, the increase was less dramatic, with the ideal weight rising from 177 pounds (80 kg) in 2001 to 180 pounds (82 kg) in 2008. (See Figure 11.2.) About two-thirds of middle-aged adults said they would like to lose weight—65% of people aged 30 to 49 and 65% of people aged 50 to 64. (See Figure 11.3.)

In *In U.S., More Would Like to Lose Weight Than Are Trying To* (November 20, 2009, http://www.gallup.com/poll/124448/In-U.S.-More-Lose-Weight-Than-Trying-To.aspx), Jeffrey M. Jones of the Gallup Organization reveals that in 2009, 62% of Americans described themselves as "over ideal weight," but only 27% said they were "seriously trying to lose weight." (See Figure 11.4.) Even though the Centers for Disease Control and Prevention (CDC) indicates that over two-thirds of Americans are overweight or obese, Jones finds that just 36% of Americans considered themselves overweight, down

from 41% in 2008. (See Figure 11.5.) More than half (58%) considered their weight to be "about right" and 6% said they are underweight.

According to Jones, the average adult is 14 pounds (6 kg) heavier than his or her ideal weight. In 2009 Jones stated that women weighed an average of 154 pounds (70 kg), and their average ideal weight was 138 pounds (63 kg), so they were 16 pounds (7 kg) above their average ideal weight. Men weighed an average of 194 pounds (88 kg), and their average ideal weight was 182 pounds (83 kg), so they were 12 pounds (5 kg) above their average ideal weight. (See Figure 11.6.) When compared with CDC estimates, the poll respondents underestimated their ideal weight, given that the CDC reports in "CDC Weight of the Nation Press Briefing" (July 27, 2009, http://www.cdc.gov/media/transcripts/2009/t090727.htm) that the average American is 23 pounds (10 kg) above an ideal or healthy weight. Table 11.1 shows that a minority of people are at an ideal weight—just 18% of women and 19% of men.

In 2009 more than half (55%) of Americans said they would like to lose weight, but this percentage had declined from 62% in 2005. (See Figure 11.7.) A little more than one-third (37%) wanted to stay at their current weight and 7% wanted to gain weight. Clearly, there is a difference between wanting to lose weight and actually making the effort to do so. Jones notes that only half (49%) of those who said they would like to lose weight in 2009 were seriously trying to do so. The percent of people expressing the desire to lose weight in 2009 was the lowest in recent years.

AMERICANS FEEL OBESITY IS AN URGENT HEALTH PROBLEM

In 2009, despite the widespread prevalence of H1N1 influenza, Americans still named obesity as one of the top five most urgent health problems facing

FIGURE 11.1

Public assessment of approximate current weight, 2001–08

WHAT IS YOUR APPROXIMATE CURRENT WEIGHT?

Average reported weight, in pounds

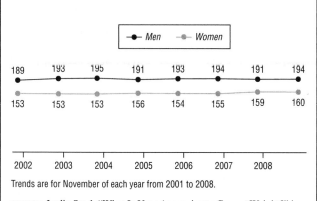

Trends are for November of each year from 2001 to 2008.

SOURCE: Lydia Saad, "What Is Your Approximate Current Weight?" in *Americans' Weight Issues Not Going Away*, The Gallup Organization, November 26, 2008, http://www.gallup.com/poll/112426/Americans-Weight-Issues-Going-Away.aspx (accessed November 23, 2009). Copyright © 2008 by The Gallup Organization. Reproduced by permission of The Gallup Organization.

FIGURE 11.3

Public opinion on desire to lose, gain, or remain at the same weight, 2008

Personal weight preferences, by age

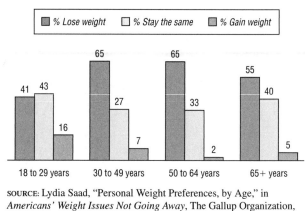

SOURCE: Lydia Saad, "Personal Weight Preferences, by Age," in *Americans' Weight Issues Not Going Away*, The Gallup Organization, November 26, 2008, http://www.gallup.com/poll/112426/Americans-Weight-Issues-Going-Away.aspx (accessed November 23, 2009). Copyright © 2008 by The Gallup Organization. Reproduced by permission of The Gallup Organization.

FIGURE 11.2

Public opinion about ideal weight by gender, 2001–08

Average "ideal weight," by gender

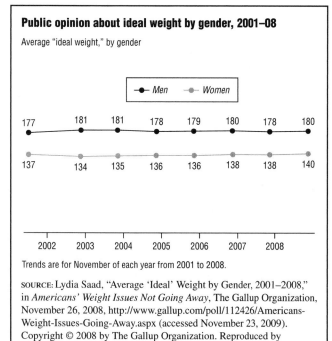

Trends are for November of each year from 2001 to 2008.

SOURCE: Lydia Saad, "Average 'Ideal' Weight by Gender, 2001–2008," in *Americans' Weight Issues Not Going Away*, The Gallup Organization, November 26, 2008, http://www.gallup.com/poll/112426/Americans-Weight-Issues-Going-Away.aspx (accessed November 23, 2009). Copyright © 2008 by The Gallup Organization. Reproduced by permission of The Gallup Organization.

FIGURE 11.4

Public opinion about ideal weight and efforts to lose weight, 2002–09

Americans' attitudes and behaviors regarding their weight, 2002–2009 Gallup Health Polls

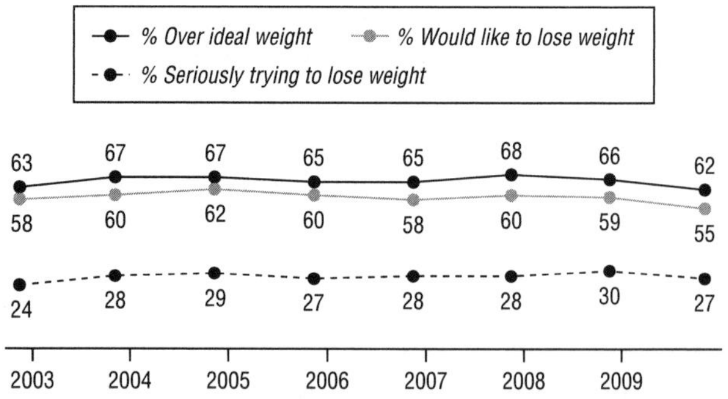

SOURCE: Jeffrey M. Jones, "Americans' Attitudes and Behaviors Regarding Their Weight, 2002–2009 Gallup Health Polls," in *In U.S., More Would Like to Lose Weight Than Are Trying To*, The Gallup Organization, November 20, 2009, http://www.gallup.com/poll/124448/In-U.S.-More-Lose-Weight-Than-Trying-To.aspx (accessed November 23, 2009). Copyright © 2009 by The Gallup Organization. Reproduced by permission of The Gallup Organization.

the nation. (See Figure 11.8.) Health care access (30% in 2008 and 32% in 2009) and costs (25% in 2008 and 18% in 2009) were the most frequently mentioned urgent health concerns, but obesity (12% in 2008 and 8% in 2009) still outranked other leading public health problems in 2009, including heart disease (2%), diabetes (1%), and smoking (less than 0.5%). Even though obesity remained in the top five most urgent health problems, it is interesting to observe that concern about obesity rose fairly steadily from 1998 to 2006, peaked at 12% in 2008, and then fell to 8% at the close of 2009. (See Figure 11.9.)

FIGURE 11.5

Public opinion about personal weight status, 2002–09

HOW WOULD YOU DESCRIBE YOUR OWN PERSONAL WEIGHT SITUATION RIGHT NOW—VERY OVERWEIGHT, SOMEWHAT OVERWEIGHT, ABOUT RIGHT, SOMEWHAT UNDERWEIGHT, OR VERY UNDERWEIGHT?

Selected trend

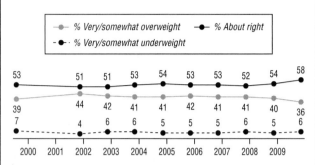

SOURCE: Jeffrey M. Jones, "How Would You Describe Your Own Personal Weight Situation Right Now—Very Overweight, Somewhat Overweight, Somewhat Underweight, or Very Under-weight?" in *In U.S., More Would Like to Lose Weight Than Are Trying To*, The Gallup Organization, November 20, 2009, http://www.gallup.com/poll/124448/In-U.S.-More-Lose-Weight-Than-Trying-To.aspx (accessed November 23, 2009). Copyright © 2009 by The Gallup Organization. Reproduced by permission of The Gallup Organization.

FIGURE 11.6

Public opinion about the difference between self-reported weight and ideal weight, 2009

Difference between self-reported weight and ideal weight, in pounds

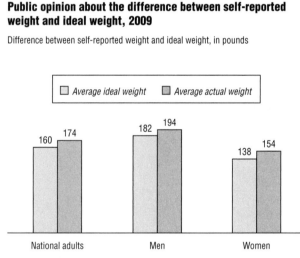

SOURCE: Jeffrey M. Jones, "Difference between Self-Reported Weight and Ideal Weight, in Pounds," in *In U.S., More Would Like to Lose Weight Than Are Trying To*, The Gallup Organization, November 20, 2009, http://www.gallup.com/poll/124448/In-U.S.-More-Lose-Weight-Than-Trying-To.aspx (accessed November 23, 2009). Copyright © 2009 by The Gallup Organization. Reproduced by permission of The Gallup Organization.

CONSUMER KNOWLEDGE OF NUTRIENTS AND THEIR HEALTH BENEFITS

In *Experimental Study of Health Claims on Food Packages: Preliminary Topline Frequency Report* (May 2007), Chung-Tung Jordan Lin of the U.S. Food and Drug Administration reports the findings from research that considered

TABLE 11.1

Public opinion of actual and ideal weight, 2009

Comparison of actual and ideal weight

	National adults	Men	Women
More than 50 lbs. over ideal weight	6%	6%	6%
2I–50 lbs. over ideal weight	17%	15%	19%
11–20 lbs. over ideal weight	15%	14%	16%
1–10 lbs. over ideal weight	24%	27%	21%
At ideal weight	18%	19%	18%
1–10 lbs. under ideal weight	7%	8%	6%
11–20 lbs. under ideal weight	3%	4%	2%
More than 20 lbs. under ideal weight	1%	2%	<1%
Undesignated	9%	6%	12%

SOURCE: Jeffrey M. Jones, "Comparison of Actual and Ideal Weight," in *In U.S., More Would Like to Lose Weight Than Are Trying To*, The Gallup Organization, November 20, 2009, http://www.gallup.com/poll/124448/In-U.S.-More-Lose-Weight-Than-Trying-To.aspx (accessed November 23, 2009). Copyright © 2009 by The Gallup Organization. Reproduced by permission of The Gallup Organization.

FIGURE 11.7

Public opinion about desire to lose weight, maintain present weight, or gain weight, 1991–2009

WOULD YOU LIKE TO [ROTATED: LOSE WEIGHT, STAY AT YOUR PRESENT WEIGHT, OR PUT ON WEIGHT]?

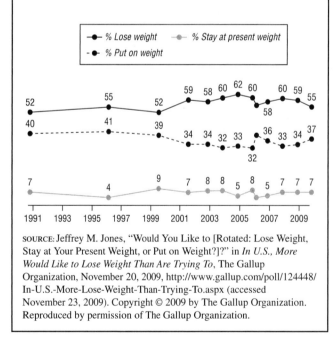

SOURCE: Jeffrey M. Jones, "Would You Like to [Rotated: Lose Weight, Stay at Your Present Weight, or Put on Weight?]?" in *In U.S., More Would Like to Lose Weight Than Are Trying To*, The Gallup Organization, November 20, 2009, http://www.gallup.com/poll/124448/In-U.S.-More-Lose-Weight-Than-Trying-To.aspx (accessed November 23, 2009). Copyright © 2009 by The Gallup Organization. Reproduced by permission of The Gallup Organization.

consumer perceptions of health and other claims (nutrient content claims, structure/function claims, and dietary guidance statements) on food packages. Because the study was based on survey results from an Internet consumer panel, it only represents respondents' knowledge, attitudes, and behavior, rather than the beliefs of all Americans. Still, it offers insight into consumer understanding of health claims that do not name the specific nutrients that are involved in the diet-disease relationship (e.g., "Yogurt may reduce the risk of osteoporosis") and health claims that name the nutrient (e.g., "Calcium-rich foods, such as yogurt, may reduce the risk of osteoporosis").

The study had two phases. The first phase collected information about the awareness of foods and nutrients and their possible health benefits. The second phase assessed consumer understanding of various health claims and messages. Lin was especially eager to learn whether consumers were able to identify the nutrient linked to a specific health benefit, and whether they knew the food sources from which these nutrients might be obtained. In the first phase, respondents were asked about their awareness of three foods (yogurt, orange juice, and pasta), the nutrients these foods contained, and their possible health benefits.

Lin notes that of the three foods, yogurt and orange juice were considered healthier than pasta, with orange juice garnering the highest percentage (58%) of "very healthful" ratings. (See Table 11.2.) Nearly two-thirds (62%) of respondents queried about the health benefits of yogurt named reducing the risk of osteoporosis, and reducing the risk of hypertension (high blood pressure) was identified as a health benefit of orange juice by a quarter (24%) of respondents questioned about it. (See Table 11.3.) Just 9% of respondents asked about the health benefit of pasta associated it with heart disease.

According to Lin, nearly all the respondents (99%) who linked yogurt to osteoporosis named calcium as the nutrient that might help reduce the risk; three out of four (74%) of those who associated orange juice with hypertension said potassium might help reduce the risk; and 17% of those who associated pasta with heart disease said the fictitious compound lysoton might help reduce the risk. (See Table 11.4.)

FIGURE 11.8

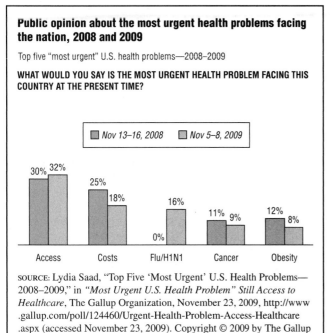

Public opinion about the most urgent health problems facing the nation, 2008 and 2009

Top five "most urgent" U.S. health problems—2008–2009

WHAT WOULD YOU SAY IS THE MOST URGENT HEALTH PROBLEM FACING THIS COUNTRY AT THE PRESENT TIME?

SOURCE: Lydia Saad, "Top Five 'Most Urgent' U.S. Health Problems—2008–2009," in *"Most Urgent U.S. Health Problem" Still Access to Healthcare*, The Gallup Organization, November 23, 2009, http://www.gallup.com/poll/124460/Urgent-Health-Problem-Access-Healthcare.aspx (accessed November 23, 2009). Copyright © 2009 by The Gallup Organization. Reproduced by permission of The Gallup Organization.

FIGURE 11.9

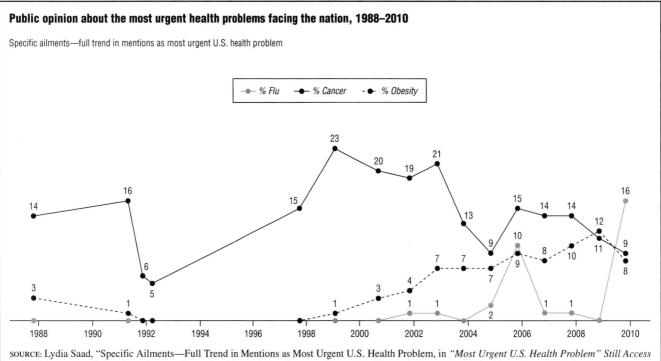

Public opinion about the most urgent health problems facing the nation, 1988–2010

Specific ailments—full trend in mentions as most urgent U.S. health problem

SOURCE: Lydia Saad, "Specific Ailments—Full Trend in Mentions as Most Urgent U.S. Health Problem, in *"Most Urgent U.S. Health Problem" Still Access to Healthcare*, The Gallup Organization, November 23, 2009, http://www.gallup.com/poll/124460/Urgent-Health-Problem-Access-Healthcare.aspx (accessed November 23, 2009). Copyright © 2009 by The Gallup Organization. Reproduced by permission of The Gallup Organization.

TABLE 11.2

Consumer assessment of the healthfulness of yogurt, orange juice, and pasta, 2007

ON A SIX POINT SCALE, WHERE 6 MEANS "VERY HEALTHFUL" AND 1 MEANS "NOT HEALTHFUL AT ALL," HOW HEALTHFUL WOULD YOU SAY THESE FOODS ARE? PLEASE SELECT ONE FOR EACH ITEM.

Answer	Yogurt (n=693)	Orange juice (n=686)	Pasta (n=693)
6 very healthful	44%	58%	11%
5	31%	25%	14%
4	14%	11%	36%
3	4%	4%	24%
2	1%	2%	10%
1 not healthful at all	*	*	3%
Don't know	5%	0%	1%

"n" denotes number of respondents.
*Less than 0.5%.

SOURCE: Chung-Tung Jordan Lin, "A2. On a six point scale, where 6 means 'very healthful' and 1 means 'not healthful at all,' how healthful would you say these foods are? Please select one for each item," in *Experimental Study of Health Claims on Food Packages: Preliminary Topline Frequency Report*, U.S. Food and Drug Administration, Center for Food Safety and Applied Nutrition, May 2007

TABLE 11.3

Consumer knowledge of foods that may reduce health risks, 2007

HAVE YOU EVER HEARD OR READ THAT [EATING/DRINKING FOOD] REGULARLY MAY HELP LOWER THE RISK OF THE FOLLOWING HEALTH PROBLEMS? PLEASE SELECT AN ANSWER FOR EACH HEALTH PROBLEM.

Health problem	Yogurt (n=693)		
	Yes	No	Don't know
Hypertension or high blood pressure	17%	67%	17%
Cancer	12%	70%	18%
Osteoporosis or bone problem	62%	28%	11%
Diabetes or high blood sugar	15%	68%	17%
Heart disease	24%	61%	15%

Health problem	Orange juice (n=686)		
	Yes	No	Don't know
Hypertension or high blood pressure	24%	60%	16%
Cancer	35%	50%	15%
Osteoporosis or bone problem	39%	47%	14%
Diabetes or high blood sugar	16%	68%	16%
Heart disease	46%	40%	14%

Health problem	Pasta (n=693)		
	Yes	No	Don't know
Hypertension or high blood pressure	7%	80%	13%
Cancer	4%	83%	13%
Osteoporosis or bone problem	7%	80%	13%
Diabetes or high blood sugar	7%	80%	12%
Heart disease	9%	78%	12%

"n" denotes number of observations.

SOURCE: Chung-Tung Jordan Lin, "B2. Have you ever heard or read that [eating/drinking food] regularly may help lower the risk of the following health problems? Please select an answer for each health problem. [RANDOMIZE LIST; RECORD FIRST ITEM]," in *Experimental Study of Health Claims on Food Packages: Preliminary Topline Frequency Report*, U.S. Food and Drug Administration, Center for Food Safety and Applied Nutrition, May 2007

TABLE 11.4

Consumer knowledge of nutrients that may help to reduce health risks, 2007

FOR EACH OF THE FOLLOWING NUTRIENTS, WOULD YOU SAY IT MIGHT HELP REDUCE THE RISK OF [HEALTH PROBLEM]? IF YOU HAVE NEVER HEARD OF A NUTRIENT, PLEASE SELECT THAT OPTION.

	Osteoporosis or bone problem (n=428)			
Nutrient	Yes	No	Have not heard	Don't know
Calcium	99%	*	0%	1%
Potassium	54%	14%	*	32%
Vitamin A	46%	13%	*	40%
Phosphorus	44%	11%	4%	41%

	Hypertension or high blood pressure (n=161)			
Nutrient	Yes	No	Have not heard	Don't know
Calcium	60%	15%	*	25%
Potassium	74%	6%	*	19%
Vitamin C	68%	6%	*	25%
Vitamin A	62%	7%	*	30%

	Heart disease (n=65)			
Nutrient	Yes	No	Have not heard	Don't know
Lysoton	17%	12%	48%	23%
Fiber	89%	5%	0%	6%
Calcium	58%	18%	0%	23%
Potassium	74%	8%	0%	18%

"n" denotes number of observations.
*Less than 0.5%.

SOURCE: Chung-Tung Jordan Lin, "B5. For each of the following nutrients, would you say it might help reduce the risk of [health problem]? If you have never heard of a nutrient, please select that option. [RANDOMIZE LIST IN EACH FOOD]," in *Experimental Study of Health Claims on Food Packages: Preliminary Topline Frequency Report*, U.S. Food and Drug Administration, Center for Food Safety and Applied Nutrition, May 2007

TABLE 11.5

Consumer use of various diets, 2007

WHICH OF THESE DIET PLANS HAVE YOU YOURSELF BEEN ON DURING THE PAST 30 DAYS? SELECT ALL THAT APPLY.

Diet	(n=1036)
Low fat diet	19%
Low carb or carbohydrate diet	16%
Low sodium diet	13%
Low calorie diet	11%
Low cholesterol diet	11%
Low sugar diet	15%
Weight loss diet	15%
None of these	55%
Don't know	1%
Prefer not to answer	*

"n" denotes number of respondents.
*Less than 0.5%.

SOURCE: Chung-Tung Jordan Lin, "C2. Which of these diet plans have you yourself been on during the past 30 days? Select all that apply," in *Experimental Study of Health Claims on Food Packages: Preliminary Topline Frequency Report*, U.S. Food and Drug Administration, Center for Food Safety and Applied Nutrition, May 2007

Interestingly, Lin indicates that just 15% of respondents said they were dieting to lose weight. (See Table 11.5.) Nineteen percent of respondents were on a low-fat diet, 16% were on a low-carbohydrate diet, 13% were on a low-sodium diet, and 11% each were on a low-cholesterol and low-sugar diet. Because respondents were permitted to choose more than one diet, some were probably adhering to more than one plan. For example, it is likely that many people who are on a low-fat diet also aim to consume a diet that is low in cholesterol. Similarly, a low-carbohydrate diet is generally also a low-sugar diet.

HOW MANY AMERICANS EAT WELL AND EXERCISE?

The Gallup-Healthways Well-Being Index, a measure that tracks the health habits of Americans, finds that a subindex of selected health behaviors—healthy eating, exercising, and smoking—improved slightly in January 2009. In *In U.S., Health Habits Improving, but Uphill Climb Remains* (February 12, 2009, http://www.gallup.com/poll/114589/Health-Habits-Improving-Uphill-Climb-Remains.aspx#1), Elizabeth Mendes of the Gallup Organization observes that in January 2009 older adults (aged 65 and older) were much more likely than any other age group to report healthy behaviors. (See Figure 11.10.) Older adults earned a score of 71 on the Healthy Behavior subindex, 9.8 points above the national average score of 61.2. People who made over $7,500 per month (63.6), people who were married (63.3), and women (62.7) also had Healthy Behavior scores higher than the national average score. Younger adults (57.1), people who made less than $500 per month (56.9), and unmarried people (56.2) had the lowest Healthy Behavior scores.

According to Mendes, two-thirds (66%) of adults said they had eaten healthily all day on the day preceding the poll, but only about half (54%) had consumed at least five servings of fruits and vegetables on three or more of the past seven days. (See Figure 11.11.) Less than half (46%) had exercised for at least 30 minutes on two or more of the past seven days.

Are Americans Getting Enough Exercise to Help Them Manage Their Weight?

Mendes finds that about a quarter (27%) of Americans were exercising 30 minutes or more on five or more days per week in 2009. (See Figure 11.12.) Another quarter (24%) said they exercised for at least 30 minutes on three or four of the last seven days, and nearly half (49%) reported exercising for at least 30 minutes less than three days per week.

Brett W. Pelham of the Gallup Organization indicates in *Exercise and Well-Being: A Little Goes a Long Way* (November 3, 2009, http://www.gallup.com/poll/124073/Exercise-Little-Goes-Long.aspx) that Americans' self-reports of the frequency with which they exercise is associated with their risk for obesity. Pelham observes that compared with those who said they did not exercise at all in the past week (35%), people who claimed they

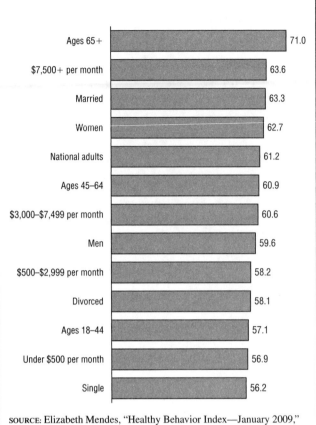

FIGURE 11.10

Healthy behavior scores, by age, gender, income, and marital status, January 2009

Ages 65+	71.0
$7,500+ per month	63.6
Married	63.3
Women	62.7
National adults	61.2
Ages 45–64	60.9
$3,000–$7,499 per month	60.6
Men	59.6
$500–$2,999 per month	58.2
Divorced	58.1
Ages 18–44	57.1
Under $500 per month	56.9
Single	56.2

SOURCE: Elizabeth Mendes, "Healthy Behavior Index—January 2009," in *In U.S., Health Habits Improving, but Uphill Climb Remains*, The Gallup Organization, February 12, 2009, http://www.gallup.com/poll/114589/health-habits-improving-uphill-climb-remains.aspx (accessed November 23, 2009). Copyright © 2009 by The Gallup Organization. Reproduced by permission of The Gallup Organization.

exercised for at least 30 minutes on one or two days (28%) were less likely to be obese. (See Figure 11.13.) Among those who said they exercised five or six days (19%), the likelihood of obesity was reduced by nearly half.

Normal-weight Americans are the most likely to exercise for 30 minutes, five or more days per week than people who are overweight or obese. Mendes notes that the percentage of people exercising at least 30 minutes per day, five or more days per week declined with increasing body mass index (BMI; body weight in kilograms divided by height in meters squared). Among poll respondents with a BMI within the normal weight range in 2009, 32% reported exercising on five days or more, compared with 28% of those who were overweight and 20% of those who were obese. (See Figure 11.14.)

AMERICANS KNOW OBESITY IS HARMFUL

The American public is, however, certain that obesity is harmful. As Table 11.6 shows, in 2007 nearly five out of six (83%) Gallup poll survey respondents said they

FIGURE 11.11

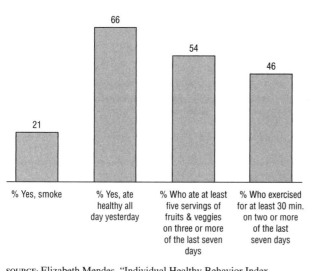

Percent of adults practicing selected healthy behaviors, January 2009

Individual healthy behavior index questions

SOURCE: Elizabeth Mendes, "Individual Healthy Behavior Index Questions," in *In U.S., Health Habits Improving, but Uphill Climb Remains*, The Gallup Organization, February 12, 2009, http://www.gallup.com/poll/114589/health-habits-improving-uphill-climb-remains.aspx (accessed November 23, 2009). Copyright © 2009 by The Gallup Organization. Reproduced by permission of The Gallup Organization.

FIGURE 11.12

Self-report of frequency of exercise, 2009

IN THE LAST SEVEN DAYS, ON HOW MANY DAYS DID YOU: EXERCISE FOR 30 OR MORE MINUTES?

Adults aged 18 and older

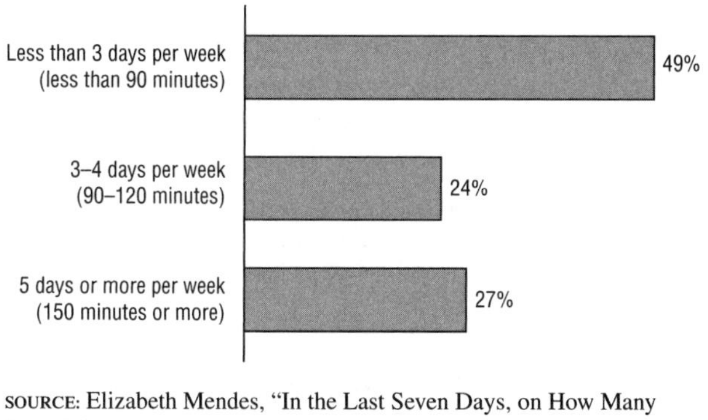

SOURCE: Elizabeth Mendes, "In the Last Seven Days, on How Many Days Did You: Exercise for 30 or More Minutes?" in *In U.S., Nearly Half Exercise Less Than Three Days a Week*, The Gallup Organization, May 26, 2009, http://www.gallup.com/poll/118570/Nearly-Half-Exercise-Less-Three-Days-Week.aspx (accessed November 23, 2009). Copyright © 2009 by The Gallup Organization. Reproduced by permission of The Gallup Organization.

FIGURE 11.13

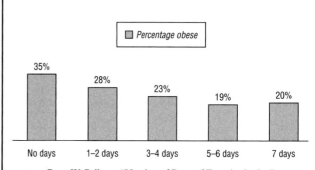

Relationship between self-reported days of exercise and obesity, 2009

Number of days of exercise in the past week and obesity

SOURCE: Brett W. Pelham, "Number of Days of Exercise in the Past Week and Obesity," *Exercise and Well-Being: A Little Goes a Long Way*, The Gallup Organization, November 3, 2009, http://www.gallup.com/poll/124073/Exercise-Little-Goes-Long.aspx (accessed November 23, 2009). Copyright © 2009 by The Gallup Organization. Reproduced by permission of The Gallup Organization.

FIGURE 11.14

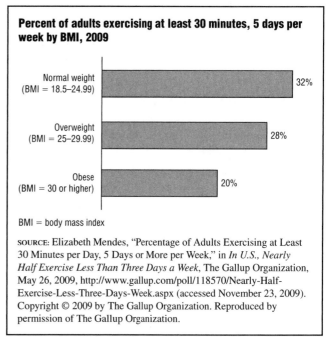

Percent of adults exercising at least 30 minutes, 5 days per week by BMI, 2009

BMI = body mass index

SOURCE: Elizabeth Mendes, "Percentage of Adults Exercising at Least 30 Minutes per Day, 5 Days or More per Week," in *In U.S., Nearly Half Exercise Less Than Three Days a Week*, The Gallup Organization, May 26, 2009, http://www.gallup.com/poll/118570/Nearly-Half-Exercise-Less-Three-Days-Week.aspx (accessed November 23, 2009). Copyright © 2009 by The Gallup Organization. Reproduced by permission of The Gallup Organization.

feel obesity is "very harmful" and an additional 15% considered it "somewhat harmful." Interestingly, survey respondents' own self-reported weight did not appear to influence their belief that being overweight is harmful. The vast majority of both respondents who considered themselves about the right weight (86%) and those who said they were overweight (79%) were aware that being significantly overweight is very harmful. (See Table 11.7.)

In fact, Americans equate the health risks associated with obesity to those of smoking. The overwhelming majority of Gallup poll survey respondents said that being obese is "very harmful" (83%) or "somewhat harmful" (15%) to one's health. (See Table 11.8.) Comparable percentages of respondents deemed smoking "very harmful" (79%) or "somewhat harmful" (14%) to health.

TABLE 11.6

Public opinion on the harm posed by obesity, 2007

IN GENERAL, HOW HARMFUL DO YOU FEEL OBESITY IS TO ADULTS WHO ARE SIGNIFICANTLY OVERWEIGHT—VERY HARMFUL, SOMEWHAT HARMFUL, NOT TOO HARMFUL, OR NOT AT ALL HARMFUL?

	Very harmful	Somewhat harmful	Not too harmful	Not at all harmful	Depends (vol.)	No opinion
2007 Jul 12–15	83%	15	*	*	*	1

*Less than 0.5%.

SOURCE: "In General, How Harmful Do You Feel Obesity Is to Adults Who Are Significantly Overweight—Very Harmful, Somewhat Harmful, Not Too Harmful, or Not at All Harmful?" in *Personal Weight Situation*, The Gallup Organization, 2009, http://www.gallup.com/poll/7264/Personal-Weight-Situation.aspx#1 (accessed November 23, 2009). Copyright © 2009 by The Gallup Organization. Reproduced by permission of The Gallup Organization.

TABLE 11.7

Percent of adult poll respondents who believe overweight is harmful, by survey respondents' body weight, July 2007

IN GENERAL, HOW HARMFUL DO YOU FEEL OBESITY IS TO ADULTS WHO ARE SIGNIFICANTLY OVERWEIGHT—VERY HARMFUL, SOMEWHAT HARMFUL, NOT TOO HARMFUL, OR NOT AT ALL HARMFUL?

	Very harmful %	Somewhat harmful %	Not too harmful %	Not at all harmful %	Depends (vol.) %	No opinion %
Describe self as overweight	79	20	*	*	—	*
Describe self as "about right" as far as weight is concerned	86	11	1	1	1	1

*Less than 0.5%.
Note: Too few Americans classify themselves as "underweight" to provide meaningful results.

SOURCE: Frank Newport, "In General, How Harmful Do You Feel Obesity Is to Adults Who Are Significantly Overweight—Very Harmful, Somewhat Harmful, Not Too Harmful, or Not at All Harmful?" in *Americans Put Obesity on Par with Smoking in Terms of Harmful Effects*, Gallup News Service, The Gallup Organization, July 20, 2007, http://www.gallup.com/poll/28177/Americans-Put-Obesity-par-Smoking-Terms-Harmful-Effects.aspx (accessed November 23, 2009). Copyright © 2007 by The Gallup Organization. Reproduced by permission of The Gallup Organization.

How Do Americans Feel about People Who Are Overweight?

In view of instances of discrimination against people who are overweight or obese and the stigma associated with being overweight, Frank Newport of the Gallup Organization finds in *Impact of Smoking, Being Overweight on a Person's Image* (July 21, 2008, http://www.gallup.com/poll/108925/Impact-Smoking-Being-Overweight-Persons-Image.aspx) that a majority of Americans claimed in a 2008 Gallup poll that whether a person is significantly overweight has no effect on their opinion of that individual. About two-thirds (67%) of Gallup respondents said their opinion of someone who is significantly overweight is not affected. (See Figure 11.15.) However, it is important to note that 29% of poll respondents said they would view someone who is significantly overweight more negatively. Interestingly, smoking appears to have more of a negative impact on a person's image than does being overweight.

Newport notes that a somewhat counterintuitive finding is that a quarter (25%) of people who are themselves overweight said they think more negatively of a person who is significantly overweight. (See Figure 11.16.) Of respondents who said their weight is "about right," one-third (33%)

have negative impressions of people who are significantly overweight.

Even though a majority of Americans do not think more negatively of people who are significantly overweight, Newport finds that most Americans believe overweight is the result of personal lifestyle choices (80%) as opposed to genetic factors (8%). (See Figure 11.17.) Just 10% of respondents felt that overweight or obesity arises from a combination of lifestyle habits and genetic factors.

AMERICANS' CHANGING SHAPES AND SIZES

The results of a national size survey that gathered measurements from more than 10,000 people across the United States confirmed that Americans are not only getting heavier but also are changing in proportion. The "SizeUSA" project is an anthropometric research study (a study of human body measurements that makes comparisons of these measurements). Using a three-dimensional body scanner, researchers compiled measurements and analyzed them by gender, age group, and four ethnicities, as well as by geography, annual household income, marital status, education, and employment status.

TABLE 11.8

Public opinion on how harmful obesity is to health, 2007

HOW HARMFUL ARE THE FOLLOWING TO ONE'S HEALTH?

	Very harmful %	Some-what harmful %	Not too harmful %	Not at all harmful %	Depends (vol.) %	No opinion %
Being obese	83	15	*	*	*	1
Smoking	79	14	3	2	1	*

*Less than 0.5%.

SOURCE: Frank Newport, "How Harmful Are the Following to One's Health," in *Americans Put Obesity on Par with Smoking in Terms of Harmful Effects*, Gallup News Service, The Gallup Organization, July 20, 2007, http://www.gallup.com/poll/28177/Americans-Put-Obesity-par-Smoking-Terms-Harmful-Effects.aspx (accessed November 23, 2009). Copyright © 2007 by The Gallup Organization. Reproduced by permission of The Gallup Organization.

FIGURE 11.15

Public opinion about whether being significantly overweight affects a person's image, 2008

EVERYTHING ELSE BEING EQUAL, PLEASE TELL ME WHETHER EACH OF THE FOLLOWING MAKES YOU [ROTATED: VIEW A PERSON MORE POSITIVELY, DOES NOT AFFECT YOUR OPINION, OR MAKES YOU VIEW A PERSON MORE NEGATIVELY]?

A. If a person smokes
B. If a person is significantly overweight

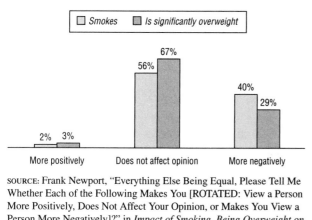

SOURCE: Frank Newport, "Everything Else Being Equal, Please Tell Me Whether Each of the Following Makes You [ROTATED: View a Person More Positively, Does Not Affect Your Opinion, or Makes You View a Person More Negatively]?" in *Impact of Smoking, Being Overweight on a Person's Image*, July 21, 2008, The Gallup Organization, http://www.gallup.com/poll/108925/Impact-Smoking-Being-Overweight-Persons-Image.aspx (accessed November 23, 2009). Copyright © 2008 by The Gallup Organization. Reproduced by permission of The Gallup Organization.

The survey was performed to assist apparel manufacturers in producing clothing that will offer a better fit to more consumers. In "Sizing up America: Signs of Expansion" (*New York Times*, March 1, 2004), Kate Zernike reports that the last such national survey of Americans was performed in 1941 by the U.S. Department of Agriculture (USDA). The USDA survey described the average American woman as a size 8, with a 35-inch (89-cm) bust, a 27-inch (69-cm) waist, and a 37.5-inch (95-cm)

FIGURE 11.16

Public opinion of persons who are significantly overweight, by respondents weight status, 2008

HOW DO YOU VIEW A PERSON WHO IS SIGNIFICANTLY OVERWEIGHT?

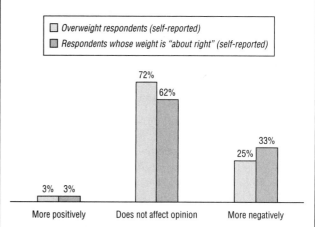

SOURCE: Frank Newport, "How Do You View a Person Who is Significantly Overweight?" in *Impact of Smoking, Being Overweight on a Person's Image*, July 21, 2008, The Gallup Organization, http://www.gallup.com/poll/108925/Impact-Smoking-Being-Overweight-Persons-Image.aspx (accessed November 23, 2009). Copyright © 2008 by The Gallup Organization. Reproduced by permission of The Gallup Organization.

FIGURE 11.17

Public opinion about the contributions of genetic and lifestyle factors to overweight and obesity, 2008

THINKING ABOUT THE REASONS WHY SOME PEOPLE ARE SIGNIFICANTLY OVERWEIGHT OR OBESE, DO YOU THINK IT IS DUE MORE TO: [ROTATED: GENETIC FACTORS A PERSON IS BORN WITH OR EATING AND LIFESTYLE HABITS]?

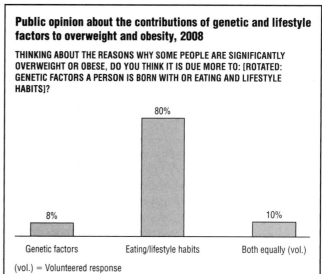

(vol.) = Volunteered response

SOURCE: Frank Newport, "Thinking about the Reasons Why Some People Are Significantly Overweight or Obese, Do You Think It Is Due More to: [ROTATED: Genetic Factors a Person Is Born With or Eating and Lifestyle Habits?" in *Impact of Smoking, Being Overweight on a Person's Image*, July 21, 2008, The Gallup Organization, http://www.ga llup.com/poll/108925/Impact-Smoking-Being-Overweight-Persons-Image.aspx (accessed November 23, 2009). Copyright © 2008 by The Gallup Organization. Reproduced by permission of The Gallup Organization.

hip circumference. The 2003 "SizeUSA" survey found that the average white woman's bust, waist, and hip measurements in inches were 38-32-41 (96.5-81-104 cm) for women aged 18 to 25, and 41-34-43 (104-86-109 cm) for women aged 36 to 45. On average, African-American women measured 43-37-46 (109-94-117 cm), Hispanic women measured 42.5-36-44 (108-91-112 cm), and an "other" category, consisting primarily of Asian-American women, measured 41-35-43 (104-89-109 cm). Based on the "SizeUSA" survey, the average American woman wears a size 12 or 14, rather than a size 8.

According to Zernike, American men have also increased in size. The size 40 regular, which measures 40 inches (102 cm) at the chest with a 34-inch (86 cm) waist, a 40-inch hip (102 cm), and a 15.5-inch (39 cm) collar, once considered the average, would be too small for many American men. The 2003 "SizeUSA" survey found that white men aged 18 to 25 measured 41-35-41 (104-89-104 cm) and older white men aged 36 to 45 measured 44-38-42 (112-96.5-107 cm). African-American men measured an average of 43-37-42 (109-94-107 cm), Hispanic men measured 44-38-42 (112-96.5-107 cm), and an "other" category, consisting primarily of Asian-American men, measured 42-37-41 (107-94-104 cm).

Interestingly, Zernike notes that measurements did not vary significantly by geography, education, or even income. The most significant variations in body shape were attributed to race, ethnicity, and age. For example, 11% of white women were described as having protruding stomachs, compared with 3% of Hispanic women and 4% of African-American women. More Hispanic women (20%) were described as having "full waists" than white (10%) or African-American (15%) women. Nearly a quarter (24%) of African-American men were described as having a "prominent seat," compared with 9% of white men and 8% of Hispanic men.

According to Zernike, the study concluded that along with expanding waists, American men over the age of 45 were the most likely to have increased abdominal girth ("potbellies") and women older than 36 were the most likely to have big hips. Nineteen percent of men were described as "portly" and another 19% had "lower front waists," meaning the researchers had to look behind the overhanging belly to find the waist.

AMERICANS' ATTITUDES ABOUT OVERWEIGHT

Despite escalating media coverage of overweight and obesity, and their associated health risks, many Americans do not appear to be overly concerned about overweight and obesity—their own or others'. They demonstrate little support for policy initiatives intended to prevent and combat obesity, and persist in the belief that obesity results from individual personal failings rather than from a combination of genetic and environmental factors.

Manasee Mankar et al. of Abasaheb Garware College examine in "Obesity as a Perceived Social Signal" (*PLoS*

One, vol. 3, no. 9, September 11, 2008) whether body proportions, and abdominal obesity in particular, are perceived as signals revealing personality traits. The researchers presented faceless drawings of three male body forms—lean, muscular, and feminine—each with and without abdominal obesity to 222 respondents. A list of 30 different adjectives or short descriptions of personality traits was given to each respondent, who was then asked to assign the most appropriate description or trait to each figure. Some of the traits were directly related to physique and others such as "selfish," "miser," "dominating," "kind," "brave," "friendly," "loving," "money-minded," and "status conscious" related to nature, attitude, moral character, and social status.

Mankar et al. find that 29 of the 30 adjectives were consistently attributed to specific body forms. The 30 traits were clustered into distinct personalities that were strongly associated with each body form. A centrally obese body type (abdominal obesity, or apple-shaped) was perceived as "lethargic, greedy, political, money-minded, selfish and rich." The researchers conclude, "Body proportions are perceived not only as indicators of health and physique … but also of nature, attitude, moral character and social status of an individual."

CHILDHOOD OBESITY

Public health professionals and practitioners are researching and evaluating interventions aimed at preventing children and teenagers from becoming overweight as well as programs to help them lose weight. Children's and teenagers' attitudes about food, exercise, and weight influence the success of prevention and treatment programs.

In "Adolescents' Attitudes about Obesity and What They Want in Obesity Prevention Programs" (*Journal of School Nursing*, vol. 23, no. 4, August 2007), Louise F. Wilson of Beaver Dam Unified School District in Beaver Dam, Wisconsin, seeks to characterize adolescents' attitudes about overweight and obesity and to identify the features and attributes they value in prevention programs. She used a written questionnaire to survey middle school students to determine the program characteristics students felt would be the most effective. Wilson finds that adolescents would be more likely to participate in, and adhere to, programs encouraging them to consume more water, fruits, and vegetables, to eat less junk food, and to exercise more. They expressed unwillingness to forgo soda, video games, computer activities, or watching television to improve their health.

Childhood Obesity Is among the Top 10 Concerns for U.S. Adults

In March 2007 researchers for the C. S. Mott Children's Hospital and Knowledge Networks conducted the

National Poll on Children's Health, a national online survey with a random sample of 2,076 adults, and reported their findings in "Smoking, Drugs, and Obesity Top Public's List of Health Problems for Children" (*CHEAR: National Poll on Children's Health*, vol. 1, no. 2, May 2, 2007). Of 17 different health concerns for children, obesity was ranked third, following smoking and drug abuse.

The poll found that Hispanics were more likely to express concern about obesity (42%) than African-Americans (36%) or whites (31%). The researchers opine that greater concern among Hispanics and African-Americans may reflect overall higher prevalence of obesity among Hispanic and African-American children and teens. Respondents that had a bachelor's degree or higher considered childhood obesity to be the number-one health issue for children, with 40% believing it was a significant problem. By contrast, respondents that had less than a high school education ranked childhood obesity 10th, with only 25% describing it as a major problem.

Are Parents to Blame for Children's Obesity?

There is no question that parents play a pivotal role in terms of preventing childhood obesity by shaping their children's early eating and physical activity habits. However, should overweight children be taken away from parents? Gaëlle Faure reports in "Should Parents of Overweight Kids Lose Custody?" (*Time*, October 16, 2009) that in recent years there have been several cases in which a child's obesity resulted in parents losing custody of the child. Removing children from their home is a controversial move, but some health professionals believe there are instances in which it can literally save a child's life or at least prevent the development of serious health problems such as Type 2 diabetes, hypertension, sleep apnea, and high cholesterol. For example, in South Carolina a 14-year-old boy who weighed 555 pounds (252 kg) was removed from his mother's custody in May 2009, and child-neglect charges were leveled against the mother.

According to Faure, health professionals who do not support the practice of removing obese children from their home observe that multiple factors affect a child's weight and that parents are but one of these influences. They point to genetic predisposition, socioeconomic status, and environmental factors as contributing to children's excess weight. They also note that children of all ages have been found to undermine their parents' best intentions by "sneaking extra food behind their parents' backs."

Faure indicates that many parents deny that their obese children have a weight problem. The parents of obese children, who often are overweight or obese themselves, may be reluctant to address the many challenges inherent in modifying their diet and increasing physical activity. Parents may also be hampered in their efforts by a lack of community resources. In some communities there are no weight-loss programs for children and teens with clinically severe obesity. For example, in the case of the South Carolina teen all the services for obese children considered him beyond the maximum weight their programs could accommodate.

Todd Varness et al. of the University of Wisconsin School of Medicine and Public Health suggest in "Childhood Obesity and Medical Neglect" (*Pediatrics*, vol. 123, no. 1, January 2009) that removal of a child from the home is only justified when three of the following conditions are met:

1. A high likelihood that serious imminent harm will occur;

2. A reasonable likelihood that coercive state intervention will result in effective treatment; and

3. The absence of alternative options for addressing the problem.

The researchers indicate that even though all three criteria are met quite infrequently, when they are, "a trial of enforced treatment outside the home may be indicated, to protect the child from irreversible harm."

Americans Blame Parents, Schools, and the Food Industry for Children's Weight Gain

In "Poll Shows Growing Concern about Role of Advertising in Child Obesity" (*Wall Street Journal*, August 20, 2007), Beckey Bright reports on the *Wall Street Journal*/Harris Interactive August 2007 poll that surveyed attitudes about childhood obesity among 2,503 adults. Bright notes that 84% of Americans viewed childhood obesity as a major problem and that 78% of parents with children under the age of 12 saw it as an issue of growing concern. Eighty-three percent of Americans and 85% of parents with children under the age of 12 believed parents have the greatest impact in terms of reducing childhood obesity.

Most of the survey respondents blamed the lack of exercise as a cause of children's overweight and felt that encouraging more physical activity will help solve the problem. The overwhelming majority (94%) felt schools should promote regular exercise. Nearly the same proportion (89%) favored parental efforts to limit time spent using computers, playing video games, and watching television to encourage children to spend more time being physically active.

According to Bright, most respondents also felt that children's diets must change. They believe schools and parents should restrict children's access to snack foods, sugary soft drinks, and fast food—88% said schools must do more to ensure that healthful foods are available and 83% said parents must be more vigilant about their children's diets.

More than three-quarters (78%) of respondents cited food advertising that targets children as a "major contributor" to the problem, up from 65% the previous year. Despite the recent move by major food industry companies to improve the nutritional value of many of their offerings and engage in more responsible marketing and advertising practices, 60% of respondents favored government regulation of food industry advertising aimed at children.

There was strong support for measures that the food industry might take to address the problem. Bright indicates that 91% of respondents expressed support for "using child-friendly characters to promote healthier foods like fruits and vegetables," and 73% favored "limiting advertising to children to healthier foods that are lower in calories, fat and/or sugar." About two-thirds (64%) said that "no longer using popular characters from television shows and movies to market products to children" would help.

Parents Misjudge Children's Weight

Several studies find that parents often misperceive their children's weight and underestimate their risk for obesity in adulthood. For example, in "Perception versus Reality: An Exploration of Children's Measured Body Mass in Relation to Caregivers' Estimates" (*Journal of Health Psychology*, vol. 12, no. 6, November 2007), Anna Akerman, Marsha E. Williams, and John Meunier compare parents' reports of their children's height and weight against the measurements the researchers obtained. The researchers find that their measurements varied from the parents' perceptions of their children's body status. Parents of overweight children consistently underestimated their children's BMI, and parents of underweight children overestimated their children's BMI. Akerman, Williams, and Meunier believe parents have a "positive bias in human cognition" that enables them to selectively interpret and correct for their children's deviations from a healthy body weight. In turn, this creates an alternative reality for them, one in which undesirable imperfections in their children do not exist.

The American College of Gastroenterology (ACG) reports in the press release "Parents Foster Significant Misperceptions of Children's Weight and Often Misjudge Risk for Obesity in Adulthood" (October 6, 2008, http://www.acg.gi.org/media/releases/2008am/ACG08Parents Misperception.pdf) that Rona L. Levy et al. gave a presentation at the ACG's 73rd Annual Scientific Meeting in Orlando, Florida, in October 2008. Levy et al. surveyed 46 parents of children aged five to nine with BMIs that placed them in the 70th percentile or higher. The parents were given a questionnaire that "included questions on their perception of their child's current weight, and whether they perceived that their child was at risk for developing obesity as an adult." The researchers noted "that even though all of the children had elevated BMI, less than 13 percent of the parents of overweight kids reported their child as currently overweight. Fewer than one-third perceived that their child's risk for adult obesity was above average or very high."

In another study, Jessica Doolen, Patricia T. Alpert, and Sally K. Miller of the University of Nevada, Las Vegas, find in "Parental Disconnect between Perceived and Actual Weight Status of Children: A Metasynthesis of the Current Research" (*Journal of the American Academy of Nurse Practitioners*, vol. 21, no, 3, March 2009) that parents were less able to recognize their child's risk for obesity if they themselves were overweight. The researchers also note that cultural influences had an impact on parents' perceptions of children's weight, in that African-American mothers were more satisfied with their larger children than were white mothers. Doolen, Alpert, and Miller conclude, "If parents do not recognize their child as at risk for overweight or overweight, they cannot intervene to diminish the risk factors for pediatric obesity and its related complications. More research is needed to identify why this phenomenon occurs. Only then can effective interventions be initiated."

The Cost of Healthful Foods and Other Stressors Play a Role in Children's Weight

Craig Gundersen et al. wondered whether mental, physical, or emotional stress experienced by mothers, called *maternal stressors*, coupled with food insecurity (living in a household that does not have the financial means to access enough food to sustain active, healthy living for all members), might worsen rates of childhood obesity in low-income families. In "Food Security, Maternal Stressors, and Overweight among Low-Income US Children: Results from the National Health and Nutrition Examination Survey (1999–2002)" (*Pediatrics*, vol. 122, no. 3, September 2008), the researchers examine the relationship between stress and childhood overweight by considering the stress that children face in response to their mother's stress. Stress experienced by mothers may be translated into behaviors such as diminished parenting, lack of time with children, or inability to shop for or cook nutritional foods, which in turn might heighten stress among children and/or reduce their overall well-being.

Gundersen et al. created a total cumulative stressor index by summing each of four measures of stress:

• Mental stress such as depression, anxiety, or difficulty concentrating

- Physical stress such as health problems or activity limitations

- Financial stress such as unemployment or lack of health insurance

- Family structure stress such as mothers who were unmarried or lacked child care

The researchers then analyzed these stressors along with the indices of food insecurity. They find that when these factors were considered together, children in food-secure households suffering from maternal stressors were more likely to be overweight or obese than children in food-insecure households with mothers suffering from similar stressor levels. In other words, increases in maternal stressors increased the likelihood of being overweight or obese for children in food-secure households but decreased these odds for children in food-insecure households.

Gundersen et al. speculate that maternal stressors did not strengthen the relationship between food insecurity and overweight for three reasons. First, children in food-secure homes may consume more calories than children in food-insecure households because of sufficient food supplies. Second, children in food-secure households may have more opportunities to consume more "comfort foods," which are often high in calories, fat, and sugar, to assuage stress. Third, there may also be a biological response to higher stress, which in the presence of excessive calorie consumption, precipitates metabolic disturbances that result in obesity. Because the majority of low-income children in the United States live in food-secure households, Gundersen et al. conclude that "maternal stressors (via its interaction with food insecurity) may be an important factor for children in the United States that are overweight or obese."

IMPORTANT NAMES
AND ADDRESSES

Academy for Eating Disorders
111 Deer Lake Rd., Ste. 100
Deerfield, IL 60015
(847) 498-4274
FAX: (847) 480-9282
E-mail: info@aedweb.org
URL: http://www.aedweb.org/

American Academy of Sleep Medicine
One Westbrook Corporate Center, Ste. 920
Westchester, IL 60154
(708) 492-0930
FAX: (708) 492-0943
URL: http://www.aasmnet.org/

American Cancer Society
1599 Clifton Rd. NE
Atlanta, GA 30329-4251
(404) 320-3333
URL: http://www.cancer.org/

American Diabetes Association
1701 N. Beauregard St.
Alexandria, VA 22311
1-800-342-2383
E-mail: AskADA@diabetes.org
URL: http://www.diabetes.org/

American Dietetic Association
120 S. Riverside Plaza, Ste. 2000
Chicago, IL 60606-6995
1-800-877-1600
URL: http://www.eatright.org/

American Heart Association
7272 Greenville Ave.
Dallas, TX 75231
1-800-242-8721
URL: http://www.americanheart.org/

American Society of Bariatric Physicians
2821 S. Parker Rd., Ste. 625
Aurora, CO 80014
(303) 770-2526
FAX: (303) 779-4834
URL: http://www.asbp.org/

American Society for Metabolic and Bariatric Surgery
100 SW. 75th St., Ste. 201
Gainesville, FL 32607
(352) 331-4900
FAX: (352) 331-4975
E-mail: info@asbs.org
URL: http://www.asbs.org/

Arthritis Foundation
PO Box 7669
Atlanta, GA 30357-0669
1-800-283-7800
URL: http://www.arthritis.org/

Atkins Nutritionals Inc.
1050 17th St., Ste. 1000
Denver, CO 80265
1-800-628-5467
URL: http://www.atkins.com/

Center for Science in the Public Interest
1875 Connecticut Ave. NW, Ste. 300
Washington, DC 20009
(202) 332-9110
FAX: (202) 265-4954
E-mail: cspi@cspinet.org
URL: http://www.cspinet.org/

Centers for Disease Control and Prevention
1600 Clifton Rd.
Atlanta, GA 30333
1-800-232-4636
URL: http://www.cdc.gov/

Council on Size and Weight Discrimination
PO Box 305
Mt. Marion, NY 12456
(845) 679-1209
FAX: (845) 679-1206
E-mail: info@cswd.org
URL: http://www.cswd.org/

Eating Disorders Coalition
720 Seventh St. NW, Ste. 300
Washington, DC 20001
(202) 543-9570
URL: http://www.eatingdisorderscoalition.org/

Federal Trade Commission
600 Pennsylvania Ave. NW
Washington, DC 20580
1-877-382-4357
URL: http://www.ftc.gov/

International Food Information Council
1100 Connecticut Ave. NW, Ste. 430
Washington, DC 20036
(202) 296-6540
FAX: (202) 296-6547
E-mail: foodinfo@ific.org
URL: http://www.foodinsight.org/

National Association to Advance Fat Acceptance
PO Box 22510
Oakland, CA 94609
(916) 558-6880
URL: http://www.naafa.org/

National Association of Anorexia Nervosa and Associated Disorders
PO Box 7
Highland Park, IL 60035
(847) 831-3438
FAX: (847) 831-4632
URL: http://www.anad.org/

National Association of Cognitive-Behavioral Therapists
203 Three Springs Dr., Ste. 4
Weirton, WV 26062
(304) 723-3982
1-800-853-1135
E-mail: nacbt@nacbt.org
URL: http://www.nacbt.org/

National Center for Health Statistics
3311 Toledo Rd.
Hyattsville, MD 20782
1-800-232-4636
URL: http://www.cdc.gov/nchs/

National Center on Sleep Disorders Research
National Heart, Lung, and Blood Institute
6701 Rockledge Dr.
Bethesda, MD 20892
(301) 435-0199
FAX: (301) 480-3451
URL: http://www.nhlbi.nih.gov/about/ncsdr/

National Diabetes Information Clearinghouse
One Information Way
Bethesda, MD 20892-3560
1-800-860-8747
FAX: (703) 738-4929
E-mail: ndic@info.niddk.nih.gov
URL: http://diabetes.niddk.nih.gov/

National Digestive Diseases Information Clearinghouse
Two Information Way
Bethesda, MD 20892-3570
1-800-891-5389
FAX: (703) 738-4929
E-mail: nddic@info.niddk.nih.gov
URL: http://digestive.niddk.nih.gov/about/

National Eating Disorders Association
603 Stewart St., Ste. 803
Seattle, WA 98101
(206) 382-3587

1-800-931-2237
FAX: (206) 829-8501
E-mail: info@NationalEatingDisorders.org
URL: http://www.nationaleatingdisorders.org/

National Heart, Lung, and Blood Institute
PO Box 30105
Bethesda, MD 20824-0105
(301) 592-8573
FAX: (240) 629-3246
E-mail: nhlbiinfo@nhlbi.nih.gov
URL: http://www.nhlbi.nih.gov/

National Institute of Diabetes and Digestive and Kidney Diseases
Bldg. 31, Rm. 9A06
31 Center Dr., MSC 2560
Bethesda, MD 20892-2560
(301) 496-3583
URL: http://www.niddk.nih.gov/

National Mental Health Association
2000 N. Beauregard St., Sixth Floor
Alexandria, VA 22311
(703) 684-7722
1-800-969-6642
FAX: (703) 684-5968
URL: http://www.nmha.org/

National Women's Health Information Center
8270 Willow Oaks Corporate Dr.
Fairfax, VA 22031
1-800-994-9662
URL: http://www.4woman.gov/

The Obesity Society
8630 Fenton St., Ste. 814
Silver Spring, MD 20910
(301) 563-6526
FAX: (301) 563-6595
URL: http://www.obesity.org/

Rudd Center for Food Policy and Obesity
Yale University
309 Edwards St.
New Haven, CT 06511
(203) 432-6700
URL: http://www.yaleruddcenter.org/

TOPS Club Inc.
4575 S. Fifth St.
Milwaukee, WI 53207-0360
(414) 482-4620
E-mail: topsinteractive@tops.org
URL: http://www.tops.org/

Weight-Control Information Network
1 WIN Way
Bethesda, MD 20892-3665
1-877-946-4627
FAX: (202) 828-1028
E-mail: win@info.niddk.nih.gov
URL: http://win.niddk.nih.gov/index.htm

Weight Watchers International Inc.
175 Crossways Park West
Woodbury, NY 11797
(516) 390-1400
URL: http://www.weightwatchers.com/

RESOURCES

The Centers for Disease Control and Prevention (CDC) tracks nationwide health trends, including overweight and obesity, and reports its findings in several periodicals, especially its *Health, United States* and *Morbidity and Mortality Weekly Reports*. The *National Vital Statistics Reports*, which is issued by the CDC's National Center for Health Statistics (NCHS), gives detailed information on U.S. births, birth weights, and death data and trends. The NCHS also compiles and analyzes demographic data—the heights and weights of a representative sample of the U.S. population—to develop standards for desirable weights. The National Health Interview Surveys, the National Health Examination Surveys, the National Health and Nutrition Examination Surveys, and the Behavioral Risk Factor Surveillance System offer ongoing information about the lifestyles, health behaviors, and health risks of Americans. Working with other agencies and professional organizations, the CDC produced *Healthy People 2010* (2007), which serves as a blueprint for improving the health status of Americans.

The U.S. Department of Agriculture provides nutrition guidelines for Americans, and the Federal Trade Commission (FTC) has launched initiatives to educate consumers and the media about false and deceptive weight-loss advertising. The FTC is one of about 50 members of the Partnership for Healthy Weight Management, a coalition of scientific, academic, health care, government, commercial, and public-interest representatives, that aims to increase public awareness of the obesity epidemic and to promote responsible marketing of weight-loss products and programs.

The relationship between birth weight and future health risks has been examined by many researchers, and the studies cited in this text were reported in *American Journal of Epidemiology, American Journal of Obstetrics and Gynecology, British Medical Journal, Circulation, International Journal of Cancer, Journal of Clinical Endocrinology and Metabolism, Journal of Women's Health,*

Obesity, and *Pediatrics*. Data from the CDC Pregnancy Nutrition Surveillance System show that very overweight women benefit from reduced weight gain during pregnancy to help reduce the risk for high-birth-weight infants.

The World Health Organization and the National Institutes of Health provide definitions, epidemiological data, and research findings about a comprehensive range of public health issues, including diet, nutrition, overweight, and obesity. The Central Intelligence Agency's *World Factbook* provides longevity estimates. The National Heart, Lung, and Blood Institute conducts research about obesity and overweight. Weight-control information and updated weight-for-height tables that incorporate height, weight, and body mass index are published by the National Institute of Diabetes and Digestive and Kidney Diseases (the part of the National Institutes of Health that is primarily responsible for obesity- and nutrition-related research). The National Institute of Mental Health offers information about eating disorders as well as the mental health issues related to obesity.

The origins, causes, and consequences of the obesity epidemic have been described in numerous professional and consumer publications, including *Ageing Research Reviews, Alternative Medicine Review, American Journal of Clinical Nutrition, American Journal of Health Promotion, American Journal of Managed Care, American Journal of Obstetrics and Gynecology, American Journal of Preventive Medicine, American Journal of Psychiatry, American Journal of Public Health, Annals, Academy of Medicine, Singapore, Annals of Behavioral Medicine, Annals of Internal Medicine, Archives of Disease in Childhood, Archives of Internal Medicine, Archives of Pediatrics and Adolescent Medicine, Arthritis and Rheumatism, Bariatric Nursing and Surgical Patient Care, Behaviour Research and Therapy, Biological Psychiatry, BMC Medicine, British Journal of Diabetes and Vascular Disease, British Journal of Gynecology, Canadian Medical Association Journal, Cancer Epidemiology*

Biomarkers and Prevention, Consumer Reports, Current Opinion in Lipidology, Diabetes Care, Disease Management, Eating Behaviors, Eating Disorders, Endocrinology and Metabolism Clinics, Epidemiology, European Eating Disorders Review, Health Affairs, International Journal of Behavioral Nutrition and Physical Activity, International Journal of Cancer, International Journal of Eating Disorders, International Journal of Obesity, Journal of the American Academy of Orthopedic Surgeons, Journal of the American Dietetic Association, Journal of the American Medical Association, Journal of Cardiovascular Nursing, Journal of Clinical Endocrinology and Metabolism, Journal of Clinical Psychiatry, Journal of Economic Perspectives, Journal of Family Practice, Journal of General Internal Medicine, Journal of Health Psychology, Journal of Nutrition, Journal of Occupational and Environmental Medicine, Journal of Public Policy and Marketing, Journal of School Health, Journal of School Nursing, Lancet, Medical Hypotheses, Medicine and Science in Sports and Exercise, Medscape Cardiology, Medscape Gastroenterology, Metabolism: Clinical and Experimental, New England Journal of Medicine, Nutrition Journal, Obesity, Obesity Research, Obesity Reviews, Obstetrics and Gynecology, Pediatrics, Pharmacogenetic Genomics, PLoS One, Preventing Chronic Disease, Proceedings of the National Academy of Sciences, Psychological Medicine, Science, and *Surgical Endoscopy.*

Several excellent books and publications provided valuable insight into the obesity epidemic. Peter N. Stearns, in *Fat History: Bodies and Beauty in the Modern West* (1997), and Laura Fraser, in *Losing It: False Hopes and Fat Profits in the Diet Industry* (1998), offer detailed histories of magical cures and weight-loss fads. Other titles referenced in this edition include books by Kelly D. Brownell and Katherine Battle Horgen, *Food Fight: The Inside Story of the Food Industry, America's Obesity Crisis, and What We Can Do about It* (2004), and Greg Critser, *Fat Land: How Americans Became the Fattest People in the World* (2004). In *Diabesity: The Obesity-Diabetes Epidemic That Threatens America—And What We Must Do to Stop It* (2005), Francine Ratner Kaufman, the former president of the American Diabetes Association, contends that the diabesity epidemic "imperils human existence as we now know it." David A. Kessler, the former commissioner of the U.S. Food and Drug Administration, explains in *The End of Overeating: Taking Control of the Insatiable American Appetite* (2009) how the desire to eat and overeat originates in the brain and is triggered by a variety of combinations of salt, fat, and sugar in the American diet.

Medical and public-health societies, along with advocacy organizations, professional associations, and foundations, offer a wealth of information about the relationship between weight, health, and disease. Sources cited in this edition include the American Dietetic Association, the American Heart Association, the American Medical Association, the American Obesity Association, the Center for Consumer Freedom, the Center for Science in the Public Interest, the International Size Acceptance Association, the National Academy of Sciences, the National Association to Advance Fat Acceptance, the National Eating Disorders Association, the Pharmacy Benefit Management Institute, the Public Health Advocacy Institute, and the Trust for America's Health.

The Gallup Organization makes available valuable poll and survey data about Americans' attitudes about overweight, obesity, physical activity, diet, and nutrition. Finally, many professional associations, voluntary medical organizations, and foundations dedicated to research, education, and advocacy about eating disorders, overweight, and obesity provided up-to-date information that was included in this edition.

INDEX

Page references in italics refer to photographs. References with the letter t following them indicate the presence of a table. The letter f indicates a figure. If more than one table or figure appears on a particular page, the exact item number for the table or figure being referenced is provided.

A

Abdominal obesity, 31–34
Absenteeism, school, 76
Acesulfame K, 84
Activity limiting conditions, 39f
Actuarial data, 6, 81
Acupuncture, 112
Addiction, eating disorders as, 50
Adherence, dietary, 98
Adolescents
    blood pressure levels, 73t, 74t
    BMI, 59f, 60f
    cholesterol levels, 76t
    diet and nutrition, 63–64
    dieting, 50f, 65t
    eating disorders, 52, 79–80
    exercise, 72(t4.10)
    exercise and dieting, by race/ethnicity, 64(t4.7)
    fast food, 64–65
    food in schools, 67–69, 68f
    fruit and vegetable consumption, 63t
    hospital costs of childhood and adolescent obesity, 117
    junk food marketing, 66–67
    metabolic syndrome, 72, 75
    overweight and obese adolescents, by sex, and selected U.S. sites, 62t–63t
    overweight and obese adolescents, by sex, race/ethnicity, and grade, 61(t4.3)
    overweight and obesity prevalence, 57–58, 58t, 61
    physical education, 70, 71f
    self-described weight status and percentage trying to lose weight, 64(t4.6)
    soda consumption, 66t
    television viewing and video game use, 72(t4.11)
    weight loss, 64
    weight status categories by BMI-for-age percentiles, 61(t4.2)
Adoption, 140
Advertising
    "Campaign for Real Beauty," 55–56
    fraudulent claims, 148–149, 151–153, 151t
    frequency of weight-loss ads, 152t
    marketing foods to children, 66–67
    public opinion on factors in children's weight gain, 185–186
Advocacy groups, 142
Agatston, Arthur, 85
Age
    BMI interpretation, by age, 60f
    calorie requirements, by gender and age group, 159(t10.3)
    metabolic syndrome risk factors, 45t
    overweight and obesity prevalence, 10–11, 12(f1.4), 27t
    weight status categories by BMI-for-age percentiles, 61(t4.2)
AHA (American Heart Association), 173
Airline policies, 138–139
Alcohol use, 51, 83
Alley, Kirstie, 84
Alli, 107
Alternative weight-loss therapies, 112
American cuisine, 91t, 92t
American Heart Association (AHA), 173
American Obesity Association (AOA), 26, 132–133
Animal studies of extreme caloric restriction, 153–154
Anorexia nervosa, 49–50, 51, 53, 146–147

Anorexiant drugs, 105
AOA (American Obesity Association), 26, 132–133
Apparel industry, 125
Arizona, 135
Arthritis, 36–39
Artificial sweeteners. *See* Noncaloric sweeteners
Asian American cuisine, 93(t5.9)
Aspartame, 84
Asthma, 5
Astral Industries, 126
Atkins, Robert, and the Atkins diet, 83, 84, 85

B

Baker, Samm Sinclair, 83
Banting, William, 81
Banzhaf, John F., III, 132
Barber, Caesar, 134–135
Bariatric surgery, 78, 107–109, 108f, 124–125, 140
"Basic Seven" food guide, 82
Batesville Casket Company, 126
Bathroom scales, 81
Beauty, standards of, 54–56, 81
Bechler, Steve, 107
Behavioral treatment, 77, 109–112, 124
Bertinelli, Valerie, 84
The Beverly Hills Diet (Mazel), 84
BIA (bioelectric impedance analysis), 7, 9
Biliary system, 40f
Binge-eating, 48–49, 80
Bioelectric impedance analysis (BIA), 7, 9
Birth defects, 43
Birth weight
    morbidity, 4–6
    race/ethnicity, 4t
    trends, 3–4
Blood pressure, 31, 35t–36t, 71, 73t, 74t

Blood sugar, 90–92

BMI. *See* Body mass index

Body fat measurements, 7, 9

Body image, 49, 55–56, 79, 142

Body mass index (BMI)

adult chart, 8*t*

boys, ages 2–20, 59*f*

calculation, 10*t*

children and adolescents, 57

interpretation, by age, 60*f*

overweight and obesity classification, 9*t*

weight loss treatment guide, 105(*t*6.4)

weight status categories by BMI-for-age percentiles, 61(*t*4.2)

Body types, 7

Body weight

genetics, 28–31

public opinion, 175, 176*f*, 177*f*, 177*t*

public opinion on the harmfulness of obesity, 182(*t*11.7)

Boys

blood pressure levels, 73*t*

BMI, 59*f*

Bradley, Jazlyn, 135

Breakfast, 145

Breast cancer, 5

Breastfeeding, 6

Brownell, Kelly, 128–127

Bulimia, 50, 51, 53, 80, 146

Bullying, 75

Burros, Marian, 85

Bush (George W.) administration, 127, 129

Businesses

airline policies, 138–139

costs of overweight and obesity, 119–123

customer service, 139

products and services for overweight and obese persons, 125–126

work-site prevention programs, 170–171

C

Calculating BMI, 10*t*

California, 65

Caloric restriction. *See* Low-calorie diets

Caloric sweeteners, 128–130, 128*t*, 130*t*

Calories

consumption, by major food group, 87*t*

consumption trends, 86, 86*t*

fat free or reduced fat *vs.* regular food, 97*t*

high-fructose corn syrup consumption, 19*t*

intake levels, 12–13

requirements, by gender and age group, 159(*t*10.3)

See also Low-calorie diets

Calories Don't Count (Taller), 83

"Campaign for Real Beauty" (advertising campaign), 55–56

Cancer, 5, 40–41, 43

Cancer screening, 138

Cardiovascular disease

children and adolescents, 72, 75

hypertension and elevated blood pressure, 35*t*–36*t*

metabolic syndrome, 44–46

risk factors in children and adolescents, 70, 71–72

risks from overweight and obesity, 31–34, 113

Caskets, 126

CBT (cognitive-behavioral therapy), 52

CDC (Centers for Disease Control and Prevention), 167

Celebrity endorsed diet programs, 84

Cemetery lots, 126

Center for Science in the Public Interest (CSPI), 66–67

Centers for Disease Control and Prevention (CDC), 167

Centers for Medicare and Medicaid Services, 27–28

Child abuse, 48

Child Nutrition Act, 67–68, 133

Children

American Heart Association antiobesity initiative, 173

anti-fat bias in, 136–137

blood pressure levels, 73*t*, 74*t*

BMI, 57

BMI for boys, ages 2–20, 59*f*

BMI interpretation, by age, 60*f*

cholesterol levels, 76*t*

early maturation, 70–71

eating disorders, 79–80

fast food, 64–65

5 a Day for Better Health Program, 165, 167

food industry and advertising, 18

food pyramid, 161–162, 162*t*, 165, 166*f*

hospital costs of obesity, 117

junk food marketing, 66–67

metabolic syndrome, 72, 75

nutrition and health education, 69–70

obesity in low-income families, 186–187

parents' misperception of children's weight, 186

physical education, 70, 71*f*

prevalence of overweight and obesity, 58*t*

public opinion on childhood obesity, 184–186

public opinion on factors in children's weight gain, 185–186

removal of obese children from parents' custody, 185

snack foods, 170

weight status categories by BMI-for-age percentiles, 61(*t*4.2)

See also School food

Cholesterol, 31, 32*t*–33*t*, 39–40, 70, 76*t*

Chronic diseases, 116*t*

Class-action lawsuits, 134–135

Clothing sizes, 9, 125, 182–184

Cognitive decline, 45–46

Cognitive-behavioral therapy (CBT), 52

College admissions, 137

Commercial weight loss programs, 82, 84, 110, 124

Commonsense Consumption Act (Idaho), 135

Community obesity prevention strategies, 156, 157*t*–158*t*, 170

Competitive foods in schools, 67, 69*f*, 133

Complementary and alternative weight loss therapies, 112

Complex carbohydrates, 90–91, 145

Congenital heart defects, 43

Consumer goods, 125–126

Consumer knowledge of nutrition, 177–178

Consumer protection, 148–149, 151–153, 151*t*

Cookbook recipes, 17

Coronary artery disease, 31–32

Council on Size and Weight Discrimination, 142

Counseling, 109–112, 124

Craig, Jenny, and Sid Craig, 84

Creams and patches, weight loss, 151

Cremation, 126

Cruise, Jorge, 85

CSPI (Center for Science in the Public Interest), 66–67

Cultural issues

anti-fat bias, 136–137, 140–141

body image, 79

dieting, 81

eating disorders, 54–56

genetics *vs.* environmental influences on body weight, 30–31

Customer service, 139

Cyclamate, 83

D

Dairy consumption, 13

DASH (Dietary Approaches to Stop Hypertension) Eating Plan, 88, 89*t*

Definitions, 6–7, 10–11

Degenerative arthritis, 36–39

Dementia, 45–46

Depression, 75–76

"Diabesity," 36

Diabetes, 34–36, 40, 70, 72, 75

See also Metabolic syndrome

Diet and Health, with Key to the Calories (Peters), 81–82

Diet and nutrition

"Amish paradox," 99